Understanding and Using Good Grammar

Reproducible Lessons, Exercises, and Tests

by Genevieve Walberg Schaefer

J. WESTON WALCH PUBLISHER

PORTLAND, MAINE

User's Guide
to
Walch Reproducible Books

As part of our general effort to provide educational materials which are as practical and economical as possible, we have designated this publication a "reproducible book." The designation means that purchase of the book includes purchase of the right to limited reproduction of all pages on which this symbol appears:

Here is the basic Walch policy: We grant to individual purchasers of this book the right to make sufficient copies of reproducible pages for use by all students of a single teacher. This permission is limited to a single teacher, and does not apply to entire schools or school systems, so institutions purchasing the book should pass the permission on to a single teacher. Copying of the book or its parts for resale is prohibited.

Any questions regarding this policy or requests to purchase further reproduction rights should be addressed to:

Permissions Editor
J. Weston Walch, Publisher
321 Valley Street • P. O. Box 658
Portland, Maine 04104-0658

Contents

Introduction

Understanding and Using Good Grammar is the second in a two-volume set of reproducible instructive worksheets developed in logical sequence to enable students to become thoroughly proficient in the oral and written use of the English language.

The first volume, *Steps to Good Grammar*, covers in one year all the grammar instruction presented during elementary school through seventh grade. It provides students with a fundamental knowledge of the construction and function of the basic parts of a sentence. They are prepared to use basic English at a level of competence required for an adult to function satisfactorily in an English-speaking society.

The second volume provides students with instruction that leads to a thorough understanding of the construction and function of advanced, complex grammatical elements used in English sentences. It begins with an essential, concentrated review of the material covered in the first volume plus pertinent, more advanced facts about the use of each element. This review study makes certain that students have a firm knowledge of the structure and interrelationships of basic sentence parts—knowledge essential to their understanding and using more sophisticated sentence forms.

The success-oriented type of study that challenges and promotes the students' ability to think analytically which was developed in *Steps to Good Grammar* is continued and extended in this volume. In each unit, information about only one new sentence element is presented in simply worded, easily understood definitions, explanations, and instructions. Example sentences demonstrate the use of the element and show the symbol that students will use to identify it in sentence analysis, the unique feature of this study program.

In each unit students analyze numerous practice sentences containing only previously learned sentence parts and the element being studied. They label each element, whether it be a single word or a group of words, with the graphic symbol that identifies its function in the sentence. This procedure enables students to understand and remember the construction and use of each grammatical element as it is introduced and to recall and apply earlier learnings. By continuing this repetitive and cumulative method of study in successive units, students acquire the knowledge necessary for them to use all advanced forms of sentence structure.

Advanced grammatical forms include individual gerunds, infinitives, and participles, phrases containing them, and dependent clauses. Each individual word or word group can function as a single sentence element—as a noun, an adjective, or an adverb. Each advanced form is characterized by a distinctive verb word which students learn to recognize in a unit devoted to the study of verb types, principal parts, voice, and the development of tenses. With this clearer understanding of verbs coupled with the firmly established knowledge of simple, basic sentence parts, students are able to recognize the sophisticated forms and understand their function as basic elements of the sentence.

Detailed study of the construction and use of these complex forms is presented in logical, orderly progression. First, students gain an understanding of gerunds, infinitives, and phrases containing them *used as nouns* in all sentence positions in which nouns are used. Instruction is given for avoiding usage errors.

Instruction about *adjectives* begins with a complete review of basic facts and rules regarding individual word adjectives. This is followed by detailed study of the construction, factors governing usage, necessary punctuation, etc., of phrases (prepositional, infinitive, and participial) and of dependent clauses used as adjectives.

The procedure for studying *adverbs* duplicates the one developed for studying adjectives, with the exception of participial phrases which cannot be used adverbially. This comprehensive study of modifiers, both adjective and adverb, enables students to realize that they can choose from among several different descriptive devices, and use the one that creates the most accurate sensory impression.

Many students have more difficulty in conceptualizing *clauses used as nouns* in the various noun positions in sentences than they do in recognizing them used as adjectives or as adverbs. Therefore, noun clauses are studied in a separate unit, followed by a review unit in which students firm up their understanding by distinguishing among the three different uses of dependent clauses—as adjectives, as adverbs, and as nouns.

The last unit in this study series presents instruction in the use of a very effective descriptive device, the *absolute phrase*, also known as nominative absolute/absolute construction, a noun/pronoun followed by and modified by a participle or participial phrase. Young writers enjoy learning about this phrase because it enables them to create lively "word pictures" which their readers can visualize.

Students who understand the components of sophisticated grammatical forms are able to recognize them in the writings of outstanding authors and to appreciate, probably to emulate, the effective, artistic expression achieved by the writers.

Analyzing interrelationships among sentence elements is not an exercise in creative thinking. However, the knowledge regarding both simple and advanced grammatical elements that students acquire by this study method enables them to think creatively in selecting among the available options as they develop their own unique, descriptive styles of expression. (Additionally, this method provides students with valuable practice in the logical, analytical type of thinking they need to use in all forms of problem solving.)

Being able to synthesize their understanding of advanced descriptive devices with their firm knowledge of the function of basic sentence parts, and being able to apply the rules of correct usage, students have the tools necessary for communicating their ideas clearly and fluently. Each has established a fund of knowledge upon which to draw in developing her or his unique, descriptively precise, grammatically and mechanically effective style of speaking and writing English.

Using the Materials

Some reproducible worksheets are designed to be supplementary drills for students to complete after the teacher has introduced certain concepts. Such is not the case with these worksheets. All in the class, students and teacher, participate in this student-centered, teacher-directed, analytical learning program.

Introducing the materials

1. Before distributing any worksheets give the students a *verbal preview* of the material they will study in this volume. First, in a concentrated review, they will reinforce the learnings they acquired from studying *Steps to Good Grammar* and, in each unit, study important advanced information. Next, they will receive extensive and intensive instruction and practice in advanced grammatical forms, special words or word groups that function as a single sentence element—as a noun, an adjective, or an adverb. They will continue to learn through the sentence analysis technique.

   In the end, they will understand the structure of sophisticated descriptive forms, recognize them in the writings of outstanding authors, and appreciate the effective expression the writers achieve. Each student will be able to apply this understanding to devleop his or her unique, interesting, effective style, both in speaking and in writing.

2. Instruct students to *collect all worksheets* that contain instructive information. These pages provide an efficient means for you to help each student to relate his or her usage errors to the principles of correct grammar. The correcting procedure utilizes the symbols that identify the function of words in the sentence. A student might write:

   > ?
   > Me and him cleaned the old cabin. Nom. pron. P. 97

   You could help the student identify the usage error by following these steps:

   (a) Use function symbols: two lines under verb, one under subject.

   (b) Focus on the error with ? .

   (c) At the end of the sentence name the correct grammatical form and show the exact study page.

   A second reason for collecting instruction pages is that, at the end of the study, the students will have accumulated a complete handbook of English grammar and syntax to which they can refer in later years.

Teacher-directed study procedure

1. With each unit, read aloud and, as needed, visually demonstrate on the chalkboard or overhead all instructive material, occasionally quizzing students to be sure that all are comprehending.

2. For most of the practice work, on the first half of the assignment, the class silently analyzes the sentences as volunteers suggest the correct function-symbol for each word. You correct or corroborate their suggestions and instruct students to write corrections of any errors they may have made. Everyone completes the last half silently; you read correct analytical markings; students write needed corrections in order to have a perfectly correct page to hand in and, when returned, to study before the unit test.

3. Students should understand that, even though you may have only enough time to check five representative sentences, you will record a score for every page. Record 100% for error-free work; subtract 5% for every uncorrected error.

4. Help students to retain the understandings they have acquired. At the beginning of class on days when your instruction deals mainly with other aspects of the language arts program, write on the chalkboard or overhead for students to mark and label at least two sentences containing recently studied elements or examples of usage problems. Even with these, record a check to credit each student who turns one in.

5. Periodically remind students of the objectives of this unique study program and of its benefits. Tell your students:

   (a) A teacher and her students developed this study system to make it easy for you to learn and to feel confident that you understand and can use English well.

   (b) In each unit you learn about only one sentence part which is defined and explained in easy-to-understand words and is given a symbol you use to identify it in analyzing sentences; the sentence part is used in example sentences to show you clearly how it functions.

   (c) In many practice sentences that contain only the new sentence part and parts you've already learned, you mark or label the use of every word, thus adding to your previous learnings a clear understanding of each new part.

   (d) "Correct" grammar, the correct form of any word in a sentence, is determined entirely by where that word is used, how it is related to all other words in the sentence. By repeatedly analyzing sentences in successive units you come to understand thoroughly the relationships among words and can use, almost without thinking, "correct" grammar.

   (e) From the beginning of your study, most of you have worked enthusiastically because this method of learning English grammar is so systematic and easy to understand. At the beginning of the year many of you said that English was your "worst" subject. But, as you've been working through sentence study, some have actually asked in amazement, "Is *this* all there is to it?" Some of you are beginning to say, "English is my 'best' subject!"

   (f) In the advanced study, repeated analysis of the construction of sophisticated grammatical elements enables you to understand them, to recognize and appreciate their descriptive value in the writings of outstanding authors, and to experiment with those as models to improve your own expression.

   (g) You are becoming aware that good writing is the result of careful thinking—that good writers carefully choose the "right" individual word, the "right" advanced descriptive form, and the "right" sentence order to communicate their ideas as clearly, effectively. and even artistically as possible to their readers.

(h) By this method of study you develop a bank of knowledge of the English language upon which you can draw endlessly to communicate your ideas precisely, descriptively, and convincingly in speaking and in writing.

The importance of English

Intermittently during the year, present to your students philosophical and factual evidence that it is really important for each one to learn to use English well.

(a) All national and racial groups in the world need to communicate understandingly in speaking and in writing in order to develop the mutual respect and cooperation necessary to solve world-wide problems. In every country today, if English isn't the national language, it is the second language. In order to communicate well with the rest of the world you need to learn to use English effectively and correctly.

(b) Some of you may not have thought about the fact that, in public schools in the United States, every subject you take you study in English. You think, speak, read, and write the subject in English—you mentally visualize, ask questions, interpret answers, analyze—you read comics, books, advertisements, classical literature—you even become skilled in ballet or in football or in building a house in English! Actually, is any subject more used, more important to know?

(c) In a few years, you who study now and learn to use English convincingly and grammatically will be several rungs higher on the employment ladder than those who don't. Whether your application is in the form of an interview or a written letter, it will be clear to your prospective employer that you deserve thoughtful consideration. It would be safe for that person to assume that, on the job you could be counted upon to use good judgment and to act responsibly (character traits highly valued by employers!) because, when you were in school, you obviously *chose to learn* to use English well (a skill highly valued by employers!)

To these few ideas, add your own throughout the year to maintain in the students' minds the conviction that learning to use English well is of real importance to them and to society in general.

Understanding and Using

GOOD GRAMMAR

PRETEST: *Recognizing Parts of Speech, Sentence Parts, and Types of Sentences*

Distribute the Pretest. Read aloud the three groupings, *Parts of Speech, Sentence Parts,* and *Types of Sentences*. Point out to students that they should refer to these groupings when they answer the questions that follow each sentence; they may use abbreviations such as *D.O.* for direct object.

Read aloud the *Instructions*. If it is helpful to them, students may mark or label the sentence parts of each sentence. However, they will be graded only on their answers to the questions and on their underlining of the verb and subject. Remind them that the score on a pretest in no way affects their report card grade.

In *Steps to Good Grammar*, students studied in detail all the material covered in this test with the exception of dependent clauses which were included only in the punctuation section. In writing the answer to question 5 in sentence *C*, if a student does not include *around our yard*, he or she should be given half credit.

Scores on this test indicate how completely students have retained the information they learned in studying *Steps to Good Grammar*. It is not unusual for some to score low. A low score simply indicates that a complete, concise review is essential for them to firm up their understanding and to prepare for advanced instruction.

Grading scale: 32 points

–1, 97	–4, 87	–7, 78	–10, 69	–13, 59	–16, 50
–2, 94	–5, 84	–8, 75	–11, 66	–14, 56	–17, 47
–3, 91	–6, 81	–9, 72	–12, 62	–15, 53	–18, 44

PRETEST: Recognizing Parts of Speech, Sentence Parts, and Types of Sentences

Parts of Speech: noun, verb, pronoun, adjective, adverb, preposition, conjunction

Sentence Parts: verb, subject, linking verb complement—**LVC**, direct object—**D.O.**, prepositional phrase—**prep.**, **O.P.**, indirect object—**I.O.**, noun of address—**N.A.**,
appositive—**Appos.**, dependent clause

Types of Sentences: simple, compound, complex

Instructions: In sentences *A*, *B*, and *C*, underline the verb twice and the subject once.
Write answers to the questions.

A. Mom, <u>Mr. Goss</u> <u>gave</u> his daughter Sue a car for her graduation present.

   1. What word is the direct object in the sentence? *car*

   2. What word is an appositive? *Sue*

   3. What word is an indirect object? *daughter*

   4. What word is a preposition? *for*

   5. What word is the object of the preposition? *present*

   6. What word is a noun of address? *Mom*

   7. What type of sentence is sentence *A*? *Simple*

B. Of the two brothers, <u>Hiram</u> <u>has</u> the higher grade-point average, and
<u>Mario</u> <u>is</u> the more outstanding athlete.

   1. Write the one verb that is a linking verb. *is*

   2. What part of the sentence is the word *average*? *D. O.*

   3. What part of the sentence is the word *athlete*? *L V C*

   4. What part of the sentence is the word *brothers*? *O.P.*

   5. What part of speech is the word *of*? *prep.* ; *two*? *adjective*

   6. What part of speech is the word *more*? *adverb* ; *and*? *conjunction*

   7. What type of sentence is sentence *B*? *compound*

C. All the <u>leaves</u> <u>have been blown</u> off the trees which form the border
around our yard.

   1. What part of speech is the subject of the sentence? *noun*

   2. Write the words that make up two prepositional phrases.

     (a) *off the trees*   (b) *around our yard*

   3. Write the word that is modifed by the first phrase. *blown*

   4. Write the word that is modifed by the second phrase. *border*

   5. Write the words that make up a dependent clause. *which form the border around our yard*

   6. Write the word that is modified by the clause. *trees*

   7. What type of sentence is sentence *C*? *complex*

PRETEST: Recognizing Parts of Speech, Sentence Parts, and Types of Sentences

Name _____

Date _____

Parts of Speech: noun, verb, pronoun, adjective, adverb, preposition, conjunction

Sentence Parts: verb, subject, linking verb complement—**LVC**, direct object—**D.O.**, prepositional phrase—**prep.**, **O.P.**, indirect object—**I.O.**, noun of address—**N.A.**, appositive—**Appos.**, dependent clause

Types of Sentences: simple, compound, complex

Instructions: In sentences *A*, *B*, and *C*, underline the verb twice and the subject once. Write answers to the questions.

A. Mom, Mr. Goss gave his daughter Sue a car for her graduation present.

1. What word is the direct object in the sentence?_____

2. What word is an **appositive**? _____

3. What word is an indirect object? _____

4. What word is a preposition? _____

5. What word is the object of the preposition?_____

6. What word is a noun of address?_____

7. What type of sentence is sentence *A*?_____

B. Of the two brothers, Hiram has the higher grade-point average, and Mario is the more outstanding athlete.

1. Write the one verb that is a linking verb. _____

2. What part of the sentence is the word *average*? _____

3. What part of the sentence is the word *athlete*? _____

4. What part of the sentence is the word *brothers*?_____

5. What part of speech is the word *of*?_____ ; *two*? _____

6. What part of speech is the word *more*? _____ ; *and*?_____

7. What type of sentence is sentence *B*? _____

C. All the leaves have been blown off the trees which form the border around our yard.

1. What part of speech is the subject of the sentence? _____

2. Write the words that make up two prepositional phrases.

 (a) _____ (b) _____

3. Write the word that is modifed by the first phrase. _____

4. Write the word that is modifed by the second phrase. _____

5. Write the words that make up a dependent clause. _____

_____

6. Write the word that is modifed by the clause. _____

7. What type of sentence is sentence *C*?_____

Understanding and Using Good Grammar

Verbs

Pages 1 through 21 present a concise review of the instruction given in the first 26 pages of *Steps to Good Grammar*. Just enough drill is given to enable students to recall their previous learnings. If this review seems insufficient, select appropriate drill pages from *Steps to Good Grammar* to help students to reestablish their understanding.

Part I, 1: The word *sound* may also be used as a linking verb and as a noun in all other main sentence parts. Write these sentences on the chalkboard to demonstrate this fact.

(a) The alarm sounded frightening.   (linking verb)

(b) What was that sound?   (noun—linking verb complement)

(c) The hikers heard an indefinable sound.   (noun—direct object)

(d) The cattle reacted wildly to the sound.   (noun—object of preposition)

(e) Hank didn't give the sound a second thought.   (noun—indirect object)

Part II, 1: Instruct the students to memorize the definition of a verb.

Part II, 1 and 3: The term *doing verb* is more accurate than *action verb*.

In the sentence Amy had been standing quietly in the hall, there is no real action, but students readily understand "what is being done."

Part II, 4 and 5: All students should be able to write or, at the very least, to recite the helping verbs perfectly in order. Knowing them not only helps the students to recognize the main verb but also, later, helps them to understand verb tenses, participial phrases, and the makeup of clauses.

Part II, 4: **Of interest:** Many helping verbs, such as *should*, express subtly different feelings and attitudes:

1. Obligation, propriety, or duty: You *should* write that letter; His parents thought he *should* go; The school cafeteria *should* serve a hot lunch.

2. Condition—possibility: If I *should* go, he would go too.
Condition—assumption: *Should* (*Assuming that*) this seating arrangement prove practicable, as seems almost certain, it will become permanent.

3. Surprise at an unexpected event in the past: As I ran around the corner, whom *should* I run into but the principal!

4. Expectation: I *should* be home by noon.

5. (*U.S. Informal*) Irony, in positive statement with negative force: They might be fined heavily, but with all their money they *should* (*need not*) worry!

(Adapted: Funk and Wagnalls *Standard College Dictionary*, 1967)

Verbs

I. The **Parts of Speech** are the eight headings under which all words in the English language are classified: **verb, noun, pronoun, adjective, adverb, preposition, conjunction, interjection**.

   1. The part of speech of any word is determined by its usage in the sentence. *Example: sound*

     (a) The siren <u>sounded</u> the danger. (verb)

     (b) The <u>sound</u> of the alarm startled us. (noun)

     (c) Sean offered a (sound) argument. (adjective)

     (d) The unruly children were [soundly] reprimanded. (adverb)

II. The **Verb:** When you are analyzing the grammatical structure of a sentence, always locate the *verb* first.

   1. **Memorize:** A word in a sentence is a **verb** if it tells what is being done and/or if it is one of the twenty-three helping verbs.

   2. The verb is the most important part of a sentence.

     (a) It tells what is being done and, as indicated by the tense, when it is being done.

     (b) It can affect or can be affected by other main sentence parts.

     (c) It is the only sentence part that can be used alone to form a complete sentence. In a command the subject *you* is understood. Hence, "Stop!" "Look!" are complete sentences.

   3. **Doing verbs** can be done. You can do them! You can *whisper, attempt, ponder, investigate, stand, slam,* or *succeed.*

   4. **Helping verbs** used with doing verbs express exact meaning.

   5. **Memorize** and be able to write in order the twenty-three helping verbs:
     is, am, are, was, were, be, being, been; has, have, had; do, does, did; shall, will, should, would; may, might, must; can, could

PRACTICE: In each sentence below draw two lines under the verb words. The clues in parentheses will help you.

                                       (Subject)   (Verb)

   1. Carl <u>had broken</u> his hockey stick.   *had broken*
     (The verb affects the direct object *stick*.)   (sentence line)

   2. Our street <u>is being repaired</u>.
     (The verb affects the subject *street*.)

   3. <u>Does</u> Derek really <u>enjoy</u> algebra?
     (Many questions begin with a helping verb.)

   4. I <u>have</u> already <u>finished</u> my homework.
     (*Already* is not a verb; you can't *do* already and you didn't memorize it as a helping verb.)

   5. Mother <u>isn't</u> <u>going</u> to the office.
     (*n't/not* is an adverb, not a verb.)

                                                    ate

   6. Pablo hurriedly <u>ate</u> breakfast and <u>left</u> for school.   *left*
     (A verb may be compound.)

Name _____   **Verbs**

Date _____

I. The **Parts of Speech** are the eight headings under which all words in the English language are classified: **verb, noun, pronoun, adjective, adverb, preposition, conjunction, interjection**.

1. The part of speech of any word is determined by its usage in the sentence. *Example: sound*

    (a) The siren <u>sounded</u> the danger. (verb)

    (b) The <u>sound</u> of the alarm startled us. (noun)

    (c) Sean offered a (sound) argument. (adjective)

    (d) The unruly children were [soundly] reprimanded. (adverb)

II. The **Verb:** When you are analyzing the grammatical structure of a sentence, always locate the *verb* first.

1. **Memorize:** A word in a sentence is a **verb** if it tells what is being done and/or if it is one of the twenty-three helping verbs.

2. The verb is the most important part of a sentence.

    (a) It tells what is being done and, as indicated by the tense, when it is being done.

    (b) It can affect or can be affected by other main sentence parts.

    (c) It is the only sentence part that can be used alone to form a complete sentence. In a command the subject *you* is understood. Hence, "Stop!" "Look!" are complete sentences.

3. **Doing verbs** can be done. You can do them! You can *whisper, attempt, ponder, investigate, stand, slam,* or *succeed.*

4. **Helping verbs** used with doing verbs express exact meaning.

5. **Memorize** and be able to write in order the twenty-three helping verbs:
    is, am, are, was, were, be, being, been; has, have, had; do, does, did; shall, will, should, would; may, might, must; can, could

PRACTICE: In each sentence below draw two lines under the verb words. The clues in parentheses will help you.

	(Subject)	(Verb)

1. Carl had broken his hockey stick.   _____ | *had broken*
    (The verb affects the direct object *stick*.)   (sentence line)

2. Our street is being repaired. (The verb affects the subject *street*.)

3. Does Derek really enjoy algebra? (Many questions begin with a helping verb.)

4. I have already finished my homework. (*Already* is not a verb; you can't *do* already and you didn't memorize it as a helping verb.)

5. Mother isn't going to the office. (*n't/not* is an adverb, not a verb.)

6. Pablo hurriedly ate breakfast
    and left for school.
    (A verb may be compound.)   *ate* / *and* / *left*

Understanding and Using Good Grammar

Nouns

For sentences 1 through 6 have volunteers identify the verb and subject audibly. For example, in sentence 1 ask the volunteer to:

(a) Read the sentence.

(b) Draw two lines under the verb: was driving.

(c) Draw one line under the subject: dad.

Read aloud the instructional note that accompanies each sentence, 2 through 6, and direct students' attention to the diagram.

Have student volunteers identify the verb and subject in each sentence, 8 through 12. As they do so, have them quote the instructional note that applies to their sentence. For example, the instructional note with sentence 2 should be quoted with sentence 8.

Nouns

DEFINITION: A **noun** is a "name" word. It is a name we can use to refer to a *person* (Karen, custodian, man), a *place* (Chicago, island, mall, playground), a *thing* (desk, apple, assignment), or a *quality* or *idea* (kindness, cruelty, principle).

USES OF NOUNS IN SENTENCES:

1. In a sentence a noun may be used as a subject, direct object, object of a preposition, indirect object, appositive, linking verb complement (also called predicate nominative), and noun of direct address. Each use will be reviewed thoroughly.

2. A **subject** is whom or what the sentence is about. To recognize the subject, first find the verb. Then ask "Who?" or "What?" about the verb. The word that answers the question is the subject.

PRACTICE: Draw two lines under the verb, one under the subject. On the reverse side of the paper, diagram the subject and verb in sentences 7–12.

1. Arnaldo's <u>dad</u> <u>was driving</u> the car.

dad	was driving

2. There <u>is</u> no <u>milk</u> in the refrigerator.
   (Introductory *There* is never a subject.
   Diagram *there* separately before the subject.)

There	milk	is

3. (*You*) <u>Take</u> your books with you.
   (In a request or command, the understood subject is *You*, shown in parentheses.)

(You)	Take

4. The <u>crowd</u> of students <u>came</u> up the walk.
   (A noun preceded by *of* is not the subject of a sentence.)

crowd	came

5. <u>Jane and David</u> <u>have finished</u> their reports.
   (A subject may be compound.)

   Jane / David | have finished

6. On the bank of the stream <u>was sitting</u>
   an interesting-looking <u>stranger</u>.
   (Many sentences do not begin with the subject and verb.)

stranger	was sitting

7. My <u>grandmother</u> <u>has traveled</u> throughout Europe.

   grandmother | has traveled

8. There <u>will be</u> a ten-minute <u>intermission</u>.

   There   intermission | will be

9. The <u>pitcher</u> of lemonade <u>slipped</u> from my hands.

   pitcher | slipped

10. <u>Are</u> <u>Marietta and Paolo</u> <u>coming</u> with us?

    Marietta / Paolo | Are coming

11. (*You*) <u>Pass</u> your papers forward.

    (You) | Pass

12. Just over the hill <u>lies</u> my uncle's <u>farm</u>.

    farm | lies

Nouns

Name _____

Date _____

DEFINITION: A **noun** is a "name" word. It is a name we can use to refer to a *person* (Karen, custodian, man), a *place* (Chicago, island, mall, playground), a *thing* (desk, apple, assignment), or a *quality* or *idea* (kindness, cruelty, principle).

USES OF NOUNS IN SENTENCES:

1. In a sentence a noun may be used as a subject, direct object, object of a preposition, indirect object, appositive, linking verb complement (also called predicate nominative), and noun of direct address. Each use will be reviewed thoroughly.

2. A **subject** is whom or what the sentence is about. To recognize the subject, first find the verb. Then ask "Who?" or "What?" about the verb. The word that answers the question is the subject.

PRACTICE: Draw two lines under the verb, one under the subject. On the reverse side of the paper, diagram the subject and verb in sentences 7–12.

1. Arnaldo's dad was driving the car.

| dad | was driving |

2. There is no milk in the refrigerator.
   (Introductory *There* is never a subject. Diagram *there* separately before the subject.)

| There | milk | is |

3.   Take your books with you.
   (In a request or command, the understood subject is *You*, shown in parentheses.)

| (You) | Take |

4. The crowd of students came up the walk.
   (A noun preceded by *of* is not the subject of a sentence.)

| crowd | came |

5. Jane and David have finished their reports.
   (A subject may be compound.)

| Jane / David | have finished |

6. On the bank of the stream was sitting an interesting-looking stranger.
   (Many sentences do not begin with the subject and verb.)

| stranger | was sitting |

7. My grandmother has traveled throughout Europe.

8. There will be a ten-minute intermission.

9. The pitcher of lemonade slipped from my hands.

10. Are Marietta and Paolo coming with us?

11.   Pass your papers forward.

12. Just over the hill lies my uncle's farm.

Understanding and Using Good Grammar

Recognizing Complete Verbs and Subjects

Prior to beginning this worksheet, call on volunteers to define *verb* (student page 8) and *subject* (student page 11) and to distinguish *adverbs* from *verbs* (student page 8, Practice sentence 4).

When students have completed the worksheet, have volunteers tell why *early* (sentence 1) and *out* (sentence 2) are not verbs.

Reminders

Sentence 4: *Water* is an adjective telling "what kind" about *main*.

Sentence 10: *Brother* is an appositive to *Jerry*.

Sentence 15: *Feeling completely disgusted* is a participial phrase used as an adjective to describe *Joan*. Phrases of all kinds will be studied in detail later in this book.

Recognizing Complete Verbs and Subjects

Instructions: Draw two lines under each verb; draw one line under the subject.

1. Joan awakened early Monday morning.

2. From the beginning, nothing worked out well.

3. No water came from the faucet in the washbasin.

4. A water main down the street had burst during the night.

5. Dad and Mom could have no coffee.

6. Instead of frozen orange juice, the family drank canned apple juice.

7. Joan looked for her special history report.

8. It was not lying on the hall table.

9. She had put it there the night before.

10. Jerry, her older brother, had already left for school.

11. He must have accidentally taken her report with him.

12. Joan ate her toast and egg quickly and gulped a glass of milk.

13. Then she flew out the door and hurried toward the bus stop.

14. Two seconds later the loaded bus pulled away from the curb.

15. Feeling completely disgusted, Joan turned around and ran back home.

16. Fortunately, her mother could drive her to school in the car.

17. At school, things improved noticeably.

18. Best of all, the due date for her history report had been changed to Wednesday.

Instructions: In the space below, construct verb-subject diagrams for sentences 2, 8, 11, 13, 16, and 18.

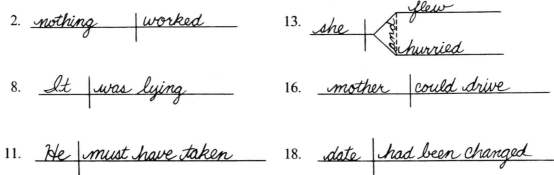

Name _____

Date _____

Recognizing Complete Verbs and Subjects

Instructions: Draw two lines under each verb; draw one line under the subject.

1. Joan awakened early Monday morning.

2. From the beginning, nothing worked out well.

3. No water came from the faucet in the washbasin.

4. A water main down the street had burst during the night.

5. Dad and Mom could have no coffee.

6. Instead of frozen orange juice, the family drank canned apple juice.

7. Joan looked for her special history report.

8. It was not lying on the hall table.

9. She had put it there the night before.

10. Jerry, her older brother, had already left for school.

11. He must have accidentally taken her report with him.

12. Joan ate her toast and egg quickly and gulped a glass of milk.

13. Then she flew out the door and hurried toward the bus stop.

14. Two seconds later the loaded bus pulled away from the curb.

15. Feeling completely disgusted, Joan turned around and ran back home.

16. Fortunately, her mother could drive her to school in the car.

17. At school, things improved noticeably.

18. Best of all, the due date for her history report had been changed to Wednesday.

Instructions: In the space below, construct verb-subject diagrams for sentences 2, 8, 11, 13, 16, and 18.

2.   13.

8.   16.

11.   18.

Understanding and Using Good Grammar

Using Adjectives

1. Read the instructional material aloud as students read silently.

2. Quiz students to assist them to retain the information:

   (a) Define *adjective*.

   (b) An adjective may tell *what* about a noun it modifies?

   (c) In your own words, explain one of the rules that governs the use of commas with adjectives; give an example sentence.

3. Give students a further explanation of parallel adjectives: Adjectives are parallel when each one "tells" something different about the noun they modify, when each one helps to make a clearer picture of the noun.

4. Students should be able to use comma rules correctly on the Test at the end of this unit.

5. Commas shown in the Answer Key for sentences 1 and 2 of the Practice are not essential, but are acceptable. In sentence 3, the comma is essential.

Answer Key—Diagramming

Using Adjectives

DEFINITION: An **adjective** is a word that describes or modifies a noun.

REMEMBER: An adjective tells *which one, what kind, how many,* or *whose* about the noun it modifies. Articles, *a, an, the,* are adjectives.

Example: (Mother's) (two,)   (closest,) (childhood) friends are coming.
             (whose) (how many)(which ones)   (what kind)

Using commas with adjectives is often a matter of individual interpretation; however, some rules may be stated.

Rule 1: When you write two or more adjectives in a series, if you can sensibly connect them with *and,* a comma may be used instead.

    Example: We are (free) and (independent) Americans. (free, independent)

Rule 2: **Parallel adjectives,** adjectives of equal importance as modifiers, used in a series may be separated by commas.

    Example: (Grandfather's)(two,) (antique,) (black) Stutz Bearcats can be driven.

    (a) Do not use a comma after the first adjective if it modifies the meaning of the other adjective(s) and noun combined.

        Examples: small delivery van   low picket fence

    (b) Do not use a comma between the last adjective and the noun it modifies.

Rule 3: Adjectives which follow a noun are separated from the noun and the rest of the sentence by commas.

    Example: (My) cousin, (tall,) (handsome,) and (athletic,) was approaching.

Notice: In your writing, work to upgrade your expression by using accurately descriptive adjectives. Use your thesaurus!

PRACTICE: Draw two lines under the verb and one line under the subject. Circle adjectives. Insert needed commas. Diagram sentences 2 through 7.

1. (All)(the)(shriveled)(brown) leaves had fallen.

2. (This)(green,)(moldy) bread should not be eaten.

3. (That)(narrow,)(potholed) road has been closed.

4. (Eric's) (well-thought-out) plans were chosen.

5. Was (the)(distinguished,)(dark-haired) woman calling?

6. (A) (new)(small,)(Chinese) restaurant is being built.

7. (My) (aunt's) (little,)(frisky,)(white) poodle was barking.

> **Notice:** Interesting adjectives may be made by joining two or more words with hyphens.

Using Adjectives

Name _____

Date _____

DEFINITION: An **adjective** is a word that describes or modifies a noun.

REMEMBER: An adjective tells *which one, what kind, how many,* or *whose* about the noun it modifies. Articles, *a, an, the,* are adjectives.

Example: (Mother's) (two), (closest), (childhood) friends are coming.
    (whose) (how many)(which ones)   (what kind)

Using commas with adjectives is often a matter of individual interpretation; however, some rules may be stated.

Rule 1: When you write two or more adjectives in a series, if you can sensibly connect them with *and,* a comma may be used instead.

Example: We are (free) and (independent) Americans. (free, independent)

Rule 2: Parallel adjectives, adjectives of equal importance as modifiers, used in a series may be separated by commas.

Example: (Grandfather's)(two), (antique), (black) Stutz Bearcats can be driven.

(a) Do not use a comma after the first adjective if it modifies the meaning of the other adjective(s) and noun combined.

Examples: small delivery van   low picket fence

(b) Do not use a comma between the last adjective and the noun it modifies.

Rule 3: Adjectives which follow a noun are separated from the noun and the rest of the sentence by commas.

Example: (My) cousin, (tall), (handsome), and (athletic), was approaching.

Notice: In your writing, work to upgrade your expression by using accurately descriptive adjectives. Use your thesaurus!

PRACTICE: Draw two lines under the verb and one line under the subject. Circle adjectives. Insert needed commas. Diagram sentences 2 through 7.

1. (All)(the)(shriveled)(brown) leaves had fallen.

2. This green moldy bread should not be eaten.

3. That narrow potholed road has been closed.

4. Eric's well-thought-out plans were chosen.

5. Was the distinguished dark-haired woman calling?

6. A new small Chinese restaurant is being built.

7. My aunt's little frisky white poodle was barking.

> **Notice:** Interesting adjectives may be made by joining two or more words with hyphens.

Understanding and Using Good Grammar

Adverbs and Effective Expression

Teaching Suggestions

Tell the students:

When we speak we can communicate our specific meaning and indicate our feelings and emotions by our tone of voice, the stress we give certain words, our facial expressions and body gestures. When we write, we must depend upon our careful choice of words and use of punctuation to convey our feelings and special meanings. Generally speaking, a writer uses a comma to suggest a pause for a specific reason.

I. Example sentence: The comma after *Finally* emphasizes the time element involved.

II. 1. A comma is placed before the conjunction *but* which indicates a contrast or something different from what was expected.

2. The adverb *yesterday* modifies the whole sentence; a comma after it emphasizes *yesterday*, not any other day.

3. Three or more short sentences that make up a compound sentence are always separated by commas.

4. *Never* modifies *again*; *again*, *back*, and *there* are basic ideas; all modify the verb *will go*. No commas are necessary.

5. *, but excited and triumphant* is a two-word contrasting adjective phrase joined by *and*; there is no comma before *and*.

PRACTICE:

1. No comma is used to separate two verb phrases joined by *and*.

2. A semicolon, rather than a period, may separate an introductory independent clause (short sentence) from closely related independent clauses which follow it.

3. The comma before the conjunction *but* gives emphasis to *extremely firmly*; the long introductory adverb phrase is separated from the subject and verb.

4. Commas set off adjectives which modify the noun they follow.

Answer Key—Diagramming

Adverbs and Effective Expression

I. *DEFINITION:* An **adverb** is a word that modifies a verb, an adjective, or another adverb. It tells *how, when, where* about a verb, and *how much* about an adjective or another adverb.

Example: [Finally], (three)[very] (tired) hikers dragged [slowly] [in].

     (when)   (how much)   (how)(where)

(Brackets identify adverbs; arrows point to words modified by adverbs.)

II. Effective expression: descriptive adverbs; varied sentence structure

Instructions: Underline verbs twice and subjects once; circle adjectives, bracket adverbs; complete given diagrams; **note placement of commas.**

1. **Simple sentence with compound verb:** (The)[really] (competent) (stage) crew had worked [systematically] and [carefully], but had[n't] finished.

2. **Simple sentence with compound subject and verb:**

   [Yesterday], Dom and Erika arrived [early] and stayed [late].

   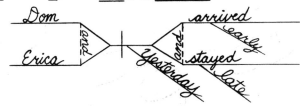

3. **Compound sentence:** Sara was walking [quickly], Michelle was dawdling, and Stacey was [purposely] lagging [behind].

4. **Adverbs at beginning of sentence:** [Never] [again] will I go [back] [there]!

5. **Adjectives following a modified noun:**

   (The) team, (exhausted), but (excited) and (triumphant) loped [slowly] [off].

   (Conjunctions are given no mark in sentence analysis and are diagrammed on dotted lines.)

   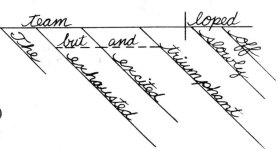

PRACTICE: Identify sentence parts as above, and insert commas. On the reverse side, construct diagrams for the sentences.

1. Beth approached [very] [cautiously] and stepped [soundlessly] [in].

2. (The) twins reacted [very] [differently]; Tomas jumped [up] [excitedly], but Pedro shrank [back] [reluctantly].

3. [Very] [quietly], but [extremely] [firmly], Dad refused.

4. Calene, (self-confident) and (smiling), came [quickly] [forward].

Name _____

Date _____

Adverbs and Effective Expression

I. DEFINITION: An *adverb* is a word that modifies a verb, an adjective, or another adverb. It tells *how, when, where* about a verb, and *how much* about an adjective or another adverb.

Example: 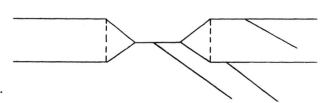 [Finally], three very tired hikers dragged [slowly] [in].

      (when)   (how much)   (how)(where)

(Brackets identify adverbs; arrows point to words modified by adverbs.)

II. Effective expression: descriptive adverbs; varied sentence structure

Instructions: Underline verbs twice and subjects once; circle adjectives, bracket adverbs; complete given diagrams; **note placement of commas.**

1. **Simple sentence with compound verb:** The really competent stage crew had worked systematically and carefully, but hadn't finished.

2. **Simple sentence with compound subject and verb:**

   Yesterday, Dom and Erika arrived early and stayed late.

   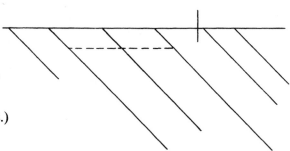

3. **Compound sentence:** Sara was walking quickly, Michelle was dawdling, and Stacey was purposely lagging behind.

4. **Adverbs at beginning of sentence:** Never again will I go back there!

5. **Adjectives following a modified noun:**

   The team, exhausted, but excited and triumphant, loped slowly off.

   (Conjunctions are given no mark in sentence analysis and are diagrammed on dotted lines.)

PRACTICE: Identify sentence parts as above, and insert commas. On the reverse side, construct diagrams for the sentences.

1. Beth approached very cautiously and stepped soundlessly in.

2. The twins reacted very differently; Tomas jumped up excitedly but Pedro shrank back reluctantly.

3. Very quietly but extremely firmly Dad refused.

4. Calene self-confident and smiling came quickly forward.

           Understanding and Using Good Grammar

FINAL PRACTICE and TEST:
Recognizing Verbs, Subjects, Adjectives, and Adverbs; Using Commas

> The next reproducible page contains one half-page Final Practice and one half-page Test. Before passing out the page, cut it in two to remove the Test.

Final Practice

Have volunteers analyze sentences 1, 2, and 3 for the class. When they have finished, corroborate their markings. Give students the correct markings for sentences 4 through 7 after they have completed their work individually. Have students correct their own errors and take home their papers to prepare for the Test.

Sentence 1: Students might suggest that *newly elected* could be a hyphenated adjective. Point out that adverbs that end in *-ly* function as separate adverbs and should not be joined to another word.

Sentence 2: A comma may be used after *Recently,* but it is not essential since the word modifies the meaning of the whole sentence.

Sentence 5: *Both* is not an adjective; *Both . . . and* is a two-word conjunction which is not given an identification mark.

Sentence 6: A comma used after *seriously* emphasizes place and time of *here* and *now.*

Sentence 7: A comma *is used* after an introductory parenthetical adverb, an adverb that isn't necessary to the meaning of the sentence.

Test

Suggested Grading: Required identification and commas total 60 points.

–1, 98	–4, 93	–7, 88	–10, 83	–13, 78	–16, 73	–19, 68	–22, 63
–2, 97	–5, 92	–8, 87	–11, 82	–14, 77	–17, 72	–20, 67	–23, 62
–3, 95	–6, 90	–9, 85	–12, 80	–15, 75	–18, 70	–21, 65	–24, 60

FINAL PRACTICE:
Recognizing Verbs, Subjects, Adjectives, and Adverbs; Using Commas

Instructions: Underline verbs twice, subjects once; circle adjectives, bracket adverbs; insert necessary commas.

1. (Our) [newly] (elected) (class) president [just] <u>ran</u> [past].

2. [Recently] (many) (new) (science-fiction) books <u>have been purchased</u>.

3. <u>Chad</u> <u>had studied</u> [carefully], but <u>Jesse</u> <u>had studied</u> [even] [more] [carefully].

4. (The) principal <u>entered</u>, <u>looked</u> [around] [thoughtfully], and <u>smiled</u> [pleasantly].

5. Both (the) doorbell and (the) telephone <u>have rung</u> [repeatedly] [today].

6. <u>Shouldn't</u> <u>we</u> <u>rehearse</u> [really] [seriously], [here] and [now]?

7. [Incidentally], (that) (historic) (old) mansion <u>will be</u> [completely] <u>restored</u>.

TEST:
Recognizing Verbs, Subjects, Adjectives, and Adverbs; Using Commas

Instructions: Underline verbs twice, subjects once; circle adjectives, bracket adverbs; insert necessary commas.

1. (The) (narrow), (wobbly), (old) (wooden) bridge <u>had been washed</u> [completely] [away].

2. <u>Sara</u> <u>was walking</u> [quickly], <u>Michelle</u> <u>was dawdling</u>, and <u>Stacey</u> <u>was</u> [purposely] <u>lagging</u> [behind].

3. [Yesterday], (my) (seven-year-old) brother and (his) (neighborhood) friends <u>were skateboarding</u>.

4. (The) team, (exhausted) but (excited) and (triumphant), <u>loped</u> [slowly] [off].

5. [Suddenly], <u>Jon</u> <u>stood</u> [up], <u>looked</u> [around] [questioningly], and <u>walked</u> [off].

6. <u>Shouldn't</u> <u>we</u> <u>rehearse</u> [really] [seriously], [here] and [now]?

FINAL PRACTICE:
Recognizing Verbs, Subjects, Adjectives, and Adverbs; Using Commas

Name _____

Date _____

Instructions: Underline verbs twice, subjects once; circle adjectives, bracket adverbs; insert necessary commas.

1. Our newly elected class president just ran past.

2. Recently many new science-fiction books have been purchased.

3. Chad had studied carefully but Jesse had studied even more carefully.

4. The principal entered looked around thoughtfully and smiled pleasantly.

5. Both the doorbell and the telephone have rung repeatedly today.

6. Shouldn't we rehearse really seriously here and now?

7. Incidentally that historic old mansion will be completely restored.

TEST: Recognizing Verbs, Subjects, Adjectives, and Adverbs; Using Commas

Name _____

Date _____

Instructions: Underline verbs twice, subjects once; circle adjectives, bracket adverbs; insert necessary commas.

1. The narrow wobbly old wooden bridge had been washed completely away.

2. Sara was walking quickly Michelle was dawdling and Stacey was purposely lagging behind.

3. Yesterday my seven-year-old brother and his neighborhood friends were skateboarding.

4. The team exhausted but excited and triumphant loped slowly off.

5. Suddenly Jon stood up looked around questioningly and walked off.

6. Shouldn't we rehearse really seriously here and now?

      Understanding and Using Good Grammar

Using Verbs Effectively

Practice—Verbs of Motion

Suggestions for evaluating students' writing:

1. Divide class into groups of five students.

2. Each group member reads own sentences.

3. Other members evaluate according to requirements in Instructions.

   (a) The verb meaning in the sentence is same as in dictionary.

   (b) Adverbs and adjectives add to clear-cut picture.

4. Each student reads to class his or her sentence judged by group to be most descriptive.

Practice—Proofreading for Clear Meaning

Suggested answers:

1. Will you ask Nathan before you ask Jacob?
   Will you ask Nathan before Jacob asks him?

2. I see Lisa more often than I see Nancy.
   I see Lisa more often than Nancy sees her.

3. Do you know Mary as well as Susan knows her?
   Do you know Mary as well as you know Susan?

4. Dad asks me to help him more than he asks my brother.
   Dad asks me to help him more than my brother asks me.

Name _____

Using Verbs Effectively

Date _____

In writing or speaking, no one makes a serious effort to be dull! Actually, everyone tries not to be! One area in which one can work to avoid being dull is in the choice of verbs.

Verbs tell what is being done . . . what is happening. Therefore, in what you write or say, choose verbs that create a clear-cut picture of the event. Use verbs that describe not only the action, but also tell something of the feelings and thoughts of the person performing the action. For example, look at these alternatives to using *say* or *said*:

"He was there," Carrie **murmured**. What thoughts and feelings caused her merely to *murmur*?

"He was there," Carrie **averred**. Why did she insist it was *true*?

         . . . **asserted**. Why was she so *sure*?

The verbs listed here express motion:

gallop	lope	stroll	loiter	toddle	lag
spring	jog	saunter	dawdle	wiggle	slink
trot	strut	meander	straggle	squirm	glide
vault	swagger	shuffle	plod	creep	amble

PRACTICE: Select six verbs from the list. For each, on a separate sheet of paper:

1. Write the dictionary definition to be sure of the precise meaning.
2. Write a sentence using the verb to create a clear-cut picture in your reader's mind.
3. Use picture-making adverbs and adjectives in your sentence.

   Example: straggle—to proceed or spread out in a scattered or irregular group

On that ⌐miserably¬ (hot) day, the <u>students</u>

<u>straggled</u> ⌐listlessly¬ into the classroom.

> **Reminder:** picture-producing adverbs help.

Proofreading for Clear Use of Verbs

A. In using verbs, *be sure your meaning is clear*; repeat the verb if it is needed for clarity.

Confusing: At the mall, I saw Mother before Dad.
Clear: At the mall, I saw Mother before Dad saw her.
Clear: At the mall, I saw Mother before I saw Dad.

PRACTICE: Write each sentence in two different, clear ways.

1. Will you ask Nathan before Jacob?

2. I see Lisa more often than Nancy.

3. Do you know Mary as well as Susan?

4. Dad asks me to help him more than my brother.

B. *Do not mix verb tenses* within a sentence.

Example: The <u>stranger</u> <u>sees</u> me and <u>hurried</u> around the corner.

      Both verbs should be present tense: <u>sees</u> . . . <u>hurries</u> *or*

                     past tense: <u>saw</u> . . . <u>hurried</u>

Understanding and Using Good Grammar

Recognizing Nouns Used as Direct Objects

Attention Teachers!

Pages 30 and 33 present a complete review of facts concerning the use of direct objects in sentences. The bottom half of page 33 is a seven-sentence test that requires students to identify verbs, subjects, direct objects, adjectives, and adverbs, and to insert needed commas.

If one-fourth of the students score below 75% on this test, it would be advisable for the class to discontinue using this advanced book and to repeat *Steps to Good Grammar*. The dual objectives in this system of study are to provide students with a clear understanding of the makeup of a sentence and to enable them to feel good about themselves for each small success. A score lower than 75% at this point does not indicate that the objectives have been or are being met.

A second year of studying *Steps to Good Grammar* can be very beneficial. More time can be spent on correct usage. More writing and speaking assignments can be given in which students can apply their learnings.

Having one more year of mental maturity, students have a greater ability to understand the relationships among the various parts of a sentence. Clearer comprehension leads to firmer retention. Students who repeat will be better able, in the following year, to benefit from the advanced instruction in *Using and Understanding Good Grammar* which helps students understand the components of effective expression.

Teaching Suggestions

Read the instructional material on the worksheet aloud as students read silently. Then quiz students:

1. What is the question-answer method used to locate the direct object?
2. In diagramming, what mark is used to indicate a direct object (**D.O.**)?

Practice

Have the class work together in analyzing sentences 1–7. Ask volunteers to suggest markings. Approve correct markings and demonstrate for the students how to diagram the sentences. Tell students to correct their own errors.

Have students complete sentences 8–14 individually. When they have finished, give them the correct markings and have them correct their own work and turn in their worksheets.

For an adequate sample of students' work check sentences 1, 2, 3, 9, 10, 11, and 12. Record the scores and return the worksheets the following day. Tell students to save their worksheets to use in preparing for the first test.

(continued)

Answer Key—Diagramming

8.

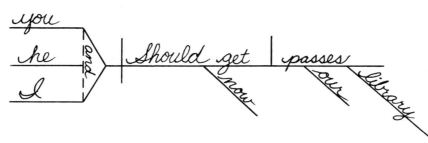

10.

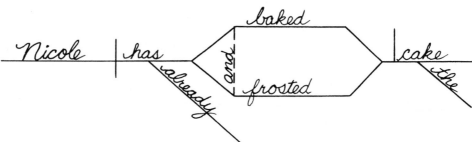

11.

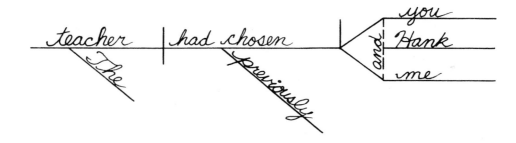

12.

Pronouns

Note that pages 93–161 are devoted to the study of the complete paradigm of pronouns. Concerning pronouns in the Practice sentences, remind students of the following:

Sentence   3:   *You* is always used first in a series of pronouns: *he*, not *him*, is a subject pronoun.

Sentence   7:   Think "they" where *and* connects compound subject words; draw a box around *and*, write *they* in parentheses above *and*, and draw an arrow from *they* to the verb *have*.

Sentence   8:   (*You*) is the understood subject in a request or command.

Sentence 10:   Demonstrates correct word and order in subject pronouns.

Sentence 12:   Demonstrates correct words and order in object pronouns.

Recognizing Nouns Used
as Direct Objects

REMEMBER:

1. The direct object, abbreviated **D.O.**, receives the action performed by the subject. Only *doing* verbs may take a direct object.

2. To locate the direct object, say the subject and verb and ask "What object?" The word that answers the question is the direct object.

   Example: The handsome stranger was carrying a large briefcase.

   Stranger was carrying "what object?" *Briefcase* is the **D.O.**

3. In diagramming, a short line perpendicular to the sentence line identifies the direct object.

stranger	was carrying	briefcase

PRACTICE: Draw two lines under the verb, one under the subject; label **D.O.**; mark adjectives and adverbs. On the reverse side diagram sentences 8, 10, 11, and 12.

1. Jeremy baked (some) cookies and (a) pie.

   (The direct object may be compound.)

2. Chris ate (a) sandwich and drank (some) milk.

   (A sentence may have compound verbs with direct objects.)

3. You and he should wash and dry (the) dishes.

   (*should* = helping verb to *wash* and *dry*;

   dishes = **D.O.** to two *doing* verbs)

4. Vic must have seen (the) culprit.

5. [Actually], Ron did dial (the) (wrong) number.

6. (The) students will have completed (their) autobiographies [soon].

7. Selma (and) Tony have written (a) [really] (good) (one-act) play.
   (they)

8. *You* Put (the) cat [out] and turn [off] (the) lights.

9. (The) teacher graded (the) tests and returned them.

10. Should you, he, and I get (our) (library) passes [now]?

11. Nicole has [already] baked and frosted (the) cake.

12. (The) teacher had [previously] chosen you, Hank, and me.

13. (The) (little) (red-haired) girl was clapping (her) hands [excitedly].

14. [Not] [even] (one) student had given (a) [completely] (correct) answer.

Name _____

Date _____

Recognizing Nouns Used as Direct Objects

REMEMBER:

1. The direct object, abbreviated **D.O.**, receives the action performed by the subject. Only *doing* verbs may take a direct object.

2. To locate the direct object, say the subject and verb and ask "What object?" The word that answers the question is the direct object.

   Example: (The)(handsome) stranger was carrying a large briefcase.

   <u>Stranger</u> <u>was carrying</u> "what object?" *Briefcase* is the **D.O.**

3. In diagramming, a short line perpendicular to the sentence line identifies the direct object.

stranger	was carrying	briefcase

PRACTICE: Draw two lines under the verb, one under the subject; label **D.O.**; mark adjectives and adverbs. On the reverse side diagram sentences 8, 10, 11, and 12.

1. Jeremy baked some cookies and a pie.

   (The direct object may be compound.)

2. Chris ate a sandwich and drank some milk.

   (A sentence may have compound verbs with direct objects.)

3. You and he should wash and dry the dishes.

   (*should* = helping verb to *wash* and *dry*;

   dishes = **D.O.** to two *doing* verbs)

4. Vic must have seen the culprit.

5. Actually, Ron did dial the wrong number.

6. The students will have completed their autobiographies soon.

7. Selma and Tony have written a really good one-act play.

8. Put the cat out and turn off the lights.

9. The teacher graded the tests and returned them.

10. Should you, he, and I get our library passes now?

11. Nicole has already baked and frosted the cake.

12. The teacher had previously chosen you, Hank, and me.

13. The little red-haired girl was clapping her hands excitedly.

14. Not even one student had given a completely correct answer.

Understanding and Using Good Grammar

FINAL PRACTICE and TEST:
The Basic Sentence; Nouns Used as Direct Objects

> The next reproducible page contains one half-page Final Practice and one half-page Test. Before passing out the page, cut it in two to remove the Test.

Final Practice

Inform students that the sentences on the Test are very similar to those in the Final Practice. Tell them to study the Final Practice and page 30 to prepare for the Test.

To assist students in remembering previous learnings, point out the special features of each sentence as indicated here:

1. Commas set off compound introductory adverbs; there is a compound subject.

2. A helping verb may be the first word in a question; there is a compound direct object.

3. Adverbs may modify adjectives; one subject, *pitcher*, has compound verb phrases each containing a direct object.

4. Commas set off adjectives that follow the noun they modify.

5. The understood subject in a request is *You.*

6. There is a comma after *actually* because it is an introductory adverb that is not essential to the meaning of the sentence; there is a compound verb with a single direct object; the three adjectives, *her little sister's*, require no comma because they form one modifying idea.

7. There is a comma after *really* because it is an introductory adverb that is not essential to the meaning of the sentence.

8. In the three-word compound subject, commas are required after *you* and after *Jenny.*

Test

Suggested Grading: Required identification and commas total 60 points.

–1, 98	–4, 93	–7, 88	–10, 83	–13, 78	–16, 73	–19, 68	–22, 63
–2, 97	–5, 92	–8, 87	–11, 82	–14, 77	–17, 72	–20, 67	–23, 62
–3, 95	–6, 90	–9, 85	–12, 80	–15, 75	–18, 70	–21, 65	–24, 60

FINAL PRACTICE:
The Basic Sentence; Nouns Used as Direct Objects

Instructions: Draw two lines under the verb, one under the subject; label **D.O.**; mark adjectives and adverbs; insert necessary commas.

1. [Slowly] and [cautiously], Lizzy and I ascended (the)(steep)(spiral) staircase. **D.O.**

2. Does (your) mother have (any) brothers or sisters? **D.O.**

3. (The) pitcher walked [only] (one) man and allowed [just] (one) hit. **D.O.** **D.O.**

4. (The)(little) child, (wide-eyed) and (frightened) watched (the)(big) dog. **D.O.**

5. (You) Call her and me [tomorrow]. **D.O.**

6. [Actually], Keri designed and sewed (her)(little)(sister's) costume. **D.O.**

7. [Really], Ted swam (1,000) laps [yesterday]. **D.O.**

8. You, Jenny, and I will do (our)(comedy) routine [tomorrow]. **D.O.**

TEST:
The Basic Sentence; Nouns Used as Direct Objects

Instructions: Draw two lines under the verb, one under the subject; label **D.O.**; mark adjectives and adverbs; insert necessary commas.

1. Will Mother and Dad take you, Jerry, and me? **D. O.**

2. (The)(little) girl, (serious-looking) and (interested) asked (several)[very] (perceptive) questions. **D. O.**

3. He and I built (the) campfire and [then] called (the)(other) hikers. **D.O.** **D.O.**

4. [Calmly] and [thoughtfully] (the) principal considered (the)(students') request. **D. O.**

5. (You) Bring (your) book and (your)(book) report [tomorrow]. **D.O.** **D.O.**

6. [Actually], you and I should wash and wax (the) car [right][now]. **D.O.**

7. [Never][before] had Dad and I seen [so](many)(wild) ducks and geese. **D. O.**

FINAL PRACTICE:
The Basic Sentence; Nouns
Used as Direct Objects

Name _____

Date _____

Instructions: Draw two lines under the verb, one under the subject; label **D.O.**; mark adjectives and adverbs; insert necessary commas.

1. Slowly and cautiously Lizzy and I ascended the steep spiral staircase.

2. Does your mother have any brothers or sisters?

3. The pitcher walked only one man and allowed just one hit.

4. The little child wide-eyed and frightened watched the big dog.

5. Call her and me tomorrow.

6. Actually Keri designed and sewed her little sister's costume.

7. Really Ted swam 1,000 laps yesterday.

8. You Jenny and I will do our comedy routine tomorrow.

TEST: The Basic Sentence;
Nouns Used as Direct
Objects

Name _____

Date _____

Instructions: Draw two lines under the verb, one under the subject; label **D.O.**; mark adjectives and adverbs; insert necessary commas.

1. Will Mother and Dad take you Jerry and me?

2. The little girl serious-looking and interested asked several very perceptive questions.

3. He and I built the campfire and then called the other hikers.

4. Calmly and thoughtfully the principal considered the students' request.

5. Bring your book and your book report tomorrow.

6. Actually you and I should wash and wax the car right now.

7. Never before had Dad and I seen so many wild ducks and geese.

© 1992, 1997 J. Weston Walch, Publisher

Understanding and Using Good Grammar

Recognizing Prepositional Phrases

Before you read aloud the **Remember** items, write these sentences for the students to copy:

1. Clara was running down the street.
2. Should the book on the table be mended?
3. A box of oranges had been ordered.

As you read each **Remember** item, call on volunteers to answer these questions about the sentences:

- What word shows the *position* relationship between (1) *running* and *street* (down); (2) *book* and *table* (on); (3) *box* and *orange* (of)?

- What words should be enclosed in parentheses? Which words should be labeled **prep.** and **O.P.**?

$$\underset{\text{(down the street)}}{\overset{\text{prep.} \quad \text{O.P.}}{}} \quad \underset{\text{(on the table)}}{\overset{\text{prep.} \quad \text{O.P.}}{}} \quad \underset{\text{(of oranges)}}{\overset{\text{prep.} \quad \text{O.P.}}{}}$$

- What added meaning does each prepositional phrase give to the modified word?
    1. *Down the street* tells *where* about *running.*
    2. *On the table* tells *which one* about *book.*
    3. *Of oranges* tells *what kind* about *box.*

Practice Diagrams

Call on volunteers to construct the diagrams. As you check their work, explain the concepts noted here with each diagram.

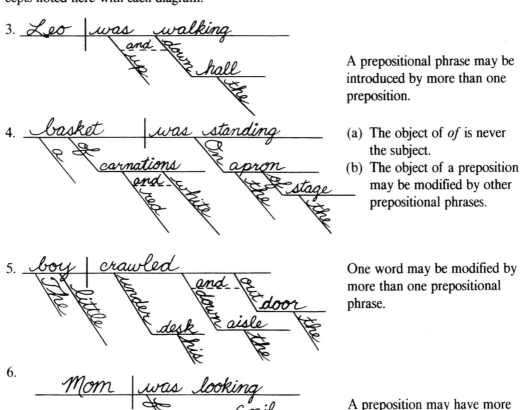

3. A prepositional phrase may be introduced by more than one preposition.

4. (a) The object of *of* is never the subject.
   (b) The object of a preposition may be modified by other prepositional phrases.

5. One word may be modified by more than one prepositional phrase.

6. A preposition may have more than one object.

Recognizing Prepositional Phrases

Words Frequently Used as Prepositions

about	around	besides	during	like	outside	under
above	at	between	except	near	over	until
across	before	beyond	for	of	past	up
after	behind	but (except)	from	off	since	upon
against	below	by	in	on	through	with
along	beneath	concerning	inside	onto	to	within
among	beside	down	into	out	toward	without

REMEMBER:

1. A **preposition** shows a relationship in position between the object of the preposition and the word it modifies.

2. A **prepositional phrase** (to be enclosed in parentheses in this study) begins with a preposition (**prep.**) and ends with a noun or pronoun object (**O.P.**).

3. A prepositional phrase gives the same added meaning to the word it modifies as does a simple adjective or adverb.

   (a) **Used as an adjective:** *which one:* sweater (from Norway); *what kind:* winner (of the contest); *how many:* reports (by seven boys); *whose:* cousin (of Jerry's).

   (b) **Used as an adverb:** *when:* arrived (on time); *where:* returned (to school); *why:* came (for advice); *how:* watched (with amazement).

4. Labeling and diagramming prepositional phrases:

   Two (of the books) were written (by Mark Twain).

PRACTICE: Underline the verb twice, the subject once; label **D.O.**, **prep.**, **O.P.**; draw an arrow from the phrase to the modified word; mark adjectives and adverbs. On the reverse side diagram sentences 3–6.

1. The bridge (over that stream) needs repair.

2. Dad had [not] noticed the YIELD sign (on the corner).

3. Leo was walking (up and down the hall).

4. (On the apron) (of the stage) stood a basket (of red and white carnations).

5. The little boy crawled (under his desk), (down the aisle), and (out the door).

6. Mom is looking (for Emil and Hilda).

7. The book (on the library table) was written (by Hemingway).

8. Joel arrived (at school) (on time).

Recognizing Prepositional Phrases

Name _____

Date _____

Words Frequently Used as Prepositions

about	around	besides	during	like	outside	under
above	at	between	except	near	over	until
across	before	beyond	for	of	past	up
after	behind	but (except)	from	off	since	upon
against	below	by	in	on	through	with
along	beneath	concerning	inside	onto	to	within
among	beside	down	into	out	toward	without

REMEMBER:

1. A **preposition** shows a relationship in position between the object of the preposition and the word it modifies.

2. A **prepositional phrase** (to be enclosed in parentheses in this study) begins with a preposition (**prep.**) and ends with a noun or pronoun object (**O.P.**).

3. A prepositional phrase gives the same added meaning to the word it modifies as does a simple adjective or adverb.

    (a) **Used as an adjective:** *which one*: sweater (from Norway); *what kind*: winner (of the contest); *how many*: reports (by seven boys); *whose*: cousin (of Jerry's).

    (b) **Used as an adverb:** *when*: arrived (on time); *where*: returned (to school); *why*: came (for advice); *how*: watched (with amazement).

4. Labeling and diagramming prepositional phrases:

    Two (of the books) were written (by Mark Twain).

PRACTICE: Underline the verb twice, the subject once; label **D.O., prep., O.P.**; draw an arrow from the phrase to the modified word; mark adjectives and adverbs. On the reverse side diagram sentences 3–6.

1. The bridge over that stream needs repair.

2. Dad had not noticed the YIELD sign on the corner.

3. Leo was walking up and down the hall.

4. On the apron of the stage stood a basket of red and white carnations.

5. The little boy crawled under his desk, down the aisle, and out the door.

6. Mom is looking for Emil and Hilda.

7. The book on the library table was written by Hemingway.

8. Joel arrived at school on time.

Understanding and Using Good Grammar

Use of Prepositional Phrases (1)

Read aloud all the instructional material in sections *A* and *B* as students read silently. Demonstrate the material as it is used in the example sentences. Quiz students to establish their understanding and retention.

For the Practice sentences, corroborate volunteers' markings. Emphasize commas as you go over the sentences. Tell students to correct all their errors. Then collect the worksheets, check the work, and record the scores. The next day return the worksheets to the students so that they can use them when preparing for the unit test.

For the Practice in section *A* emphasize:

Sentence 1: The indefinite pronoun, *everyone's*, uses an apostrophe to show possession.

Sentence 2: *Scratching* is not a verb; *scratching*, the thing the boys heard, is a gerund used as a direct object in the sentence. Gerunds will be studied later.

Use of Prepositional Phrases (1)

A. Use a comma after an introductory prepositional phrase if the phrase does not modify the sentence part which immediately follows it.

Examples: Today, (in class), Mr. Grant assigned a (one-page) composition.

(Under a (pine) tree) stood the (little) (lost) child.

PRACTICE: In the sentences, identify the sentence parts as in the examples.

1. (In his (ridiculous) costume) the clown attracted (everyone's) attention.

2. (After dark), the boys heard the scratching (of a (clawed) animal).

3. (In her (new) dress) the (little) girl was smiling [happily].

4. (From the (top floor) windows), a cloud (of confetti) was falling (like a snowstorm) (to the street).

5. (From the distance) came the howl (of a (lone) coyote).

6. (At the (country) store), you and she can buy (some) sodas (for them and us).

7. (At the end) (of the performance), the actors were applauded [enthusiastically].

B. A preposition may be formed of two or more words.

Example: [How] can we get (out of (this) predicament)?

PRACTICE: In the sentences, identify the sentence parts as in the example.

1. We stayed [home] (because of the storm).

2. He and she left (in spite of the rain).

3. (According to Sue), you and Liz scored [highest] (on the test).

4. (In addition to (new) jeans), Rachele and I bought (new) (tennis) shoes.

5. (You) Sort (these) books (as to author).

6. (As for me), I [really] tried.

7. We had fun (on our (backpack) trip) (in spite of the (cold) weather).

8. (Because of her (mother's) illness), Jane will stay [home] [today].

9. Mom wrote (to the (mail order) company) (in regard to the (damaged) items).

10. (In response to (your) question), I can [not] give an (immediate) answer.

Name _____

Date _____

Use of Prepositional Phrases (1)

A. Use a comma after an introductory prepositional phrase if the phrase does not modify the sentence part which immediately follows it.

Examples: [Today], (in class), Mr. Grant assigned a (one-page) composition.

(Under a (pine) tree) stood (the) (little) (lost) child.

PRACTICE: In the sentences, identify the sentence parts as in the examples.

1. In his ridiculous costume the clown attracted everyone's attention.

2. After dark, the boys heard the scratching of a clawed animal.

3. In her new dress the little girl was smiling happily.

4. From the top floor windows, a cloud of confetti was falling like a snowstorm to the street.

5. From the distance came the howl of a lone coyote.

6. At the country store, you and she can buy some sodas for them and us.

7. At the end of the performance, the actors were applauded enthusiastically.

B. A preposition may be formed of two or more words.

Example: [How] can we get (out of (this) predicament)?

PRACTICE: In the sentences, identify the sentence parts as in the example.

1. We stayed home because of the storm.

2. He and she left in spite of the rain.

3. According to Sue, you and Liz scored highest on the test.

4. In addition to new jeans, Rachele and I bought new sneakers.

5. Sort these books as to author.

6. As for me, I really tried.

7. We had fun on our backpack trip in spite of the cold weather.

8. Because of her mother's illness, Jane will stay home today.

9. Mom wrote to the mail order company in regard to the damaged items.

10. In response to your question, I cannot give an immediate answer.

Use of Prepositional Phrases (2)

Read all instructional material in *A*, *B*, and *C* as students read silently. Work with the students in completing the Practice sentences, quizzing them to establish understanding and correct marking. Collect and check papers, record scores, and return papers for students to use in preparing for the unit test.

In section *A*, sentence 1, point out that *else's* (possessive form) must be used after *everyone*; without it, Josh's ideas would be different from his own—a purely nonsensical statement.

Repetitive oral drill can be helpful in establishing correct usage in the students' minds. It may seem childish for the class to say repeatedly, "different from" and "off my bike," but try it! Years from now, some tall, bearded young man may say, "Ms./Mr. _____ , I still remember 'different from' and 'get off my bike'!"

Use of Prepositional Phrases (2)

A. After the word **different**, in making a comparison, use a prepositional phrase beginning with **from**. *Than*, which is not a preposition, should not be used. Identify the parts in sentences 2 and 3 as in sentence 1.

1. Josh's ideas are [usually] different (from everyone else's).

2. Rick has interests [quite] different (from his brother's).

3. Your recommendation was [not] [very] different (from his and hers).

B. **Exact meaning of similar prepositions.** Identify the sentence parts.

1. in (motion within something):   Cecilia and I walked [around] (in the mall) (with him and her).

   into (motion from one place into another)   We stepped [cautiously] (into the dilapidated house).

2. beside (next to):   Louis will sit (beside them or us).

   besides (in addition to):   No one is going (besides you, Ed, and me).

3. between (concerns two):   I'll divide the profit (between Dawn and her).

   among (concerns more than two):   We'll divide it (among the four) (of us).

C. **Usage to avoid.** Cross out the incorrect form in parentheses.

1. Do not use *of* after the preposition *off*: The little boy got (off, ~~off of~~) his bike.
   Notice: As a type of proof, no one uses *of* after *on*: The little boy got (on, ~~on of~~) his bike.

2. Do not use *a* or *an* after *kind of* or *sort of*: What kind (of, ~~of a~~) pie is that? What sort (of, ~~of an~~) explanation did he give?

PRACTICE: Cross out each error; above it, write the correct form.

1. Our choice will be ~~among~~ *between* him and her.

2. Adam looks very different ~~than~~ *from* his brother.

3. It was a lazy kind of ~~a~~ day.

4. We helped the injured hiker off ~~of~~ the mountain.

5. A really competitive spirit exists ~~between~~ *among* all the teams.

6. Carl went ~~in~~ *into* the gym before anyone else.

7. Take the book off ~~of~~ the shelf.

8. ~~Beside~~ *Besides* history, I have homework in English.

9. Her opinion was different ~~than~~ *from* mine.

10. My little cousin certainly gets ~~in~~ *into* trouble easily.

Use of Prepositional Phrases (2)

Name _____

Date _____

A. After the word **different**, in making a comparison, use a prepositional phrase beginning with **from**. *Than*, which is not a preposition, should not be used. Identify the parts in sentences 2 and 3 as in sentence 1.

1. (Josh's) ideas are [usually] different (from everyone else's)

   L.V. LVC-A prep. O.P.

2. Rick has interests quite different from his brother's.

3. Your recommendation was not very different from his and hers.

B. Exact meaning of similar prepositions. Identify the sentence parts.

1. in (motion within something):   Cecilia and I walked around in the mall with him and her.

   into (motion from one place into another)   We stepped cautiously into the dilapidated house.

2. beside (next to):   Louis will sit beside them or us.

   besides (in addition to):   No one is going besides you, Ed, and me.

3. between (concerns two):   I'll divide the profit between Dawn and her.

   among (concerns more than two):   We'll divide it among the four of us.

C. Usage to avoid. Cross out the incorrect form in parentheses.

1. Do not use *of* after the preposition *off*: The little boy got (off, ~~off of~~) his bike.
   Notice: As a type of proof, no one uses *of* after *on*: The little boy got (on, ~~on of~~) his bike.

2. Do not use *a* or *an* after *kind of* or *sort of*: What kind (of, ~~of a~~) pie is that? What sort (of, ~~of an~~) explanation did he give?

PRACTICE: Cross out each error; above it, write the correct form.

1. Our choice will be among him and her.

2. Adam looks very different than his brother.

3. It was a lazy kind of a day.

4. We helped the injured hiker off of the mountain.

5. A really competitive spirit exists between all the teams.

6. Carl went in the gym before anyone else.

7. Take the book off of the shelf.

8. Beside history, I have homework in English.

9. Her opinion was different than mine.

10. My little cousin certainly gets in trouble easily.

Understanding and Using Good Grammar

TRIAL TEST:
Prepositional Phrases and Prepositions

Students should complete this Trial Test individually. When everyone has finished, have volunteers suggest the marking of the sentence parts; then corroborate their marking. Have students correct their mistakes and keep the worksheet to use in preparing for the Test.

In section *A* point out to students:

Sentences 5 and 6: The introductory phrase modifies the verb which immediately follows the phrase; therefore no comma is needed.

Sentence 8: The two introductory phrases modify the meaning of the whole sentence; therefore no comma is necessary.

Suggested Grading:

Have students estimate their grade as follows:

Part A 1 point for each mark of identification (For a prepositional phrase, the parentheses and the arrow count as ½ point each.)

Total points: 136 (Subtract ¾ point for each error.)

Part B 12 items: Subtract 8 points for each error.

TRIAL TEST:
Prepositional Phrases and Prepositions

A. Recognizing Prepositional Phrases

Instructions: Underline verbs twice and subjects once; label **D.O.**, (**prep.**, **O.P.**), draw an arrow from the phrase to the word it modifies; insert commas where necessary; mark adjectives and adverbs.

1. (You) Put this quart (of milk) (in the refrigerator).

2. The small five-dollar gold coin slipped (between my fingers) and disappeared (through a crack) (in the attic floor).

3. Bryan has written his report (about the field trip).

4. Have many people been going (into and out of that house) [today]?

5. (Beside our cabin) flows a sparkling mountain stream.

6. (After the rehearsal) will you and she go (with Erin and me) (to the library)?

7. I spoke (to the carpenter) (with regard to his progress) (on the job).

8. (From the top) of Mt. Diablo a person can see snow-capped mountains (in the Sierras).

9. [Suddenly] an unkempt-looking stranger stepped (into the clearing) (beside our cabin), looked [around] (in a puzzled manner), turned (on his heel), and disappeared (into the forest).

B. Correct Usage of Prepositions

Instructions: Cross out each error; above it, write the correct form.

1. There is not much difference ~~among~~ *between* the two candidates.

2. She and I walked ~~in~~ *into* the room from the hall.

3. *Besides* ~~Beside~~ you and her, I will invite Leann and Jennifer.

4. Probably this book is not very different ~~than~~ *from* the other one.

5. What sort of ~~a~~ book are you looking for?

6. Dad lifted the ladder off ~~of~~ the garage rafters.

7. *Among* ~~Between~~ all of the candidates, three of you have the best qualifications.

8. That family lived ~~besides~~ *beside* us for many years.

9. Is your report very different ~~than~~ *from* Emily's?

10. What kind of ~~a~~ coat did you have in mind?

11. We edged carefully off ~~of~~ the crumbling ledge.

12. Will Janelle enter her name ~~into~~ *in* the contest?

Name _____

Date _____

TRIAL TEST:
Prepositional Phrases and Prepositions

A. Recognizing Prepositional Phrases

Instructions: Underline verbs twice and subjects once; label **D.O.**, (**prep.**, **O.P.**), draw an arrow from the phrase to the word it modifies; insert commas where necessary; mark adjectives and adverbs.

1. Put this quart of milk in the refrigerator.

2. The small five-dollar gold coin slipped between my fingers and disappeared through a crack in the attic floor.

3. Bryan has written his report about the field trip.

4. Have many people been going into and out of that house today?

5. Beside our cabin flows a sparkling mountain stream.

6. After the rehearsal will you and she go with Erin and me to the library?

7. I spoke to the carpenter with regard to his progress on the job.

8. From the top of Mt. Diablo a person can see snow-capped mountains in the Sierras.

9. Suddenly an unkempt-looking stranger stepped into the clearing beside our cabin looked around in a puzzled manner turned on his heel and disappeared into the forest.

B. Correct Usage of Prepositions

Instructions: Cross out each error; above it, write the correct form.

1. There is not much difference among the two candidates.

2. She and I walked in the room from the hall.

3. Beside you and her, I will invite Leann and Jennifer.

4. Probably this book is not very different than the other one.

5. What sort of a book are you looking for?

6. Dad lifted the ladder off of the garage rafters.

7. Between all of the candidates, three of you have the best qualifications.

8. That family lived besides us for many years.

9. Is your report very different than Emily's?

10. What kind of a coat did you have in mind?

11. We edged carefully off of the crumbling ledge.

12. Will Janelle enter her name into the contest?

TEST: *Prepositional Phrases*
and Prepositions

Suggested Grading:

Part A

All sentences are taken from information and practice pages in this unit. Scores should be high. In scoring, identification marks and commas count as 1 point, except that the prepositional phrase parentheses and the arrow count as ½ point each. Total points: 76 (1.32 each).

–1, 99	–5, 93	–9, 88	–13, 83	–17, 78	–21, 72	–25, 67
–2, 97	–6, 92	–10, 87	–14, 82	–18, 76	–22, 71	–26, 66
–3, 96	–7, 91	–11, 85	–15, 80	–19, 75	–23, 70	–27, 64
–4, 95	–8, 89	–12, 84	–16, 79	–20, 74	–24, 68	–28, 63

Part B

15 items = 6.67 each

–1, 93	–3, 80	–5, 67	–7, 53
–2, 87	–4, 73	–6, 60	–8, 47

Averaging the two scores for recording would be justified since recognition, correct punctuation, and correct usage are equally important.

TEST: Prepositional Phrases and Prepositions

A. Recognizing Prepositional Phrases

Instructions: Underline verbs twice, and subjects once; label **D.O.**, (**prep., O.P.**); draw an
arrow from the phrase to the word it modifies; insert commas where necessary;
mark adjectives and adverbs.

1. (Because of her mother's illness), Jane stayed [home] [yesterday].

2. Have many people been going (into and out of that house) today?

3. (From the distance) came the howl (of a lone coyote).

4. (At the country store) you and she can buy some sodas (for them and us).

5. [Suddenly] a stranger stepped (into the clearing)(beside our cabin),
   looked [around](in a puzzled manner), turned (on his heel), and
   disappeared (into the forest).

B. Correct Usage of Prepositions

Instructions: Cross out each error; above it, write the correct form.

1. We ran from the car, up the walk, and ~~in~~ *into* the school.

2. Accidentally, I knocked the vase off ~~of~~ the shelf.

3. The principal must decide ~~between~~ *among* the three plans.

4. No one ~~beside~~ *besides* you, Carla, and me volunteered to help.

5. Sue is the sort of ~~a~~ girl whom everyone admires.

6. For many years the Dosses have lived ~~besides~~ *beside* us.

7. What kind of ~~a~~ job are you looking for?

8. Was today's performance different ~~than~~ *from* yesterday's?

9. If you are always late for school, you will get ~~in~~ *into* trouble.

10. ~~Between~~ *Among* all those dresses, must I choose just one?

11. ~~Beside~~ *Besides* raking the leaves, we mowed the lawn.

12. I slipped off ~~of~~ the diving board right ~~in~~ *into* the pool.

13. That sort of ~~an~~ assembly is different ~~than~~ *from* our usual ones.

TEST: Prepositional Phrases and Prepositions

Name _____

Date _____

A. Recognizing Prepositional Phrases

Instructions: Underline verbs twice, and subjects once; label **D.O., (prep., O.P.)**; draw an arrow from the phrase to the word it modifies; insert commas where necessary; mark adjectives and adverbs.

1. Because of her mother's illness Jane stayed home yesterday.

2. Have many people been going into and out of that house today?

3. From the distance came the howl of a lone coyote.

4. At the country store you and she can buy some sodas for them and us.

5. Suddenly a stranger stepped into the clearing beside our cabin looked around in a puzzled manner turned on his heel and disappeared into the forest.

B. Correct Usage of Prepositions

Instructions: Cross out each error; above it, write the correct form.

1. We ran from the car, up the walk, and in the school.

2. Accidentally, I knocked the vase off of the shelf.

3. The principal must decide between the three plans.

4. No one beside you, Carla, and me volunteered to help.

5. Sue is the sort of a girl whom everyone admires.

6. For many years the Dosses have lived besides us.

7. What kind of a job are you looking for?

8. Was today's performance different than yesterday's?

9. If you are always late for school, you will get in trouble.

10. Between all those dresses, must I choose just one?

11. Beside raking the leaves, we mowed the lawn.

12. I slipped off of the diving board right in the pool.

13. That sort of an assembly is different than our usual ones.

Use of Prepositional Phrases

This page is self-explanatory. In the example sentences the arrows show why misplaced prepositional phrases create confusion.

If students have difficulty getting started on the Confusing/Clear assignment, you might give them this sentence:

Aunt Em just bought a red sports car (from that dealer) (with spoked wheels).

You might add to **Not acceptable** this sentence which students often use:

What did you do that *for*?

Better: *For what reason* did you do that?

Preferred: *Why* did you do that?

Students are not tested on the information presented on this page. They should keep it for future reference.

Use of Prepositional Phrases

Name _____

Date _____

A. Placement of Prepositional Phrases

A prepositional phrase should be placed as close as possible to the word it modifies. A misplaced phrase may confuse the reader.

1. *Confusing:* We read a report (of the accident)(in today's paper).

   Clear: (In today's paper) we read a report (of the accident).

2. *Confusing:* Mom bought some strawberries (at the store)(with a delicious flavor).

   Clear: (At the store), Mom bought some strawberries (with a delicious flavor).

3. *Confusing:* (In the aspen grove)(near the stream) I watched two beavers hard at work.

   Clear: I watched two beavers hard at work (in the aspen grove)(near the stream).

PRACTICE: Write two pairs of original Confusing/Clear sentences.

1. *Confusing:* _____

   Clear: _____

2. *Confusing:* _____

   Clear: _____

B. Placement of a Preposition

Many grammarians accept these statements: A preposition may be used at the end of a sentence if (a) it has an object of the preposition somewhere in the sentence or (b) that position adds emphasis to the preposition or sounds more natural.

Examples:

1. What are you staring *at*? The demonstrative pronoun, *What*, is the object of *at*; this structure sounds more natural than: At what are you staring?

2. Which design did you vote *for*? The demonstrative pronoun, *Which*, is the object of *for*, this structure emphasizes *for* as opposed to *against*.

Not acceptable: 1. Where are you going to?   Omit the prepositions;
                      2. Where is your book at?   adverbs *where/why* are
                      3. Why are they leaving for?   not objects of prepositions.

More formal and completely acceptable:

1. With whom are you going?
2. In which drawer did you find it?
3. For whom did you buy that watch?
4. At which theater did you see that movie?
5. To whom did you send the package?

Understanding and Using Good Grammar

Recognizing Nouns Used
as Indirect Objects

Read aloud **Remember** items 1, 2, 3, and 4 as students read silently; quiz students to check their understanding.

Practice

1. Encourage students to use the "ask and say" device to recognize the indirect object:

   Sentence 4: *Ask:* "The people sent what object?" *Say:* "tons" (**D.O.**)
   Ask: "Who got it?" *Say:* "victims" (**I.O.**)

2. Remind students:

   Sentence 2: In a request or command, *you* is frequently the understood subject.

   Sentence 4: *Tons* is the direct object; *of clothing* is a prepositional phrase that tells "what kind" about *tons*.

Answer Key—Diagramming

2.

4.

6.

8.

Recognizing Nouns Used as Indirect Objects

REMEMBER:

1. An **indirect object** (abbreviated **I.O.**) is a kind of prepositional phrase. A preposition is not used, but the meaning is understood.

    Examples: Dad handed Al (the) keys. (to Al)

    We bought Mother (some) perfume. (for Mother)

2. The sentence must have a direct object in order to have an indirect object. The **I.O.** gets, or receives, the **D.O.**

3. To locate the indirect object, ask: "Dad handed *what object?*"
    Answer: "the keys" (**D.O.**); ask: "Who got it?" Answer: "Al" (**I.O.**)

4. In diagramming, an (x) takes the place of the understood preposition. Indirect objects may be compound.

    Example: (My) parents have given (my) sister and me (their) permission.

PRACTICE: Underline verbs twice and subjects once. Label **D.O.**, (**prep.**, **O.P.**), and **I.O.** Draw an arrow from the prepositional phrase to the word it modifies. Mark adjectives and adverbs. On the reverse side, diagram sentences 2, 4, 6, and 8.

1. Dad has given Shiloh (the) money.
2. (You) Tell (the) man (your) name.
3. Coach granted Scott (the) request.
4. (The) people (in (that) town) sent (the)(flood) victims tons (of clothing).
5. (The) pitcher threw (the) batter (a)(sharp) curve.
6. Did Marcel give Ben (the) information (about (the)(field) trip)?
7. Has Molly given Mr. Alexander (her)(history) report?
8. (Without question), (my)(little) brother had told Mom and Dad (the) truth.

Rewrite these sentences substituting indirect objects (**I.O.**'s) for prepositional phrases. Identify sentence parts in the sentences you write.

1. Kaspar has made some sandwiches for us. *Kaspar has made us (some) sandwiches.*

2. The judge showed no mercy to the hardened criminal. *(The) judge showed (the)(hardened) criminal (no) mercy.*

3. Hasn't your uncle built a mountain chalet for his family? *Hasn't your uncle built (his) family (a)(mountain) chalet?*

Recognizing Nouns Used as Indirect Objects

Name _____

Date _____

REMEMBER:

1. An **indirect object** (abbreviated **I.O.**) is a kind of prepositional phrase. A preposition is not used, but the meaning is understood.

   Examples: Dad handed Al (the) keys. (to Al)
   We bought Mother (some) perfume. (for Mother)

2. The sentence must have a direct object in order to have an indirect object. The **I.O.** gets, or receives, the **D.O.**

3. To locate the indirect object, ask: "Dad handed *what object*?"
   Answer: "the keys" (**D.O.**); ask: "Who got it?" Answer: "Al" (**I.O.**)

4. In diagramming, an (x) takes the place of the understood preposition. Indirect objects may be compound.

   Example: (My) parents have given (my) sister and me (their) permission.

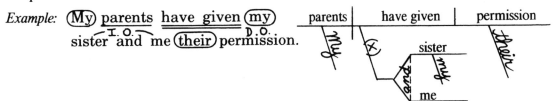

PRACTICE: Underline verbs twice and subjects once. Label **D.O.**, (**prep.**, **O.P.**), and **I.O.** Draw an arrow from the prepositional phrase to the word it modifies. Mark adjectives and adverbs. On the reverse side, diagram sentences 2, 4, 6, and 8.

1. Dad has given Shiloh the money.

2.   Tell the man your name.

3. Coach granted Scott the request.

4. The people in that town sent the flood victims tons of clothing.

5. The pitcher threw the batter a sharp curve.

6. Did Marcel give Ben the information about the field trip?

7. Has Molly given Mr. Alexander her history report?

8. Without question, my little brother had told Mom and Dad the truth.

   Rewrite these sentences substituting indirect objects (**I.O.**'s) for prepositional phrases. Identify sentence parts in the sentences you write.

1. Kaspar has made some sandwiches for us. _____

   _____

2. The judge showed no mercy to the hardened criminal. _____

   _____

3. Hasn't your uncle built a mountain chalet for his family? _____

   _____

Understanding and Using Good Grammar

PRACTICE: Recognizing Indirect Objects and All Other Sentence Parts

Several pairs of sentences show the similarity between an indirect object and a prepositional phrase. Using sentences 1 and 2, demonstrate to students the reasons for choosing to use one form or the other:

1. The verb is the most important part of a sentence.
2. The sentence part most closely following the verb receives emphasis.
3. Main sentence parts receive more emphasis than do modifying elements.

Use sentence 1 to emphasize the direct object:

Arvid bought (some) lunch (for (his) friend).

Use sentence 2 to emphasize the indirect object:

Arvid bought (his) friend (some) lunch.

Call on volunteers to analyze sentences 7–8, 10–11, and 12–13 in this manner.

On the chalkboard or overhead, construct the diagram for sentence 15 to show the position of adverbs/adverb phrases that modify a compound verb.

The following worksheet, along with the worksheet on page 55, will help students prepare for the Test.

PRACTICE: Recognizing Indirect Objects and All Other Sentence Parts

Instructions: Underline verbs twice and subjects once; label **D.O.** (**prep.**, **O.P.**), and **I.O.**; draw an arrow from a prepositional phrase to the word it modifies; insert commas; mark adjectives and adverbs.

1. Arvid bought some lunch (for his friend).

2. Arvid bought his friend some lunch.

3. (After the election) will you give Jean and me your honest opinion?

4. The teacher might ask you or Dennis that same question.

5. (You) Hand me your test paper (on your way) (out of the room).

6. The secretary (in the office) lent Joe some lunch money.

7. No, the principal did not give her permission (to them).

8. No, the principal did not give them her permission.

9. Have their parents sent Wendy and Randy the money (for the entry fee)?

10. Aunt Kay bought us some very nice souvenirs.

11. Aunt Kay bought some very nice souvenirs (for us).

12. Curtis had left careful instructions (for her and me).

13. Curtis had left her and me careful instructions.

14. Unfortunately not until (after Curtis's return) did we notice his note (of instructions) (on the family bulletin board).

15. Yesterday early (in the morning) (during a heavy downpour) (of rain), Mr. Scott saw me (at the bus stop) and gave me a ride (to school).

16. The shrill scream gave all (of us) the chills.

17. Keri always makes a clever Halloween costume (for her little sister).

18. Hasn't the school sent you and your brother your report cards?

19. Tomorrow, the teacher will give you a test similar (to this practice).

PRACTICE: Recognizing Indirect Objects and All Other Sentence Parts

Name _____

Date _____

Instructions: Underline verbs twice and subjects once; label **D.O. (prep., O.P.)**, and **I.O.**; draw an arrow from a prepositional phrase to the word it modifies; insert commas; mark adjectives and adverbs.

1. Arvid bought some lunch for his friend.

2. Arvid bought his friend some lunch.

3. After the election will you give Jean and me your honest opinion?

4. The teacher might ask you or Dennis that same question.

5.   Hand me your test paper on your way out of the room.

6. The secretary in the office lent Joe some lunch money.

7. No the principal did not give her permission to them.

8. No the principal did not give them her permission.

9. Have their parents sent Wendy and Randy the money for the entry fee?

10. Aunt Kay bought us some very nice souvenirs.

11. Aunt Kay bought some very nice souvenirs for us.

12. Curtis had left careful instructions for her and me.

13. Curtis had left her and me careful instructions.

14. Unfortunately not until after Curtis's return did we notice his note of instructions on the family bulletin board.

15. Yesterday early in the morning during a heavy downpour of rain Mr. Scott saw me at the bus stop and gave me a ride to school.

16. The shrill scream gave all of us the chills.

17. Keri always makes a clever Halloween costume for her little sister.

18. Hasn't the school sent you and your brother your report cards?

19. Tomorrow the teacher will give you a test similar to this practice.

TEST: Recognizing Indirect Objects and All Other Sentence Parts

The next reproducible page contains two copies of one half-page Test. Before passing out the page, cut each duplicated page in half; give each student one half-page.

Sentences 2 and 3: No commas should be used after the prepositional phrases *after the election* and *after his return* because both phrases modify the verbs which follow them immediately.

Suggested Grading: No point value is given the parentheses around prepositional phrases.

There are 70 markings, including commas = 1.4 each.

–1, 99	–7, 90	–13, 82	–19, 73	–25, 65
–2, 97	–8, 89	–14, 80	–20, 72	–26, 64
–3, 96	–9, 87	–15, 79	–21, 71	–27, 62
–4, 94	–10, 86	–16, 78	–22, 69	–28, 61
–5, 93	–11, 85	–17, 76	–23, 68	–29, 59
–6, 92	–12, 83	–18, 75	–24, 66	

TEST: Recognizing Indirect Objects and All Other Sentence Parts

Instructions: Underline verbs twice and subjects once; label **D.O., I.O., (prep., O.P.)**; insert commas; mark adjectives and adverbs.

1. Have (your) parents given you and (your) sister (their) permission?

2. (After (the) election) will you give Jean and me (your)(honest) opinion?

3. Actually, not until (after (his) return) did we notice (Curtis's) note (of instructions)(on (the)(family)(bulletin) board).

4. Yesterday, early (in (the) morning)(during (a)(heavy) downpour)(of rain), Mr. Hanson saw me (at (the) bus stop) and gave me (a) ride (to school).

5. (The) judge showed (no) mercy (to (the)(hardened) criminal).

TEST: Recognizing Indirect Objects and All Other Sentence Parts

Name _____

Date _____

Instructions: Underline verbs twice and subjects once; label **D.O.**, **I.O.**, (**prep.**, **O.P.**); insert commas; mark adjectives and adverbs.

1. Have your parents given you and your sister their permission?

2. After the election will you give Jean and me your honest opinion?

3. Actually not until after his return did we notice Curtis's note of instructions on the family bulletin board.

4. Yesterday early in the morning during a heavy downpour of rain Mr. Hanson saw me at the bus stop and gave me a ride to school.

5. The judge showed no mercy to the hardened criminal.

TEST: Recognizing Indirect Objects and All Other Sentence Parts

Name _____

Date _____

Instructions: Underline verbs twice and subjects once; label **D.O.**, **I.O.**, (**prep.**, **O.P.**); insert commas; mark adjectives and adverbs.

1. Have your parents given you and your sister their permission?

2. After the election will you give Jean and me your honest opinion?

3. Actually not until after his return did we notice Curtis's note of instructions on the family bulletin board.

4. Yesterday early in the morning during a heavy downpour of rain Mr. Hanson saw me at the bus stop and gave me a ride to school.

5. The judge showed no mercy to the hardened criminal.

Recognizing Linking Verbs

Read aloud the instructive material as students read silently. Then cover the following points:

1. Tell students they are to memorize the seventeen linking verbs to write in order the next day; emphasize the *Notice* item.

2. Quiz students regarding the instructive notes that apply to the **Example** sentences.

    Sentence 2: Remind students that nominative (meaning "having to do with the subject") personal pronouns (*I, he, she, we, they*) are correctly used after linking verbs.

    Sentence 3: Point out that *Winner* wasn't "doing" *surprised*; the only verb word is *was*, a linking verb; *surprised* is the **LVC–A** that describes the subject, *winner*.

3. In the **Diagramming** section demonstrate the slanted line that points back to the subject.

4. For item 1 in the **Remember** section, emphasize *only* verb word; for item 2, emphasize *last* word.

5. Have students complete the Practice in the usual manner. When they have finished, have volunteers analyze the sentence parts; corroborate their markings. Have students correct their own papers and hand them in. Check the papers, record the scores, and return them to students to use in preparing for the Test.

    As they review their work, students should be able to give reasons for using commas as follows:

    Sentence 4: A comma is used after the introductory adverb, which is not necessary to the meaning of the sentence.

    Sentence 5: A comma is used to separate parallel adjectives.

    Sentence 6: A comma is always used before the conjunction *but*, which expresses a contrast.

Answer Key—Diagramming

5.

6.

Recognizing Linking Verbs

DEFINITION: A **linking verb** (**LV**) connects or links the subject and the linking verb complement, the noun/pronoun (**LVC–N**) or adjective (**LVC–A**) that follows the linking verb.

MEMORIZE: Words frequently used as linking verbs are: **is, am, are, was, were, be, being, been, become, seem, appear, feel, taste, smell, sound, grow, look.**

> Notice: The first eight linking verbs are the same as the first eight helping verbs. The rest of the 23 helping verbs, *has, have, had, do,* etc., are *never* used as linking verbs.

Examples: 1. (The) winner <u>was</u> Gabriella.   The **LVC–N** identifies the subject;

2. (The) winner <u>was</u> she.   it tells who or what the subject is.

A sentence with an **LVC–N** can be reversed and the meaning remains the same:

<u>Gabriella</u> <u>was</u> (the) winner.   <u>She</u> <u>was</u> (the) winner.

3. (The) winner <u>was</u> surprised.   The **LVC–A** describes the subject.

DIAGRAMMING: The line following the linking verb slants back toward the subject, indicating that the **LVC** either identifies the subject or modifies it.

REMEMBER: 1. When *is, am, are, was,* or *were* is the only verb word in the sentence, it is *always* a linking verb.

2. When *be, being,* or *been* is the last word in a verb phrase, it is *always* a linking verb:

<u>Theo</u> <u>will be</u> / <u>is being</u> / <u>should have been</u> cautious.

PRACTICE: Mark verbs, subjects, adjectives (except **LVC–A**), and adverbs; label **LV, LCV–N, LVC–A**; insert commas. Diagram sentences 5 and 6.

1. (Our) <u>dog</u> <u>is</u> (a)(German) shepherd.

2. <u>Uncle Evan</u> <u>had been</u> (a)(U.S. Navy) pilot.

3. <u>Maria</u> <u>is</u> [certainly] <u>being</u> careful.

4. [Hopefully,] (our)(school) <u>band</u> <u>will be</u> (the) winner.

5. (Aunt Cathy's) <u>twins</u> <u>are</u> (darling)(little,)(freckled) redheads.

6. (The) <u>carpenters</u> <u>were</u> slow, but [very] careful.

7. (Several)(capable) <u>women</u> <u>are</u> candidates.

8. <u>Has</u> <u>he</u> <u>been</u> [really] angry?

9. <u>Elizabeth</u> <u>could have</u> and <u>should have been</u> (the)(squad) leader.

Recognizing Linking Verbs

Name _____

Date _____

DEFINITION: A **linking verb** (**LV**) connects or links the subject and the linking verb complement, the noun/pronoun (**LVC–N**) or adjective (**LVC–A**) that follows the linking verb.

MEMORIZE: Words frequently used as linking verbs are: **is, am, are, was, were, be, being, been, become, seem, appear, feel, taste, smell, sound, grow, look.**

> **Notice:** The first eight linking verbs are the same as the first eight helping verbs. The rest of the 23 helping verbs, *has, have, had, do,* etc., are *never* used as linking verbs.

Examples:
1. (The) winner was Gabriella.   The **LVC–N** identifies the subject;
it tells who or what the subject is.
2. (The) winner was she.

A sentence with an **LVC–N** can be reversed and the meaning remains the same:

Gabriella was (the) winner.   She was (the) winner.

3. (The) winner was surprised.   The **LVC–A** describes the subject.

DIAGRAMMING: The line following the linking verb slants back toward the subject, indicating that the **LVC** either identifies the subject or modifies it.

winner | was \ Gabriella   *winner | was \ surprised*

REMEMBER:
1. When *is, am, are, was,* or *were* is the only verb word in the sentence, it is *always* a linking verb.

2. When *be, being,* or *been* is the last word in a verb phrase, it is *always* a linking verb:
Theo will be / is being / should have been cautious.

PRACTICE: Mark verbs, subjects, adjectives (except **LVC–A**), and adverbs; label **LV, LCV–N, LVC–A**; insert commas. Diagram sentences 5 and 6.

1. Our dog is a German shepherd.

2. Uncle Evan had been a U.S. Navy pilot.

3. Maria is certainly being careful.

4. Hopefully our school band will be the winner.

5. Aunt Cathy's twins are darling little freckled redheads.

6. The carpenters were slow but very careful.

7. Several capable women are candidates.

8. Has he been really angry?

9. Elizabeth could have and should have been the squad leader.

Understanding and Using Good Grammar

Distinguishing Between Linking Verbs and Helping Verbs

TO TEACHERS:

Specific directions for introducing instructive material, "teacher read aloud, students read silently," etc. will be omitted in succeeding pages of the Teacher's Manual. However, teachers are advised to continue the practice. Without being instructed to do so, even the most highly motivated students seldom reread and quiz themselves to be sure they fully understand and will remember new and review concepts in grammar.

The work on this page is self-explanatory. The students should have little trouble in recognizing helping verbs used in conjunction with either linking or doing verbs. Labeling helping verbs with a lower case *h* assists in the analysis.

Before students begin the review of linking verbs on page 71, point out the following:

1. The label **LVC–A** identifies an adjective that modifies the subject.

2. In using the verb *feel* with reference to health, the adjectives *well* and *bad* are used.

3. In *spoken* English, where the meaning of *bad* is "regretful," some grammarians accept the adverb *badly*:

$$\text{Elsa \underline{felt} [badly] (about (her) forgetfulness).}$$

In *written* English, the majority prefer the adjective *bad*:

$$\text{Elsa \underline{felt} bad (about it).}$$

Whether written or spoken, whether referring to health or regret, all grammarians accept:

$$\text{Elsa \underline{felt} bad.}$$

Students might as well accept it as standard!

Distinguishing Between Linking Verbs and Helping Verbs

REMEMBER: 1. A **linking verb** expresses no action; the subject doesn't do anything and nothing is done to the subject.

         2. A sentence with a linking verb simply reports a condition or asks a question about a condition.

         3. **Is**, **am**, **are**, **was**, **were**, **be**, **being**, and **been** may be used as linking verbs or as helping verbs to doing verbs:

Examples:

(a) The spectators **were** enthusiastic and noisy.   (LV, LVC-A, LVC-A)

     The spectators were not *doing* "enthusiastic" or "noisy"; *were* is a linking verb followed by **LVC-A**'s.

(b) The spectators **were shouting** [enthusiastically].   (h)

     Here, *were* is a helping verb to the doing verb, *shouting.*

PRACTICE: Distinguish between linking verbs and helping verbs. Mark verbs, subjects, adjectives, (except **LVC-A**), and adverbs; label **LV**, **LVC-A**; above helping verbs, write a lowercase **h.**

1. My friend should be a candidate.   (h, LV, LVC-N)

2. My friend should be campaigning.   (h, h)

3. My friend should be successful.   (h, LV, LVC-A)

4. The cabin was an A-frame structure.   (LV, LVC-N)

5. The cabin was [not] large.   (LV, LVC-A)

6. The cabin was [recently] built.   (h)

7. We are students.   (LV, LVC-N)

8. We are industrious.   (LV, LVC-A)

9. We are studying.   (h)

10. That woman and her brother were nurses.   (LV, LVC-N)

11. Both were [very] competent.   (LV, LVC-A)

12. They were [regularly] employed.   (h)

13. Will you be the driver?   (h, LV, LVC-N)

14. Will you be driving [today]?   (h, h)

15. He and she have been jogging.   (h, h)

16. He and she have [always] been [quite] athletic.   (h, LV, LVC-A)

17. Tanya [surely] must have been pleased.   (h, h, LV, LVC-A)

18. My horse is being stubborn.   (h, LV, LVC-A)

19. His horse is being ridden.   (h, h)

Name _____

Date _____

Distinguishing Between Linking Verbs and Helping Verbs

REMEMBER: 1. A **linking verb** expresses no action; the subject doesn't do anything and nothing is done to the subject.

2. A sentence with a linking verb simply reports a condition or asks a question about a condition.

3. **Is, am, are, was, were, be, being,** and **been** may be used as linking verbs or as helping verbs to doing verbs:

Examples:

(a) The spectators were enthusiastic and noisy.

The spectators were not *doing* "enthusiastic" or "noisy"; *were* is a linking verb followed by **LVC–A**'s.

(b) The spectators were shouting enthusiastically.

Here, *were* is a helping verb to the doing verb, *shouting*.

PRACTICE: Distinguish between linking verbs and helping verbs. Mark verbs, subjects, adjectives, (except **LVC–A**), and adverbs; label **LV, LVC–A**; above helping verbs, write a lowercase **h**.

1. My friend should be a candidate.

2. My friend should be campaigning.

3. My friend should be successful.

4. The cabin was an A-frame structure.

5. The cabin was not large.

6. The cabin was recently built.

7. We are students.

8. We are industrious.

9. We are studying.

10. That woman and her brother were nurses.

11. Both were very competent.

12. They were regularly employed.

13. Will you be the driver?

14. Will you be driving today?

15. He and she have been jogging.

16. He and she have always been quite athletic.

17. Tanya surely must have been pleased.

18. My horse is being stubborn.

19. His horse is being ridden.

Recognizing Linking Verbs

PRACTICE A:

Demonstrate on the chalkboard the correct form for diagramming linking verb complements.

Answer Key—Diagramming

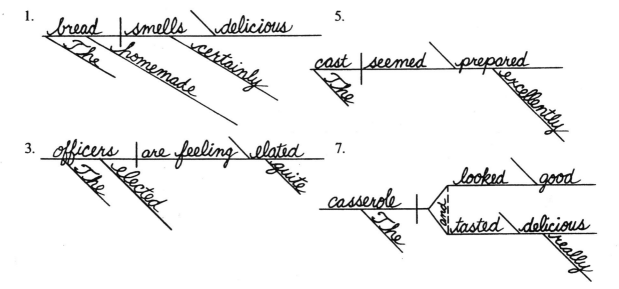

PRACTICE B:

Point out the following to students:

Sentence 1: As used here, *become* means "show to advantage"; *anyone* is a direct object.

Sentence 2: *Had become* means "had come to be" and is a linking verb.

Sentence 9: Remind students that an adverb ending in *-ly* should *not* be connected by a hyphen to an adjective that follows it.

Answer Key—Diagramming

Recognizing Linking Verbs

The other nine words frequently used as linking verbs are:

become, seem, appear, feel, taste, smell, sound, grow, look

PRACTICE A: Mark verbs, subjects, adjectives (except **LVC–A**), and adverbs; label **LV, LVC–N, LVC–A.** On the reverse side, diagram sentences 1, 3, 5, and 7. (Refer to page 65.)

1. (The)(homemade) bread [certainly] smells delicious.

2. (The) coach [usually] appeared confident.

3. (The)(elected) officers are feeling [quite] elated.

4. (The) audience was growing [more] interested.

5. (The) cast seemed [excellently] prepared.

6. (That)(little)(mountain) stream becomes (a)(raging) river.

7. (The) pizza looked good and tasted [really] delicious.

8. (The)(wolves') howls had sounded threatening.

Notice: These verbs, with the exception of *seem*, may also be used as doing verbs.

PRACTICE B: Distinguish between linking verbs and doing verbs. Mark verbs, subjects, adjectives (except **LVC–A**), adverbs, prepositional phrases; label **LV, LVC–N, LVC–A, D.O., prep.,** and **O.P.** On the reverse side diagram sentences 1, 2, 15, and 16.

1. (Selfish) behavior does [not] become anyone.

2. (The) child had become [rather] selfish.

3. (A) stranger appeared (in (the) doorway).

4. (The) stranger appeared bewildered.

5. I felt (the) rush (of (cold) air).

6. (The) air felt clammy.

7. Dad [eagerly] tasted (the) soup.

8. (The) soup tasted [quite] salty.

9. Clarice smelled (the)(freshly)(baked) brownies.

10. (The) brownies smelled tempting.

11. (The) principal sounded (the) alarm.

12. (The) alarm sounded deafening.

13. (A)(neighboring) farmer had grown (the)(huge) pumpkin.

14. (The) pumpkin had grown huge.

15. Geno looked (at (his)(brother's) project).

16. (The) project looked superior.

Recognizing Linking Verbs

Name _____

Date _____

The other nine words frequently used as linking verbs are:

become, seem, appear, feel, taste, smell, sound, grow, look

PRACTICE A: Mark verbs, subjects, adjectives (except **LVC–A**), and adverbs; label **LV**, **LVC–N**, **LVC–A**. On the reverse side, diagram sentences 1, 3, 5, and 7. (Refer to page 65.)

1. The homemade bread certainly smells delicious.

2. The coach usually appeared confident.

3. The elected officers are feeling quite elated.

4. The audience was growing more interested.

5. The cast seemed excellently prepared.

6. That little mountain stream becomes a raging river.

7. The pizza looked good and tasted really delicious.

8. The wolves' howls had sounded threatening.

Notice: These verbs, with the exception of *seem*, may also be used as doing verbs.

PRACTICE B: Distinguish between linking verbs and doing verbs. Mark verbs, subjects, adjectives (except **LVC–A**), adverbs, prepositional phrases; label **LV**, **LVC–N**, **LVC–A**, **D.O.**, **prep.**, and **O.P.** On the reverse side diagram sentences 1, 2, 15, and 16.

1. Selfish behavior does not become anyone.

2. The child had become rather selfish.

3. A stranger appeared in the doorway.

4. The stranger appeared bewildered.

5. I felt the rush of cold air.

6. The air felt clammy.

7. **Dad eagerly tasted the soup.**

8. The soup tasted quite salty.

9. Clarice smelled the freshly baked brownies.

10. The brownies smelled tempting.

11. The principal sounded the alarm.

12. The alarm sounded deafening.

13. A neighboring farmer had grown the huge pumpkin.

14. The pumpkin had grown huge.

15. Geno looked at his brother's project.

16. The project looked superior.

Understanding and Using Good Grammar

FINAL DRILL and TEST:
Recognizing Linking Verbs

The next reproducible page contains one half-page Final Drill and one half-page Test. Before passing out the page, cut it in two to remove the Test.

Final Drill

Sentences 1–6:   Have volunteers analyze, mark, and label the sentence parts. Review the drill with students to make necessary corrections.

Sentences 7–12:   Have students individually mark and label the sentences. Give them the correct markings. Tell students to correct their own papers and take them home to use, along with page 71, to prepare for the Test.

Test

In grading, count the **underlining** of a linking verb as **1 point** and the **LV** label as **1 point**. Altogether there are 80 marks/labels required on the test. Each error has a value of 1.25 points. On a paper with 10 errors, subtract 12.50 from 100 = 87.5; record 88.

FINAL DRILL:
Recognizing Linking Verbs

Instructions: Mark verbs, subjects, adjectives (except **LVC–A**), adverbs and prepositional phrases; label **LV**, **LVC–N**, **LVC–A**, **D.O.**, **prep.**, **O.P.**, and **h** above helping verb.

1. (Those)(two) women <u>are</u> [LV] officers (in [prep.] (the) U.S.A.F.) [O.P.]

2. They <u>are</u> [h] <u>stationed</u> (at [prep.] Vandenberg Air Force Base). [O.P.]

3. (That) horse <u>seems</u> [LV] [very] well-trained. [LVC–A]

4. (The) caller (on [prep.] (the) phone) [O.P.] <u>must</u> [h] <u>have</u> [h] <u>been</u> [LV] (my) aunt. [LVC–N]

5. Luigi <u>must</u> [h] <u>have</u> [h] <u>been</u> driving [very] slowly.

6. None (of us) [prep. O.P.] <u>had</u> [h] <u>felt</u> (the) earthquake. [D.O.]

7. Jake <u>had</u>n't [h] <u>felt</u> [LV] well [LVC–A] [recently].

8. (Most) members (of [prep.] (the) band) [O.P.] <u>were</u> [h] <u>cooperating</u>.

9. (Very) few <u>were</u> [LV] [not] cooperative. [LVC–A]

10. <u>Did</u> [h] (your) relatives <u>appear</u> [LV] disturbed? [LVC–A]

11. (The) superintendent <u>appeared</u> [briefly] (in [prep.] (the) hall). [O.P.]

12. Xenia <u>had</u> [h] <u>grown</u> (a)(vegetable) garden [D.O.] and <u>looked</u> [LV] [really] pleased [LVC–A] (about [prep.] it). [O.P.]

TEST:
Recognizing Linking Verbs

Instructions: Mark verbs, subjects, adjectives (except **LVC–A**), adverbs and prepositional phrases; label **LV**, **LVC–N**, **LVC–A**, **D.O.**, **prep.**, **O.P.**

1. <u>Does</u>n't (the) air <u>smell</u> [LV] fresh and clean? [LVC–A]

2. We <u>smelled</u> (the)(burning)(cedar) logs [D.O.] (in [prep.] (the) fireplace). [O.P.]

3. [Outside], (the) wind <u>was</u> <u>howling</u>.

4. (The) wind <u>was</u> [LV] freezing-cold. [LVC–A]

5. (Our) parents <u>will</u> <u>be</u> <u>preparing</u> (the) refreshments. [D.O.]

6. (The)(contest) judges <u>will</u> <u>be</u> [LV] (our) parents. [LVC–N]

7. <u>Did</u>n't (the) principal <u>sound</u> [LV] [somewhat] exasperated? [LVC–A]

8. (The)(shrill) whir (of [prep.] (the)(chain) saw) [O.P.] <u>sounded</u> (through [prep.] (the) forest). [O.P.]

9. (This) sentence <u>may</u> <u>look</u> [LV] [rather] complicated, [LVC–A] but [actually], it <u>is</u> [LV] [quite] simple. [LVC–A]

10. (The) child <u>was</u> <u>feeling</u> (the)(velvet-smooth)(flower) petal.

11. (The) child [obviously] <u>felt</u> [LV] happy. [LVC–A]

12. (Rhoda's) aunt <u>became</u> [LV] (a)(petroleum) geologist. [LVC–N]

Name _____

Date _____

FINAL DRILL:
Recognizing Linking Verbs

Instructions: Mark verbs, subjects, adjectives (except **LVC–A**), adverbs and prepositional phrases; label **LV, LVC–N, LVC–A, D.O., prep., O.P.,** and **h** above helping verb.

1. Those two women are officers in the U.S.A.F.

2. They are stationed at Vandenberg Air Force Base.

3. That horse seems very well-trained.

4. The caller on the phone must have been my aunt.

5. Luigi must have been driving very slowly.

6. None of us had felt the earthquake.

7. Jake hadn't felt well recently.

8. Most members of the band were cooperating.

9. Very few were not cooperative.

10. Did your relatives appear disturbed?

11. The superintendent appeared briefly in the hall.

12. Xenia had grown a vegetable garden and looked really pleased about it.

Name _____

Date _____

TEST:
Recognizing Linking Verbs

Instructions: Mark verbs, subjects, adjectives (except **LVC–A**), adverbs and prepositional phrases; label **LV, LVC–N, LVC–A, D.O., prep., O.P.**

1. Doesn't the air smell fresh and clean?

2. We smelled the burning cedar logs in the fireplace.

3. Outside, the wind was howling.

4. The wind was freezing-cold.

5. Our parents will be preparing the refreshments.

6. The contest judges will be our parents.

7. Didn't the principal sound somewhat exasperated?

8. The shrill whir of the chain saw sounded through the forest.

9. This sentence may look rather complicated, but actually, it is quite simple.

10. The child was feeling the velvet-smooth flower petal.

11. The child obviously felt happy.

12. Rhoda's aunt became a petroleum geologist.

Recognizing Nouns Used as Appositives

As students analyze the sentences, they should realize that the meaning of the sentence is clarified by setting off the appositive with commas. Work carefully with students to be sure they understand.

Inform students that a sentence may contain an appositive to an appositive. Write these sentences on the chalkboard or the overhead and challenge the students to identify the sentence parts.

1. One important team member, the star quarterback, Bill Hamid, was seriously injured.

2. We had a farewell party for my best friend Olga, our class president.

Point out that *Olga*, being specifically identified as *best*, does not need to be separated by a comma from *friend*.

Answer Key—Diagramming

In sentence 2 *eighth-graders* is a hyphenated noun; however, *eighth* functions as an adjective modified by the adverb *particularly*.

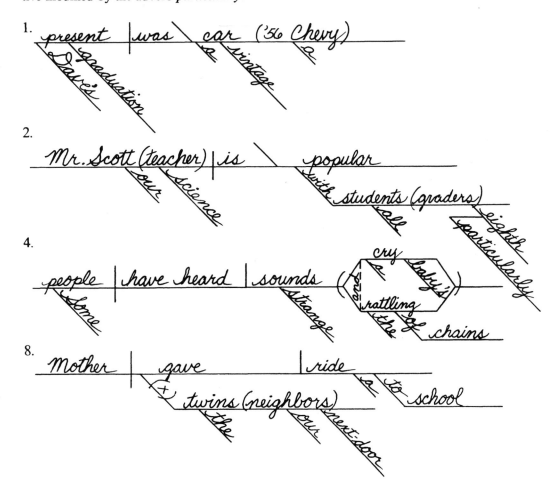

1. present | was \ car ('56 Chevy)

2. Mr. Scott (teacher) | is \ popular

4. people | have heard | sounds

8. Mother | gave | ride

Recognizing Nouns Used as Appositives

REMEMBER:

1. An **appositive**, abbreviated **Appos.**, is a noun or pronoun which identifies or explains the noun it follows.

2. An appositive may be used to identify a subject, a direct object, a linking verb complement, the object of a preposition, or an indirect object.

3. An appositive, or a phrase containing the appositive, is set off from the rest of the sentence by a comma or commas.

4. An appositive may be compound.

5. In diagramming, an appositive is shown in parentheses immediately following the word it identifies.

Example: Uncle Steve gave us, (my) brother and me, passes (to (the) A's) game.

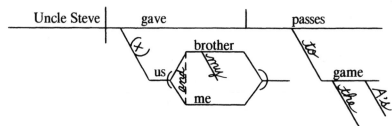

PRACTICE: Mark verbs, subjects, adjectives (except **LVC-A**), adverbs, and prepositional phrases; label **LV**, **LVC-N**, **LVC-A**, **D.O.**, **prep.**, **O.P.**, **I.O.**, and **Appos.**; draw an arrow from the appositive to the word it identifies; insert commas. On the reverse side, diagram sentences 1, 2, 4, and 8.

1. (Dave's) (graduation) present was (a) (vintage) car, (a) '56 Chevy.

2. Mr. Scott, (our) (science) teacher, is popular (with (all) students), eighth-graders, [particularly].

3. (That) house, (the) (shabby) (Victorian) one (on (the) corner), may be haunted.

4. (Some) people have heard (strange) sounds, (a) (baby's) cry and (the) rattling (of chains).

5. (Other) people, skeptics, have [never] heard (any) sounds.

6. Lucia and Dagmar won (the) (national) prize, (a) trip (to Washington, D.C.)

7. (That) (tall) boy is (my) (brother's) (best) friend, Kurt Erikson.

8. Mother gave (the) twins, (our) (next-door) neighbors, (a) ride (to school).

9. They took (a) trip (down (the) Nile, (the) (longest) river (in (the) world).

Recognizing Nouns Used as Appositives

Name _____

Date _____

REMEMBER:

1. An **appositive**, abbreviated **Appos.**, is a noun or pronoun which identifies or explains the noun it follows.

2. An appositive may be used to identify a subject, a direct object, a linking verb complement, the object of a preposition, or an indirect object.

3. An appositive, or a phrase containing the appositive, is set off from the rest of the sentence by a comma or commas.

4. An appositive may be compound.

5. In diagramming, an appositive is shown in parentheses immediately following the word it identifies.

    Example: Uncle Steve gave us, my brother and me, passes to the A's game.

PRACTICE: Mark verbs, subjects, adjectives (except **LVC–A**), adverbs, and prepositional phrases; label **LV, LVC–N, LVC–A, D.O., prep., O.P., I.O.,** and **Appos.**; draw an arrow from the appositive to the word it identifies; insert commas. On the reverse side, diagram sentences 1, 2, 4, and 8.

1. Dave's graduation present was a vintage car a '56 Chevy.

2. Mr. Scott our science teacher is popular with all students eighth-graders particularly.

3. That house the shabby Victorian one on the corner may be haunted.

4. Some people have heard strange sounds a baby's cry and the rattling of chains.

5. Other people skeptics have never heard any sounds.

6. Lucia and Dagmar won the national prize a trip to Washington D.C.

7. That tall boy is my brother's best friend Kurt Erikson.

8. Mother gave the twins our next-door neighbors a ride to school.

9. They took a trip down the Nile the longest river in the world.

Understanding and Using Good Grammar

Using Appositives

Some students may have trouble using appositives to join sentences. Suggest to them:

1. Determine the sentence that expresses the main idea.
2. In the other sentence(s), locate identifying or descriptive words to use as appositives to nouns in the main sentence.

In the *Example:*

1. The main idea is in the first sentence.
2. In the second, *my mother's brother* clearly identifies *Uncle Neil*; the phrase is used after *Neil*; *brother* is the appositive.
3. In the third, "the youngest child in our family" describes Tommy and is placed right after "Tommy"; "child" is the appositive.

PRACTICE:

Sentence 6: The main idea is "Annette sits beside me...."

Sentence 7: The main idea is "The guide answered all...."

Since this is an assignment in joining sentences through the use of appositives, sentences joined in any other way are not correct.

Using Appositives

Appositives are useful in joining two or more sentences into one, thus eliminating (doing away with) unnecessary words.

Example: Uncle Neil gave Tommy a new bicycle. Uncle Neil is my mother's brother. Tommy is the youngest child in our family.

Uncle Neil, my mother's brother, gave Tommy, the youngest child in our family, a new bicycle.

PRACTICE: Rewrite the following short sentences into one. In the sentences you write, mark: verbs, subjects, adjectives, adverbs, and prepositional phrases; label **LV, LVC–N, D.O., prep., O.P., I.O., Appos.**; draw an arrow from the appositive to the word it identifies. Insert commas.

1. My birthday was Thursday. It was a record-breaking hot day.

My birthday was Thursday, a record-breaking hot day.

2. I saw Peter Lewis at the hobby shop. He is the president of our class.

I saw Peter Lewis, president of our class at the hobby shop.

3. Peg will tell about the plans for the dance. She is the committee chairperson.

Peg, the committee chairperson, will tell about the plans for the dance.

4. We gave Tollah a can of her favorite food. Tollah is our Persian kitten.

We gave Tollah, our Persian kitten, a can of her favorite food.

5. We should look for Mr. Goss. He is the owner of that beautiful sailboat.

We should look for Mr. Goss the owner of that beautiful sailboat.

6. Annette is a girl from France. She is a very good student. She sits beside me in English.

(You may use *and* to join two appositives.)

Annette, a girl from France and a very good student, sits beside me in English.

7. Our guide was a young native. He answered all our questions about the ruins.

Our guide, a young native, answered all our questions about the ruins.

Name _____   **Using Appositives**

Date _____

Appositives are useful in joining two or more sentences into one, thus eliminating (doing away with) unnecessary words.

Example: Uncle Neil gave Tommy a new bicycle. Uncle Neil is my mother's brother. Tommy is the youngest child in our family.

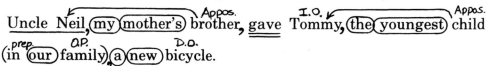

PRACTICE: Rewrite the following short sentences into one. In the sentences you write, mark: verbs, subjects, adjectives, adverbs, and prepositional phrases; label **LV, LVC–N, D.O., prep., O.P., I.O., Appos.**; draw an arrow from the appositive to the word it identifies. Insert commas.

1. My birthday was Thursday. It was a record-breaking hot day.

2. I saw Peter Lewis at the hobby shop. He is the president of our class.

3. Peg will tell about the plans for the dance. She is the committee chairperson.

4. We gave Tollah a can of her favorite food. Tollah is our Persian kitten.

5. We should look for Mr. Goss. He is the owner of that beautiful sailboat.

6. Annette is a girl from France. She is a very good student. She sits beside me in English.

    (You may use *and* to join two appositives.)

7. Our guide was a young native. He answered all our questions about the ruins.

Understanding and Using Good Grammar

FINAL DRILL:
Recognizing and Using Appositives

You may want the students to take this Final Practice as a trial test which they would correct completely in class and take home to review for next day's Test.

FINAL DRILL:
Recognizing and Using Appositives

Instructions: Mark verbs, subjects, adjectives, adverbs, and prepositional phrases; label **LV**, **LVC-N**, **D.O.**, **prep.**, **O.P.**, **I.O.**, and **Appos.**; draw an arrow from the appositive to the word it identifies. Insert necessary commas.

1. The contest manager gave the top salespersons, Todd and Erik, their prizes.

2. Have you read the book, *The Scarlet Letter*, by Nathaniel Hawthorne?

3. That speaker, the attractive blonde in the tailored suit, is my cousin.

4. This is Iola, a very good friend of mine.

5. Uncle Bob, my father's brother, was born on December 25, Christmas Day.

Instructions: Rewrite the following short sentences into one. In the sentence you write, mark and label the sentence parts as you did above; draw an arrow from the appositive to the word it identifies. Insert necessary commas.

1. I have lost my new watch. It was my Christmas present from Dad.

   I have lost my new watch, my Christmas present from Dad.

2. The judge did not smile at the attempted humor. The judge was a very serious-minded person.

   The judge, a very serious-minded person, did not smile at the attempted humor.

3. Our class president will probably be Jason. He is a very good student.

   Our class valedictorian will probably be Jason, a very good student.

4. This book about horses was given to me for my birthday. Horses are my favorite animal.

   This book about horses, my favorite animal, was given to me for my birthday.

5. The teacher gave Heidi a special test. Heidi is the new girl in our class.

   The teacher gave Heidi, the new girl in our class, a special test.

FINAL DRILL: Recognizing and Using Appositives

Name _____

Date _____

Instructions: Mark verbs, subjects, adjectives, adverbs, and prepositional phrases; label **LV**, **LVC-N**, **D.O.**, **prep.**, **O.P.**, **I.O.**, and **Appos.**; draw an arrow from the appositive to the word it identifies. Insert necessary commas.

1. The contest manager gave the top salespersons Todd and Erik their prizes.

2. Have you read the book *The Scarlet Letter* by Nathaniel Hawthorne?

3. That speaker the attractive blonde in the tailored suit is my cousin.

4. This is Iola a very good friend of mine.

5. Uncle Bob my father's brother was born on December 25 Christmas Day.

Instructions: Rewrite the following short sentences into one. In the sentence you write, mark and label the sentence parts as you did above; draw an arrow from the appositive to the word it identifies. Insert necessary commas.

1. I have lost my new watch. It was my Christmas present from Dad.

2. The judge did not smile at the attempted humor. The judge was a very serious-minded person.

3. Our class valedictorian will probably be Jason. He is a very good student.

4. This book about horses was given to me for my birthday. Horses are my favorite animal.

5. The teacher gave Heidi a special test. Heidi is the new girl in our class.

TEST: Recognizing
and Using Appositives

Before students start the second part of the Test, inform them that the main idea is in the first sentence. The second sentence has the appositive phrase which should be written as an appositive to a noun in the first.

Suggested Grading:

The marks, labels, commas, and arrows in the first part total 60, in the second, 63. The difference is negligible; therefore, the same percent scale can be used for both. The average of the two scores should be recorded.

–1, 98	–6, 90	–11, 82	–16, 74	–21, 66
–2, 97	–7, 89	–12, 81	–17, 73	–22, 65
–3, 95	–8, 87	–13, 79	–18, 71	–23, 63
–4, 94	–9, 86	–14, 78	–19, 70	–24, 62
–5, 92	–10, 84	–15, 76	–20, 68	–25, 60

TEST: Recognizing and Using Appositives

Instructions: Mark verbs, subjects, adjectives, adverbs, and prepositional phrases; label **LV, LVC–N, D.O., prep., O.P., I.O.,** and **Appos.**; draw an arrow from the appositive to the word it identifies. Insert commas.

1. Joel prepared (two) desserts, a pecan pie and a chocolate cake.

2. The child, obviously a stubborn youngster, was kicking and screaming.

3. The man (by the door) is Marilee's uncle, a highly respected lawyer.

4. Sarah wrote a book report (on her favorite American classic, *O Pioneers*.

5. The students gave the speaker, Mr. Adams, their best attention.

Instructions: Rewrite these short sentences into one. In the sentence you write, mark and label the sentence parts as you did above; draw an arrow from the appositive to the word it identifies. Insert needed commas.

1. Coach handed the winners their trophies. The winners were Adam and Cyril.

   Coach handed the winners, Adam and Cyril, their trophies.

2. Uncle Tex gave Glenn a new skateboard. It was a very expensive one.

   Uncle Tex gave Glenn a new skateboard, a very expensive one.

3. That pleasant salesperson is Michelle. She is my sister's best friend.

   That pleasant salesperson is Michelle, my sister's best friend.

4. The newspaper must have lain in the gutter overnight. It is now a soggy lump.

   The newspaper, now a soggy lump, must have lain (in the gutter) overnight.

5. Grandpa has given $1,000 to José and me for our college savings accounts. José is my cousin.

   Grandpa has given $1,000 (to José, my cousin, and me) (for our college savings accounts).

Name _____

Date _____

TEST: Recognizing and Using Appositives

Instructions: Mark verbs, subjects, adjectives, adverbs, and prepositional phrases; label **LV, LVC–N, D.O., prep., O.P., I.O.,** and **Appos.**; draw an arrow from the appositive to the word it identifies. Insert commas.

1. Joel prepared two desserts a pecan pie and a chocolate cake.

2. The child obviously a stubborn youngster was kicking and screaming.

3. The man by the door is Marilee's uncle a highly respected lawyer.

4. Sarah wrote a book report on her favorite American classic *O Pioneers.*

5. The students gave the speaker Mr. Adams their best attention.

Instructions: Rewrite these short sentences into one. In the sentence you write, mark and label the sentence parts as you did above; draw an arrow from the appositive to the word it identifies. Insert needed commas.

1. Coach handed the winners their trophies. The winners were Adam and Cyril.

2. Uncle Tex gave Glenn a new skateboard. It was a very expensive one.

3. That pleasant salesperson is Michelle. She is my sister's best friend.

4. The newspaper must have lain in the gutter overnight. It is now a soggy lump.

5. Grandpa has given $1,000 to José and me for our college savings accounts. José is my cousin.

Understanding and Using Good Grammar

Recognizing Nouns of Direct Address and All Other Sentence Parts

As the class works through the Practice, call attention to these points:

1. Commas are extremely important in producing understandable written communication; to demonstrate this point, call students' attention to sentences 2, 4, and 8.

2. The structure of the twelve sentences provides a complete review in recognizing all the main sentence parts.

3. The review of special forms studied on pages 1–86 includes the correct use of:
   - subjective (nominative) pronouns (sentences 4 and 5)
   - objective pronouns (sentences 2 and 8)
   - *different from* (sentence 3)
   - *kind of* (sentence 11)
   - acceptable ending of a sentence with a preposition (sentence 11)
   - *among* used with more than two (sentence 9)

   and recognition of:
   - a gerund (sentences 6 and 7)
   - prepositions of two or three words (sentences 2, 4, and 5)

Answer Key—Diagramming:

Recognizing Nouns of Direct Address and All Other Sentence Parts

DEFINITION: A **noun of direct address** is a person's name written as though the writer were speaking to the person, addressing him or her directly.

REMEMBER:

1. A noun of address, abbreviated **N.A.**, is set off from the rest of the sentence by a comma or commas.

2. A noun of address has no grammatical connection to the rest of the sentence.

3. In diagramming, no matter where the **N.A.** appears in the sentence, it is diagrammed ahead of the sentence, as are the introductory words: *yes, no, well, oh,* and *there.*

    Example: Oh, yes, Sandra, the boys really do need your help!

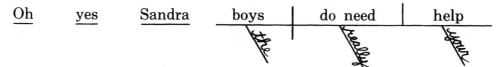

PRACTICE: Mark verbs, subjects, adjectives (except **LVC–A**), adverbs, and prepositional phrases; label **LV, LVC-N, LVC-A, D.O., prep., O.P., I.O., Appos.,** and **N.A.** Insert commas where they are needed. Be alert to special forms you have studied in this book. On the reverse, diagram sentences 1, 2, 3, 4, and 8.

1. Aaron, have you met the new student, the boy from Afghanistan?

2. (In addition to you, Jeff, and me), Alycia, is anyone else going?

3. Was your golf tournament score [very] different (from mine), Gwen?

4. (According to Caitlin), Donna, you and she are the only candidates.

5. Aunt Ruth, should you and I start [out] [now] (in spite of the bad weather)?

6. Are you becoming annoyed (by the parrot's screeching), Grandma?

7. Mr. Andrews, is walking (at a steady [moderately] fast pace) good exercise?

8. (Without question), Mom, Pepe told you and Dad the truth.

9. We will divide the prize money (among the four winners), Andrea.

10. (From this distance), Ms. Marks, can you identify those three dusty, sunburned hikers?

11. Kevin, what kind) (of book) are you looking (for?

12. Students, (you) pass your papers [forward].

Recognizing Nouns of Direct Address and All Other Sentence Parts

Name _____

Date _____

DEFINITION: A **noun of direct address** is a person's name written as though the writer were speaking to the person, addressing him or her directly.

REMEMBER:

1. A noun of address, abbreviated **N.A.**, is set off from the rest of the sentence by a comma or commas.

2. A noun of address has no grammatical connection to the rest of the sentence.

3. In diagramming, no matter where the **N.A.** appears in the sentence, it is diagrammed ahead of the sentence, as are the introductory words: *yes, no, well, oh,* and *there.*

   Example: Oh, yes, Sandra, the boys really do need your help!

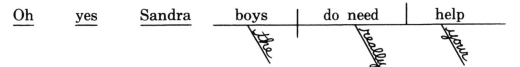

PRACTICE: Mark verbs, subjects, adjectives (except **LVC–A**), adverbs, and prepositional phrases; label **LV, LVC-N, LVC-A, D.O., prep., O.P., I.O., Appos.,** and **N.A.** Insert commas where they are needed. Be alert to special forms you have studied in this book. On the reverse, diagram sentences 1, 2, 3, 4, and 8.

1. Aaron have you met the new student the boy from Afghanistan?

2. In addition to you Jeff and me Alycia is anyone else going?

3. Was your golf tournament score very different from mine Gwen?

4. According to Caitlin Donna you and she are the only candidates.

5. Aunt Ruth should you and I start out now in spite of the bad weather?

6. Are you becoming annoyed by the parrot's screeching Grandma?

7. Mr. Andrews is walking at a steady moderately fast pace good exercise?

8. Without question Mom Pepe told you and Dad the truth.

9. We will divide the prize money among the four winners Andrea.

10. From this distance Ms. Marks can you identify those three dusty sunburned hikers?

11. Kevin what kind of book are you looking for?

12. Students pass your papers forward.

FINAL PRACTICE and TEST:
Recognizing Nouns of Direct Address and All Other Sentence Parts

> The next reproducible page contains one half-page Final Practice and one half-page Test. Before passing out the page, cut it in two to remove the Test.

Final Practice

Sentence 1: Remind students that the introductory *there* has no grammatical connection to the rest of the sentence.

Sentence 5: *was* } are linking verbs completed with prepositional phrases
Sentence 6: *is* } functioning as **LVC**'s.

Test

Sentence 3 is a request/command in which the subject is the understood *You.*

Grading Scale: 79 points:

–1, 99	–6, 92	–11, 86	–16, 80	–21, 74	–26, 67	–31, 61
–2, 97	–7, 91	–12, 85	–17, 79	–22, 72	–27, 66	–32, 60
–3, 96	–8, 90	–13, 84	–18, 77	–23, 71	–28, 65	–33, 58
–4, 95	–9, 89	–14, 82	–19, 76	–24, 70	–29, 63	–34, 57
–5, 94	–10, 87	–15, 81	–20, 75	–25, 68	–30, 62	–35, 56

FINAL PRACTICE:
Recognizing Nouns of Direct Address and All Other Sentence Parts

Instructions: Mark verbs, subjects, adjectives, adverbs, and prepositional phrases; label **LV**, **D.O.**, **prep.**, **O.P.**, **Appos.**, and **N.A.** Insert necessary commas.

1. Kyle, there have been (no) applications turned [in] (besides yours and mine).

2. (In reply to Lance's question), Letitia, can you give (a good) explanation?

3. Could you finish (your) test (within the allotted time), Karen?

4. (Because of all this homework) I can't go (to the mall) (with you), Kirsten.

5. Paula, was the list (of candidates) (for school offices) (on the bulletin board)?

6. Rochelle, (your new) neighbor, Amber, is (in my gym class).

7. (Before the tardy bell), Ms. Hunter, may I go (to my locker)?

TEST:
Recognizing Nouns of Direct Address and All Other Sentence Parts

Instructions: Mark verbs, subjects, adjectives (except LVC–A), adverbs, and prepositional phrases; label **LV**, **LVC–A**, **LVC–N**, **D.O.**, **prep.**, **O.P.**, **Appos.**, **I.O.**, and **N.A.** Insert necessary commas.

1. (At today's meeting), Ellen, did the committee make plans (for the dance)?

2. Elizabeth, have you [ever] seen R. L. Stine, (the popular) author?

3. (You) Take (your) time, Dominic, and complete the test [carefully].

4. (Your book) report was [very] different (from Richard's), Joey.

5. (Without question), Mom, Pepe told you and Dad the truth.

6. Mrs. Ward, has Mr. Heaton spoken (to you) (with regard to Tina's, Justin's, and my petition)?

7. Andy, is walking (at a steady [moderately] fast pace) good exercise?

Name _____

Date _____

FINAL PRACTICE: Recognizing Nouns of Address and All Other Sentence Parts

Instructions: Mark verbs, subjects, adjectives, adverbs, and prepositional phrases; label **LV**, **D.O.**, **prep.**, **O.P.**, **Appos.**, and **N.A.** Insert necessary commas.

1. Kyle there have been no applications turned in besides yours and mine.

2. In reply to Lance's question Letitia can you give a good explanation?

3. Could you finish your test within the allotted time Karen?

4. Because of all this homework I can't go to the mall with you Kirsten.

5. Paula was the list of candidates for school offices on the bulletin board?

6. Rochelle your new neighbor Amber is in my gym class.

7. Before the tardy bell Ms. Hunter may I go to my locker?

Name _____

Date _____

TEST: Recognizing Nouns of Address and All Other Sentence Parts

Instructions: Mark verbs, subjects, adjectives (except **LVC–A**), adverbs, and prepositional phrases; label **LV**, **LVC–A**, **LVC–N**, **D.O.**, **prep.**, **O.P.**, **Appos.**, **I.O.**, and **N.A.** Insert necessary commas.

1. At today's meeting Ellen did the committee make plans for the dance?

2. Elizabeth have you ever seen R. L. Stine the popular author?

3. Take your time Dominic and complete the test carefully.

4. Your book report was very different from Richard's Joey.

5. Without question Mom Pepe told you and Dad the truth.

6. Mrs. Ward has Mr. Heaton spoken to you with regard to Tina's Justin's and my petition?

7. Andy is walking at a steady moderately fast pace good exercise?

Understanding and Using Good Grammar

PRETEST: Recognizing Correct Use of Pronouns

Remind students that Pretest scores do not affect report card grades. Before beginning the Pretest, without telling students why, instruct them to circle sentence numbers 3, 4, 5, 7, 9, 11, 14, 19, 21, 22, 23, and 24. When the Pretests are returned to the students, point out that those sentences contain pronoun usage they didn't study in *Steps to Good Grammar*. This should make them realize that there is more for them to learn about pronoun usage, as well as some information they should recall from their previous study.

Grading scale for 42 items:

–1, 98	–5, 88	–9, 79	–13, 69	–17, 60	–21, 50
–2, 95	–6, 86	–10, 76	–14, 67	–18, 57	–22, 48
–3, 93	–7, 83	–11, 74	–15, 64	–19, 55	–23, 45
–4, 90	–8, 81	–12, 71	–16, 62	–20, 52	–24, 43

PRETEST: Recognizing Correct Use of Pronouns

Instructions: Draw a circle around the correct form in parentheses.

1. (Kristal and myself; Me and Kristal; (Kristal and I)) are leaving soon.

2. I hope (its, (it's)) (him, (he)) on the telephone.

3. Ms. Jow has chosen three students, (Katie, me, and you; I, you, and Katie; (you, Katie, and me)).

4. Is her sister taller than ((she) her) or (me, (I))?

5. Could ((we) us) girls ride with (you and he; (you and him), him and you)?

6. Was Ileane calling to (me, you, or Ramon; Ramon, you, or I; (you, Ramon, or me))?

7. Dad was pleased about (me and your; you and my; (your and my)) winning.

8. Had Peter and (him, (he)) seen (you and I; (you and me), me and you)?

9. Ms. Jones must have invited all ((us) we) eighth-grade girls.

10. Our neighbor gave (she and I; (her and me), her and I) a ride to school.

11. My brothers and (myself, (I), me) play tennis often.

12. Finally, the dog has quit (it's, (its)) barking!

13. Haven't they completed (they're, (their), there) plans yet?

14. Dad (hisself, (himself)) said that Jeff and (me, (I)) could go.

15. Beth and (her, (she)) (has, (have)) invited ((their) her) parents.

16. Neither ((he) him) nor Randy ((has) have) invited ((his), their) parents.

17. (Your, (You're)) going to invite ((yours) your's), aren't you?

18. Everybody (have, (has)) brought (their, (his or her)) books.

19. (Whom, (Who)) does Coach think is the best all-round athlete?

20. ((Has), Have) either of the boys lost ((his) their) coat?

21. (Do, (Does)) anyone among you know (whose, (who's)) bringing the drinks?

22. Everyone else among the boys ((was), were) as exhausted as (him, (he)).

23. (Is, (Are)) Joe and (him, (he)) sure it was (me, (I)) (who, (whom)) they heard?

24. Mom and (me, (I)) (was, (were)) sure we saw (ourselfs, us, (ourselves)) on the six-o'clock TV news.

PRETEST: Recognizing Correct Use of Pronouns

Name _____

Date _____

Instructions: Draw a circle around the correct form in parentheses.

1. (Kristal and myself; Me and Kristal; Kristal and I) are leaving soon.

2. I hope (its, it's) (him, he) on the telephone.

3. Ms. Jow has chosen three students, (Katie, me, and you; I, you, and Katie; you, Katie, and me).

4. Is her sister taller than (she, her) or (me, I)?

5. Could (we, us) girls ride with (you and he; you and him; him and you)?

6. Was Ileane calling to (me, you, or Ramon; Ramon, you, or I; you, Ramon, or me)?

7. Dad was pleased about (me and your; you and my; your and my) winning.

8. Had Peter and (him, he) seen (you and I; you and me; me and you)?

9. Ms. Jones must have invited all (us, we) eighth-grade girls.

10. Our neighbor gave (she and I; her and me; her and I) a ride to school.

11. My brothers and (myself, I, me) play tennis often.

12. Finally, the dog has quit (it's, its) barking!

13. Haven't they completed (they're, their, there) plans yet?

14. Dad (hisself, himself) said that Jeff and (me, I) could go.

15. Beth and (her, she) (has, have) invited (their, her) parents.

16. Neither (he, him) nor Randy (has, have) invited (his, their) parents.

17. (Your, You're) going to invite (yours, your's), aren't you?

18. Everybody (have, has) brought (their, his or her) books.

19. (Whom, Who) does Coach think is the best all-round athlete?

20. (Has, Have) either of the boys lost (his, their) coat?

21. (Do, Does) anyone among you know (whose, who's) bringing the drinks?

22. Everyone else among the boys (was, were) as exhausted as (him, he).

23. (Is, Are) Joe and (him, he) sure it was (me, I) (who, whom) they heard?

24. Mom and (me, I) (was, were) sure we saw (ourselfs, us, ourselves) on the six-o'clock TV news.

      Understanding and Using Good Grammar

Nominative and Compound (Intensive Appositive) Pronouns

TO TEACHERS:

In *Steps to Good Grammar,* students learned the correct use of personal pronouns in the various sentence parts immediately after learning the use of nouns in those parts. In a later unit, they reviewed personal pronouns and studied the use of possesssive, indefinite, and compound pronouns, verb contractions with pronouns, and finally, pronoun subject-verb agreement.

In this book, the knowledge they have acquired is reinforced with review and extended to include more facts.

Continue to reward students for turning in perfect papers. In checking their identification of sentence parts, no matter how many *words* make up a compound subject, a compound appositive, etc., it is still only one part and counts for *one* point. With *pronouns,* each word counts if separate choices are presented:

Example: Is her sister taller than (ⓢⓗⓔ her) or (me, Ⓘ?

In checking papers, deduct 5% for each error in a representative number of practice sentences; for example, the first and last four sentences on a page containing 12 to 18 sentences. Record the score and return pages for students to refer to as they complete the rest of the pages in the unit.

Remind students that nominative pronouns are used as subjects and/or in subject-related positions.

Students should be able to recite from memory (1) nominative pronouns, (2) sequence of polite order, and (3) the "hearing" clue to correct usage. If they can't recite them, assign memorizing them. Assure students that memorized concepts stored in the subconscious are readily available to them when the need arises!

Work with students to be sure they correctly mark or label the parts of the sentences given as examples of the various uses. Sentences 2, 4, and 6 present new facts; clauses will be studied in detail later. Collect students' papers, check their work, record scores, and return them to students for reference as they complete pages 101, 104, and 107. Tell students to add their papers to their collection of information sheets.

Nominative and Compound (Intensive Appositive) Pronouns

REMEMBER:

1. **Personal pronouns** may be used to replace nouns.
2. The correct use of personal pronouns in compound parts of sentences requires careful study.

NOMINATIVE PRONOUNS: I, you, he, she, we, they, who

1. Polite order: First, *you*; next, *she, he, they,* or nouns; last, *I, we.*
2. To hear the correct pronoun, say each pronoun separately *before* the verb.

Nominative pronouns may be used as:

1. **Subject:** You, Kathryn, and I could leave now.

   They and we will [probably] compete (in (the) finals).

2. **Appositive to identify a noun subject:**

   [Only] (two) girls, you and she, have volunteered.

3. **Pronoun subject followed by a noun appositive:**

   We (three) boys were candidates.

4. **Subject of an elliptical (shortened) clause.** These pronouns are used after *as* and *than* in making comparisons, are labeled **Subj. Cl.**, and enclosed with brackets.

   Teresa is [as] tall [as I]. (Think: "as tall as I am tall")

   We worked [more] [slowly] [than he and she]. (Think: "she worked")

5. **Linking Verb Complement:**

   Will (the) captains be you and he?

   (The) pranksters [certainly] weren't they or we!

6. **Appositive to identify an LVC:**

   (The) (only) volunteers were (two) girls, you and she.

7. **Pronoun LVC followed by a noun appositive:**

   (The) candidates were we (three) boys.

COMPOUND PRONOUNS (INTENSIVE APPOSITIVES): myself, yourself, himself (never *hisself*), **herself, itself, ourselves, yourselves, themselves** (never *theirselves*)

Correct Use: As an **intensive appositive** placed immediately after a noun or pronoun in a main sentence part to emphasize the noun or pronoun. Label: **Int. Appos.**

1. I myself bought (the) gift.   2. (The) burglar was (the) butler himself.

Incorrect Use: Never used as a subject or **LVC** in a sentence.

1. He and (myself, I) can go.   2. (The) winners are (yourselves, you)

   and (ourselves, we).

(Reflexive use will be studied with objective personal pronouns.)

Nominative and Compound (Intensive Appositive) Pronouns

REMEMBER:

1. **Personal pronouns** may be used to replace nouns.
2. The correct use of personal pronouns in compound parts of sentences requires careful study.

NOMINATIVE PRONOUNS: I, you, he, she, we, they, who

1. Polite order: First, *you*; next, *she, he, they*, or nouns; last, *I, we*.
2. To hear the correct pronoun, say each pronoun separately *before* the verb.

Nominative pronouns may be used as:

1. **Subject:** You, Kathryn, and I could leave now.

   They and we will probably compete in the finals.

2. **Appositive to identify a noun subject:**

   Only two girls, you and she, have volunteered.

3. **Pronoun subject followed by a noun appositive:**

   We three boys were candidates.

4. **Subject of an elliptical (shortened) clause.** These pronouns are used after *as* and *than* in making comparisons, are labeled **Subj. Cl.**, and enclosed with brackets.

   Teresa is as tall as I. (Think: "as tall as I am tall")

   We worked more slowly than he and she. (Think: "she worked")

5. **Linking Verb Complement:**

   Will the captains be you and he?

   The pranksters certainly weren't they or we!

6. **Appositive to identify an LVC:**

   The only volunteers were two girls, you and she.

7. **Pronoun LVC followed by a noun appositive:**

   The candidates were we three boys.

COMPOUND PRONOUNS (INTENSIVE APPOSITIVES): myself, yourself, himself (never *hisself*)**, herself, itself, ourselves, yourselves, themselves** (never *theirselves*)

Correct Use: As an **intensive appositive** placed immediately after a noun or pronoun in a main sentence part to emphasize the noun or pronoun. Label: **Int. Appos.**

1. I myself bought the gift.   2. The burglar was the butler himself.

Incorrect Use: Never used as a subject or **LVC** in a sentence.

1. He and (myself, I) can go.   2. The winners are (yourselves, you)

   and (ourselves, we).

(Reflexive use will be studied with objective personal pronouns.)

Understanding and Using Good Grammar

Nominative and Compound (Intensive Appositive) Pronouns

Practice sentences 1–5, 8, and 11 review previous learnings. All others are examples of new facts. Students should refer to information on page 98 for examples of marking and labeling sentence parts:

    a. Draw an arrow from an appositive to the word it modifies. (sentences 2, 3, 6, 7)

    b. Bracket elliptical clauses; label pronoun subject **Subj. Cl.** (sentence 4)

Sentences 6, 13, 14: Commas separate an appositive from the rest of sentence.

Sentences 9, 12, 17: The first *as* functions as an adverb modifying the adverb/adjective that follows it; the second *as* introduces the elliptical clause.

Sentences 2, 6, 10, 12: Regarding *he*, *she*, *it*, or *singular nouns*—When two or more are used together in a series, their positions in "polite order" are interchangeable. Show this with a two-pointed arrow drawn under the pronouns.

    EXAMPLE: Sentence 2: she and he

Nominative and Compound (Intensive Appositive) Pronouns

PRACTICE: In the blanks, write in polite order the correct pronouns or nouns in parentheses. Mark verbs, subjects, adjectives (except **LVC–A**), adverbs, prepositional phrases, and elliptical clauses. Label **LV**, **LVC–N**, **LVC–A**, **D.O.**, **I.O.**, **prep.**, **O.P.**, **Appos.**, **Subj. Cl.**, and **Int. Appos.**

1. <u>My brothers</u> and _____I_____ [often] play tennis. (Me, My brothers, I)   [D.O. over tennis]

2. Have _____you_____, _____she_____, and _____he_____ finished the test? (he, you, him, she, her)

3. (Before the storm), _____they_____ and _____we_____ closed the windows. (us, they, them, we)

4. The approved candidates are _____you_____, _____she_____, and _____I_____. (her, yourself, I, she, me, myself, you)

5. That [certainly] was [not] _____they_____ or _____we_____. (us, they, we, them)

6. Two students, _Ivan_ and _he_, have been chosen. (he, him, Ivan)

7. The highest scorers were three girls, _you_, _Audrey_, and _I_. (I, Audrey, you, me)

8. _We_ students appreciate many of our teachers. (Us, We)

9. Is your friend [as] interested (in backpacking) [as _you_ and _we_]? (we, us, you)

10. The girls were walking [more] slowly [than _he_ and _Chuck_]. (Chuck, he, him)

11. The last ones (in line) were _we_ three boys. (us, we)

12. No one else (on the team) is [as] athletic [as _Mona_ or _she_]. (she, Mona, her)

13. The winners will [likely] be two boys, _you_ and _he_. (yourself, him, you, he)

14. The doubles finalists, _they_ and _we_, play [tomorrow]. (them, ourselves, they, us, we)

15. You two played a better game [than _she_ and _I_]. (myself, she, her, me, I)

16. My brother _himself_ caught the high-fly ball. (hisself, himself)

17. Everyone else tried [as] [hard] [as _you_ and _we_]. (ourselves, you, us, we)

Nominative and Compound (Intensive Appositive) Pronouns

Name _____

Date _____

PRACTICE: In the blanks, write in polite order the correct pronouns or nouns in parentheses. Mark verbs, subjects, adjectives (except **LVC–A**), adverbs, prepositional phrases, and elliptical clauses. Label **LV, LVC–N, LVC–A, D.O., I.O., prep., O.P., Appos., Subj. Cl.,** and **Int. Appos.**

1. _____ and _____ often play tennis. (Me, My brothers, I)

2. Have _____ , _____ , and _____ finished the test?
   (he, you, him, she, her)

3. Before the storm, _____ and _____ closed the windows.
   (us, they, them, we)

4. The approved candidates are _____ , _____ , and _____ .
   (her, yourself, I, she, me, myself, you)

5. That certainly was not _____ or _____ . (us, they, we, them)

6. Two students, _____ and _____ , have been chosen. (he, him, Ivan)

7. The highest scorers were three girls, _____ , _____ , and _____ .
   (I, Audrey, you, me)

8. _____ students appreciate many of our teachers. (Us, We)

9. Is your friend as interested in backpacking as _____ and _____?
   (we, us, you)

10. The girls were walking more slowly than _____ and _____ .
    (Chuck, he, him)

11. The last ones in line were _____ three boys. (us, we)

12. No one else on the team is as athletic as _____ or _____.
    (she, Mona, her)

13. The winners will likely be two boys, _____ and _____ .
    (yourself, him, you, he)

14. The doubles finalists, _____ and _____ , play tomorrow.
    (them, ourselves, they, us, we)

15. You two played a better game than _____ and _____ .
    (myself, she, her, me, I)

16. My brother _____ caught the high-fly ball.
    (hisself, himself)

17. Everyone else tried as hard as _____ and _____ .
    (ourselves, you, us, we)

Understanding and Using Good Grammar

Nominative and Compound (Intensive Appositive) Pronouns

Several sentences offer students the opportunity of misusing compound pronouns! Tell them this is simply to help them remember to avoid such usage. Correct use is in sentences 10 and 14, with an emphasis on correct spelling.

When the papers are handed in, check at least the choice and order, and the marks and labels of the written nouns and pronouns. Return them to the students to review for the Test on page 110.

Nominative and Compound (Intensive Appositive) Pronouns

PRACTICE: In the blanks, write in polite order the correct pronouns or nouns in parentheses. Mark verbs, subjects, adjectives (except **LVC–A**), adverbs, prepositional phrases, and elliptical clauses. Label **LV, LVC–N, LVC–A, D.O., I.O., prep., O.P., Appos., Subj. Cl.,** and **Int. Appos.**

1. [Unquestionably], Lars is [as] tall [as ___you___ or ___I___]. (yourself, me, you, I)

2. ___You___, ___Louise___, and ___I___ should be prompt. (I, me, you, Louise)

3. Do ___we___ students [ever] [really] work [too] [hard]? (us, we)

4. Are (the) (new) officers ___you___, ___Ryan___, and ___he___ ? (Ryan, he, you, him)

5. Duncan studies [more] [seriously] [than (my) sister or ___I___]. (me, my sister, I)

6. [Only] (two) students, ___she___ and ___he___, finished (on time). (he, her, him, she)

7. Helen is [as] curious (about (the) package) [as ___they___ or ___we___]. (they, them, us, we)

8. ___We___ (Us, We) (three) girls, ___you___, ___she___, and ___I___, could take turns. (you, her, myself, I, me, she)

9. [Probably] (no) one could be [more] pleased [than ___you___, ___he___, and ___I___]. (him, you, he, I, me)

10. Had he ___himself___ dropped (the) pitcher? (hisself, himself)

11. [Nearly] everyone was [as] satisfied (with (the) results) (of (the) (book) sale) [as ___they___ and ___we___]. (them, we, ourselves, us, they)

12. (The) (first) arrivals will [probably] be (the) (usual) three, ___you___, ___Doug___, and ___I___. (Doug, I, me, you)

13. (According to (the) records) ___you___, ___he___, and ___she___ are tardy [too] [often]. (he, her, she, him, you)

14. (The) students ___themselves___ selected (that) program. (theirselves, themselves)

15. (The) (only) students (with (perfect) attendance) records) are (three) sopho-mores, ___Caleb___, ___Irene___, and ___I___. (Irene, myself, I, Caleb)

Name _____

Date _____

Nominative and Compound (Intensive Appositive) Pronouns

PRACTICE: In the blanks, write in polite order the correct pronouns or nouns in parentheses. Mark verbs, subjects, adjectives (except **LVC–A**), adverbs, prepositional phrases, and elliptical clauses. Label **LV, LVC–N, LVC–A, D.O., I.O., prep., O.P., Appos., Subj. Cl.,** and **Int. Appos.**

1. Unquestionably, Lars is as tall as _____ or _____ .
   (yourself, me, you, I)

2. _____ , _____ , and _____ should be prompt.
   (I, me, you, Louise)

3. Do _____ students ever really work too hard? (us, we)

4. Are the new officers _____ , _____ , and _____ ?
   (Ryan, he, you, him)

5. Duncan studies more seriously than _____ or _____ .
   (me, my sister, I)

6. Only two students, _____ and _____ , finished on time.
   (he, her, him, she)

7. Helen is as curious about the package as _____ or _____ .
   (they, them, us, we)

8. _____ (Us, We) three girls, _____ , _____ , and
   _____ , could take turns. (you, her, myself, I, me, she)

9. Probably no one could be more pleased than _____ , _____ ,
   and _____ . (him, you, he, I, me)

10. Had he _____ dropped the pitcher? (hisself, himself)

11. Nearly everyone was as satisfied with the results of the book sale as
    _____ and _____ . (them, we, ourselves, us, they)

12. The first arrivals will probably be the usual three, _____ ,
    _____ , and _____ . (Doug, I, me, you)

13. According to the records, _____ , _____ , and _____ are
    tardy too often.   (he, her, she, him, you)

14. The students _____ selected that program.
    (theirselves, themselves)

15. The only students with perfect attendance records are three sopho-
    mores, _____ , _____ , and _____ .
    (Irene, myself, I, Caleb)

Understanding and Using Good Grammar

FINAL PRACTICE: Selecting Correct Nominative and Compound (Intensive Appositive) Pronouns

You may want to have students take this Final Practice as a Trial Test in preparation for the Test on page 110. They could correct their own papers as you give them the correct write-ins, marks, and labels.

Examples:

Sentence 1: Write *she*, bracket *than she*, and label **Subj. Cl.**

Sentence 3: Write *we*, label **LVC–N**; write *you*, *Mark*, *I*, label **Appos.**, draw arrow back to *three*.

There would be no need to record the scores, and students could take the papers home to review before the Test.

FINAL PRACTICE: Selecting Correct Nominative and Compound (Intensive Appositive) Pronouns

Instructions: In the blanks, write in polite order the correct pronouns or nouns in parentheses. Mark verbs, subjects, adjectives (except **LVC–A**), adverbs, prepositional phrases, and elliptical clauses. Label **LV, LVC–N, LVC–A, D.O., I.O., prep., O.P., Appos., Subj. Cl.,** and **Int. Appos.** Draw an arrow from an appositive to the word it identifies.

1. Is *her* sister taller [than *she*]? (her, she)

2. Only *two* girls, *she* and *I*, qualified. (me, she, her, I)

3. Hopefully, the lead characters will be *we* three, *you* , *Mark* and *I* . (me, Mark, I, you, myself)

4. *Our* parents and *we* saw the accident. (us, our parents, ourselves, we)

5. Did Dad *himself* call the repair shop? (himself, hisself)

6. The last contestants will probably be *they* and *we* . (we, them, us, they)

7. You two played a better game [than *he* and *I*]. (he, me, I, him)

8. Dad plays golf more often than *we* , *Sis* , and *I* . (myself, Sis, me, I)

9. *My* brothers and *I* often play flag football. (I, myself, my brothers, me)

10. Are *they* and *we* on the committee? (they, ourselves, us, them, we)

11. Haven't we worked as quickly as *she* and *he* ? (he, her, him, she)

12. Talliers (of the votes) will be *we* three students, *Lizzy* , *Peter* , and *I* . (I, Lizzy, myself, Peter, me)

13. The students *themselves* selected that assembly program. (theirselves, themselves)

FINAL PRACTICE: Selecting Correct Nominative and Compound (Intensive Appositive) Pronouns

Name _____

Date _____

Instructions: In the blanks, write in polite order the correct pronouns or nouns in parentheses. Mark verbs, subjects, adjectives (except **LVC–A**), adverbs, prepositional phrases, and elliptical clauses. Label **LV, LVC–N, LVC–A, D.O., I.O., prep., O.P., Appos., Subj. Cl.,** and **Int. Appos.** Draw an arrow from an appositive to the word it identifies.

1. Is her sister taller than _____? (her, she)

2. Only two girls, _____ and _____, qualified. (me, she, her, I)

3. Hopefully, the lead characters will be _____ three, _____,
   (us, we)

   _____ and _____ . (me, Mark, I, you, myself)

4. _____ and _____ saw the accident.
   (us, our parents, ourselves, we)

5. Did Dad _____ call the repair shop? (himself, hisself)

6. The last contestants will probably be _____ and _____ .
   (we, them, us, they)

7. You two played a better game than _____ and _____ .
   (he, me, I, him)

8. Dad plays golf more often than _____ , _____ , and
   (us, we)

   _____ . (myself, Sis, me, I)

9. _____ and _____ often play flag football.
   (I, myself, my brothers, me)

10. Are _____ and _____ on the committee?
    (they, ourselves, us, them, we)

11. Haven't we worked as quickly as _____ and _____ ?
    (he, her, him, she)

12. Talliers of the votes will be _____ three students, _____ ,
    (we, us)

    _____ , and _____ . (I, Lizzy, myself, Peter, me)

13. The students _____ selected that assembly program.
    (theirselves, themselves)

© 1992, 1997 J. Weston Walch, Publisher

Understanding and Using Good Grammar

TEST: Selecting Correct Nominative and Compound (Intensive Appositive) Pronouns

Suggested Grading:

Sentence part identification:

2 points for appositive arrow and label
2 points for clause brackets and label
2 points for linking verb underline and label
1 point for compound sentence parts

Total points: 67 (% value each error, 1.5)

–1, 98	–8, 88	–15, 77	–22, 67
–2, 97	–9, 86	–16, 76	–23, 65
–3, 95	–10, 85	–17, 74	–24, 64
–4, 94	–11, 83	–18, 73	–25, 62
–5, 92	–12, 82	–19, 71	–26, 61
–6, 91	–13, 80	–20, 70	–27, 59
–7, 89	–14, 79	–21, 68	–28, 58

Pronoun choice and order

(% value each error, 3.57)

Sentence	Choice	Order	Points	Scale
1	2	3	5	–1, 96
2	2	2	4	–2, 93
3	2	2	4	–3, 89
4	2	3	5	–4, 86
5	2	0	2	–5, 82
6	1	2	3	–6, 79
7	2	2	4	–7, 75
8	1	0	1	–8, 71
			28	–9, 68
				–10, 64
				–11, 61
				–12, 57

TEST: Selecting Correct Nominative and Compound (Intensive Appositive) Pronouns

Instructions: In the blanks, write in polite order the correct pronouns or nouns in parentheses. Mark verbs, subjects, adjectives (except **LVC–A**), adverbs, prepositional phrases, and elliptical clauses. Label **LV, LVC–N, LVC–A, D.O., I.O., prep., O.P., Appos., Subj. Cl.,** and **Int. Appos.** Draw an arrow from an appositive to the word it identifies.

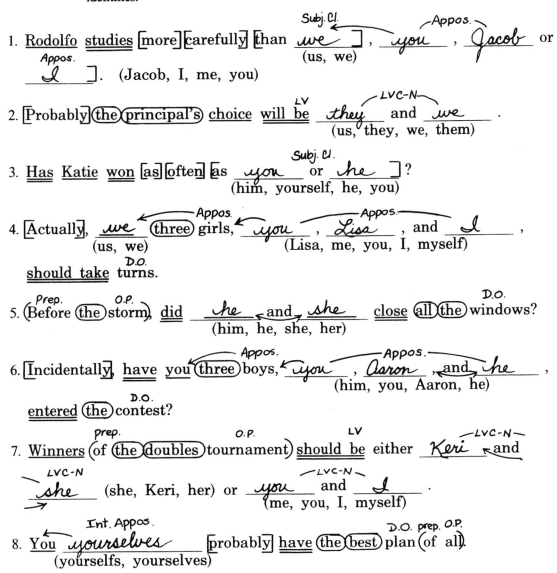

1. Rodolfo studies [more] carefully than *we*], *you* , *Jacob* or
   I]. (Jacob, I, me, you)

2. [Probably] (the) (principal's) choice will be *they* and *we* .
   (us, they, we, them)

3. Has Katie won [as] [often] as *you* or *he*]?
   (him, yourself, he, you)

4. [Actually], *we* (three) girls, *you* , *Lisa* , and *I* ,
   should take turns.

5. (Before (the) storm), did *he* and *she* close (all) (the) windows?
   (him, he, she, her)

6. [Incidentally], have you (three) boys, *you* , *Aaron* , and *he* ,
   entered (the) contest?

7. Winners (of (the) (doubles) tournament) should be either *Keri* and
   she (she, Keri, her) or *you* and *I* .
   (me, you, I, myself)

8. You *yourselves* [probably] have (the) (best) plan (of all).
   (yourselfs, yourselves)

Name _____

Date _____

TEST: Selecting Correct Nominative and Compound (Intensive Appositive) Pronouns

Instructions: In the blanks, write in polite order the correct pronouns or nouns in parentheses. Mark verbs, subjects, adjectives (except **LVC–A**), adverbs, prepositional phrases, and elliptical clauses. Label **LV, LVC–N, LVC–A, D.O., I.O., prep., O.P., Appos., Subj. Cl.,** and **Int. Appos.** Draw an arrow from an appositive to the word it identifies.

1. Rodolfo studies more carefully than _____ , _____ , _____ or
   (us, we)

   _____ . (Jacob, I, me, you)

2. Probably the principal's choice will be _____ and _____ .
   (us, they, we, them)

3. Has Katie won as often as _____ or _____ ?
   (him, yourself, he, you)

4. Actually, _____ three girls, _____ , _____ , and _____ ,
   (us, we)   (Lisa, me, you, I, myself)

   should take turns.

5. Before the storm, did _____ and _____ close all the windows?
   (him, he, she, her)

6. Incidentally, have you three boys, _____ , _____ , and _____ ,
   (him, you, Aaron, he)

   entered the contest?

7. Winners of the doubles tournament should be either _____ and

   _____ (she, Keri, her) or _____ and _____ .
   (me, you, I, myself)

8. You _____ probably have the best plan of all.
   (yourselfs, yourselves)

Objective, Compound (Reflexive), and Possessive Pronouns

This material through Objective Pronoun Use number 4 is review. Students should be able to recite from memory (1) objective pronouns, (2) sequence of polite order, and (3) the "hearing clue" to correct usage. Objective Pronoun Use number 5 and possessive pronouns are new material. Emphasize that commas should be used with appositives.

Work with students as they mark or label the parts of the example sentences. Diagram outlines are given to help students to maintain their skill, understanding, and appreciation of diagramming. On the chalkboard or overhead, write this sentence as an example of a reflexive pronoun used as the object of a preposition:

> This Christmas present I bought (for myself)
> D.O.   prep.   Refl. O.P.

Collect and check students' papers, record scores, return papers to students to refer to as they complete pages 116 and 119, and then to add to their accumulation of information pages.

Objective, Compound (Reflexive), and Possessive Pronouns

DEFINITION: **Objective pronouns** are used in object positions in sentences.

OBJECTIVE PRONOUNS: me, you, him, her, us, them, whom

1. Polite order: First, *you*; next, *him, her, them*, nouns; last, *me, us*
2. Where several pronouns are used in an object position, say each pronoun separately *after* the verb to hear the correct pronoun.

<u>Dad</u> <u>saw</u> (he, him), (her, she), (they, them), and (us, we).

Objective pronouns may be used as:

1. **Direct Object:**

(The) <u>teacher</u> <u>chose</u> you and them.

2. **Object of Preposition:**

<u>Mr. Brown</u> <u>called</u> (to her and me).

3. **Indirect Object:**

(Our) <u>neighbor</u> <u>will give</u> him and us (a) ride (to school).

4. **Object pronoun identified by noun appositive:**

Dad, <u>can</u> <u>you</u> <u>help</u> us girls?

5. **Pronoun in apposition to a noun in an object position:**

To **D.O.:** (This) <u>candidate</u> <u>has</u> (three)(strong) supporters,← ←us, you, Candy, and me!

To **O.P.:** She <u>brought</u> books (for (two) students), you and her.

To **I.O.:** (Our) <u>parents</u> <u>give</u> us, Sis and me, (generous) allowances.

COMPOUND PRONOUNS (REFLEXIVE), myself, yourself, himself, herself, itself, ouryourselves, themselves, are used in object positions and reflect the subject. Label: **Refl.**

1. <u>Jan</u> <u>gave</u> herself (a) permanent.   2. <u>I</u> <u>saw</u> myself (on (the)(TV) news).

POSSESSIVE PRONOUNS, my, your, her, etc., are used to modify gerunds—verb forms ending in *-ing* used as nouns. Label: **Poss. Ger.**

1. (No) <u>one</u> <u>knew</u> (about (your, you) winning).
2. (Him, (His)) leaving [now] <u>would be</u> (a) mistake.
3. <u>We</u> [really] <u>enjoyed</u> (them, (their)) singing.

Objective, Compound (Reflexive), and Possessive Pronouns

Name _____

Date _____

DEFINITION: **Objective pronouns** are used in object positions in sentences.

OBJECTIVE PRONOUNS: me, you, him, her, us, them, whom

1. Polite order: First, *you*; next, *him, her, them*, nouns; last, *me, us*
2. Where several pronouns are used in an object position, say each pronoun separately *after* the verb to hear the correct pronoun.

Dad saw (he, him), (her, she), (they, them), and (us, we).

Objective pronouns may be used as:

1. **Direct Object:**

   The teacher chose you and them.

2. **Object of Preposition:**

   Mr. Brown called to her and me.

3. **Indirect Object:**

   Our neighbor will give him and us

   a ride to school.

4. **Object pronoun identified by noun appositive:**

   Dad, can you help us girls?

5. **Pronoun in apposition to a noun in an object position:**

   To **D.O.**: This candidate has three strong supporters,

   us, you, Candy, and me!

   To **O.P.**: She brought books for two students, you and her.

   To **I.O.**: Our parents give us, Sis and me, generous allowances.

COMPOUND PRONOUNS (REFLEXIVE), myself, yourself, himself, herself, itself, our-yourselves, themselves, are used in object positions and reflect the subject. Label: **Refl.**

1. Jan gave herself a permanent.   2. I saw myself on the TV news.

POSSESSIVE PRONOUNS, my, your, her, etc., are used to modify gerunds—verb forms ending in *-ing* used as nouns. Label: **Poss. Ger.**

1. No one knew about (your, you) winning.   3. We really enjoyed (them, their) singing.

2. (Him, His) leaving now would be a mistake.

Understanding and Using Good Grammar

Objective, Compound (Reflexive), and Possessive Pronouns

Work with students to corroborate the sentence analysis and insertion of correct pronouns and commas suggested by volunteers. Tell students that some of these sentences are used in the unit test.

Collect papers, check sentences 1–8 or 9–16, record scores, and return papers to students to use in preparing for the Unit Test.

Objective, Compound (Reflexive), and Possessive Pronouns

PRACTICE: In the blanks, write in polite order the correct pronouns or nouns in parentheses.

Mark verbs, subjects, adjectives (except **LVC–A**), adverbs, and prepositional phrases.

Label **LV, LVC–N, LVC–A, D.O., I.O., prep., O.P., Appos., N.A., Refl.** (reflexive pronoun) and **Poss. Ger.** (possessive before a gerund).

1. The members have chosen *them* and *us* . (them, we, us, they)

2. Did Coach lend *you* and *him* the money? (you, he, him)

3. Wasn't the package sent (to *you* , *Marge* , and *me*)? (I, Marge, you, me)

4. *His* whining had gotten (on everyone's nerves) (He, Him, His)

5. We girls gave *ourselves* permanents. (us, ourselfs, ourselves)

6. Alison's dad was [not] surprised (about *her* and *my* winning) (her, I, she, my, me)

7. Doreen, did you see us, *him* and *me* , (at the game? (him, I, he, me)

8. A score (of 100%) was earned (by three students, *you* , *her* , and *me* . (her, myself, you, I, she, me)

9. Can you take *them* or *us* (in your car? (they, us, we them)

10. Richard's parents have bought *themselves* a new car. (theirselves, themselves)

11. Everyone was [really] excited (about *your* and *their* arriving) (them, you, your, their, they)

12. Ray has bought *you* , *Tom* , and *me* tickets (to the Giants game) (me, you, myself, I, Tom)

13. Lead roles are being played (by *you* , *her* , and *me*). (I, you, she, her, me)

14. The men are shouting (at someone, either *them* or *us* . (us, they, them, we)

15. My little brother told us, *Mom* and *me* , the truth. (myself, I, Mom, me)

16. Uncle Ken gave the VCR (to *us*) two, *Duane* and *me* . (we, us) (me, Duane, I)

Name _____

Date _____

Objective, Compound (Reflexive), and Possessive Pronouns

PRACTICE: In the blanks, write in polite order the correct pronouns or nouns in parentheses. Mark verbs, subjects, adjectives (except **LVC–A**), adverbs, and prepositional phrases. Label **LV, LVC–N, LVC–A, D.O., I.O., prep., O.P., Appos., N.A., Refl.** (reflexive pronoun) and **Poss. Ger.** (possessive before a gerund).

1. The members have chosen _____ and _____. (them, we, us, they)

2. Did Coach lend _____ and _____ the money? (you, he, him)

3. Wasn't the package sent to _____, _____, and _____?
   (I, **Marge**, you, me)

4. _____ whining had gotten on everyone's nerves. (He, Him, His)

5. We girls gave _____ permanents. (us, ourselfs, ourselves)

6. Alison's dad was not surprised about _____ and _____ winning.
   (her, I, she, my, me)

7. Doreen, did you see us, _____ and _____, at the game? (him, I, he, me)

8. A score of 100% was earned by three students, _____, _____,
   and _____. (her, myself, you, I, she, me)

9. Can you take _____ or _____ in your car? (they, us, we them)

10. Richard's parents have bought _____ a new car.
    (theirselves, themselves)

11. Everyone was really excited about _____ and _____ arriving.
    (them, you, your, their, they)

12. Ray has bought _____, _____, and _____ tickets to the
    Giants game.   (me, you, myself, I, Tom)

13. Lead roles are being played by _____, _____, and _____.
    (I, you, she, her, me)

14. The men are shouting at someone, either _____ or _____.
    (us, they, them, we)

15. My little brother told us, _____ and _____, the truth.
    (myself, I, Mom, me)

16. Uncle Ken gave the VCR to _____ two, _____ and _____.
    (we, us)   (me, Duane, I)

Understanding and Using Good Grammar

FINAL PRACTICE: Selecting Objective, Compound (Reflexive), and Possessive Pronouns

Advise students to work carefully as you and they complete the sentence analysis and insert the correct words and commas. There is no need to collect these papers. Students should take them home to review in preparing for the Test.

Sentence 13: *Heather* is a closely related appositive to *cousin* and does not need to be separated from it by a comma.

FINAL PRACTICE: Selecting
Objective, Compound (Reflexive), and Possessive Pronouns

Instructions: In the blanks, write in polite order the correct pronouns or nouns in parentheses. Mark verbs, subjects, adjectives (except **LVC-A**), adverbs, and prepositional phrases. Label **LV, LVC-N, LVC-A, D.O., I.O., prep., O.P., Appos., Refl.** (reflexive pronoun) and **Poss. Ger.** (possessive before a gerund). Insert necessary commas; draw an arrow from **Appos.** to the identified word.

1. (The) counselor will call us, _you_, _Adele_, and _me_. (me, Adele, myself, you, I)

2. Was Keith signaling (to _her_ or _him_)? (her, he, she, him)

3. (By now,) others will have heard (about _your_ and _my_ winning). (you, myself, my, your, me)

4. (The) (disc) jockey gave (two) students, _her_ and _him_, (his) autograph. (she, him, he, her)

5. Did Daren buy (that) book (for _himself_)? (himself, hisself)

6. _Their_ coming (at (that) time) surprised _us_ girls. (Them, Their) (we, us)

7. Did you see _her_ or _them_ (at (the) mall)? (them, her, she, they)

8. (Some) people take _themselves_ (too) (seriously). (themselfs, theirselves, themselves)

9. Mr. Weston gave _us_ boys, (my) brother and _me_, tickets (to (the) (49ers) game). (us, we) (I, my brother, myself, me)

10. Coach will present (the) trophies (to (three) boys), _you_, _him_, and _me_. (he, you, me, him, I)

11. We're buying _ourselves_ (a) (new) home. (ourselfs, ourselves)

12. _His_ disagreeing (really) annoyed _them_ and _us_. (He, His, Him) (them, we, us, they)

13. (My) aunt is giving _herself_, (my) cousin _Heather_, and _me_ (a) trip (to New Orleans). (myself, Heather, me, herself, her)

14. Elaine seems angry (about _your_, _Pat's_, and _my_ arriving) (late) (for dinner). (Pat, you, Pat's, my, me, your)

FINAL PRACTICE: Selecting Objective, Compound (Reflexive), and Possessive Pronouns

Name _____

Date _____

Instructions: In the blanks, write in polite order the correct pronouns or nouns in parentheses. Mark verbs, subjects, adjectives (except **LVC–A**), adverbs, and prepositional phrases. Label **LV, LVC–N, LVC–A, D.O., I.O., prep., O.P., Appos., Refl.** (reflexive pronoun) and **Poss. Ger.** (possessive before a gerund). Insert necessary commas; draw an arrow from **Appos.** to the identified word.

1. The counselor will call us _____ _____ and _____ . .
   (me, Adele, myself, you, I)

2. Was Keith signaling to_____ or _____ ? (her, he, she, him)

3. By now others will have heard about _____ and _____ winning.
   (you, myself, my, your, me)

4. The disc jockey gave two students _____ and _____ his autograph.
   (she, him, he, her)

5. Did Daren buy that book for _____ ? (himself, hisself)

6. _____ coming at that time surprised _____ girls.
   (Them, Their)   (we, us)

7. Did you see _____ or _____ at the mall? (them, her, she, they)

8. Some people take _____ too seriously.
   (themselfs, theirselves, themselves)

9. Mr. Weston gave _____ boys _____ and _____ tickets
   (us, we)   (I, my brother, myself, me)
   to the 49ers game.

10. Coach will present the trophies to three boys _____ _____
    and_____ . (he, you, me, him, I)

11. We're buying _____ a new home. (ourselfs, ourselves)

12. _____ disagreeing really annoyed _____ and _____ .
    (He, His, Him)   (them, we, us, they)

13. My aunt is giving _____ , my cousin _____ and _____
    (myself, Heather, me, herself, her)
    a trip to New Orleans.

14. Elaine seems angry about _____ _____ and _____ arriving
    (Pat, you, Pat's, my, me, your)
    late for dinner.

Understanding and Using Good Grammar

TEST: Selecting Correct
Objective, Compound (Reflexive),
and Possessive Pronouns

> The next reproducible page contains two copies of one half-page Test. Cut each duplicated page in half; give each student one half-page.

Suggested Grading:

1 point for all words in compound sentence part, 2 points for two separate appositives in sentence 7.

Sentence part identification and commas

–1, 98	–7, 88	–13, 78	–19, 68
–2, 97	–8, 87	–14, 77	–20, 67
–3, 95	–9, 85	–15, 75	–21, 65
–4, 93	–10, 83	–16, 73	–22, 63
–5, 92	–11, 82	–17, 72	–23, 62
–6, 90	–12, 80	–18, 70	–24, 60

Total points: 60 (53 identifications, 7 commas)

Pronoun choice and order

Sentence	Choice	Order	Points	Scale
1	2	2	4	–1, 96
2	1	3	4	–2, 93
3	2	0	2	–3, 89
4	2	2	4	–4, 85
5	2	2	4	–5, 81
6	2	2	4	–6, 78
7	2	3	5	–7, 74
			27	–8, 70
				–9, 67
				–10, 63
				–11, 59

TEST: Selecting Correct Objective, Compound (Reflexive), and Possessive Pronouns

Name _____

Date _____

Instructions: In the blanks, write in polite order the correct pronouns or nouns in parentheses. Mark verbs, subjects, adjectives (except **LVC–A**), adverbs, and prepositional phrases. Label **LV, LVC–N, LVC–A, D.O., I.O., prep., O.P., Appos., Refl.** (reflexive pronoun) and **Poss. Ger.** (possessive before a gerund). Insert necessary commas; draw an arrow from **Appos.** to the identified word.

1. Would your dad lend _**them**_ and _**us**_ the money?
   (they, us, we, them)

2. The counselor will call _**you**_, _**Adele**_, and _**me**_.
   (Adele, I, you, me)

3. Will the package be addressed (to _**him**_ or _**her**_)?
   (he, her, him, she)

4. Alison's dad was not surprised (about _**her**_ and _**my**_ winning)
   (I, her, she, me, my)

5. My aunt is giving _**herself**_, my cousin _**Heather**_, and _**me**_
   (myself, Heather, me, herself, her)
   a trip (to New Orleans)

6. The principal was really supportive (of _**their**_ and _**our**_ continuing)
   (us, their, them, our)

7. This candidate has three strong supporters: _**you**_, _**Miguel**_, and
   _**me**_. (Miguel, I, me, you)

Name _____

Date _____

TEST: Selecting Correct Objective, Compound (Reflexive), and Possessive Pronouns

Instructions: In the blanks, write in polite order the correct pronouns or nouns in parentheses. Mark verbs, subjects, adjectives (except **LVC–A**), adverbs, and prepositional phrases. Label **LV, LVC–N, LVC–A, D.O., I.O., prep., O.P., Appos., Refl.** (reflexive pronoun) and **Poss. Ger.** (possessive before a gerund). Insert necessary commas; draw an arrow from **Appos.** to the identified word.

1. Would your dad lend _____ and _____ the money?
   (they, us, we, them)

2. The counselor will call _____ _____ and _____ .
   (Adele, I, you, me)

3. Will the package be addressed to _____ or _____ ?
   (he, her, him, she)

4. Alison's dad was not surprised about _____ and _____ winning.
   (I, her, she, me, my)

5. My aunt is giving _____ , my cousin _____ and _____
   a trip to New Orleans.   (myself, Heather, me, herself, her)

6. The principal was really supportive of_____ and _____ continuing.
   (us, their, them, our)

7. This candidate has three strong supporters: _____ _____
   and _____ . (Miguel, I, me, you)

Name _____

Date _____

TEST: Selecting Correct Objective, Compound (Reflexive), and Possessive Pronouns

Instructions: In the blanks, write in polite order the correct pronouns or nouns in parentheses. Mark verbs, subjects, adjectives (except **LVC–A**), adverbs, and prepositional phrases. Label **LV, LVC–N, LVC–A, D.O., I.O., prep., O.P., Appos., Refl.** (reflexive pronoun) and **Poss. Ger.** (possessive before a gerund). Insert necessary commas; draw an arrow from **Appos.** to the identified word.

1. Would your dad lend _____ and _____ the money?
   (they, us, we, them)

2. The counselor will call _____ _____ and _____ .
   (Adele, I, you, me)

3. Will the package be addressed to _____ or _____ ?
   (he, her, him, she)

4. Alison's dad was not surprised about _____ and _____ winning.
   (I, her, she, me, my)

5. My aunt is giving _____ , my cousin _____ and _____
   a trip to New Orleans.   (myself, Heather, me, herself, her)

6. The principal was really supportive of_____ and _____ continuing.
   (us, their, them, our)

7. This candidate has three strong supporters: _____ _____
   and _____ . (Miguel, I, me, you)

Understanding and Using Good Grammar

REVIEW:
Use of Pronouns

This page summarizes all the uses of both nominative and objective pronouns. Students should review information pages 98 and 113. Work with them to be sure they write the correct forms in the blanks and mark and label sentence parts correctly. In sentence 3 *there* is an introductory word that has no grammatical connection to the rest of the sentence. There is no need to collect this page; students should take it home to review before the Test on page 128.

REVIEW:
Nominative and Objective
Personal Pronouns

Instructions: In the blanks, write in polite order the correct pronouns or nouns in parentheses. Mark or label all sentence parts as usual, including **Subj. Cl.** (subject of clause), **Int. Appos.** (intensive appositive), **Refl.** (reflexive pronoun), and **Poss. Ger.** (possessive before gerund); draw an arrow from **Appos.** to the identified word. Insert necessary commas.

1. _____He_____ and _____they_____ must have seen _us_ girls, (them, he, him, they)   (we, us)
   you, _Michelle_, and _me_ . (I, Michelle, me, you)

2. My parents [just] bought _themselves_, _my sister_ _Sally_, and (my sister, theirselves, me, Sally, themselves, I)
   _me_ (new) in-line skates.

3. [Possibly] there could be (four) winners (of (the) contest), _they_ and _we_ . (us, they, we, them)

4. _We_ two [usually] get (better) grades [than _she_ and _he_] . (her, she, him, he)

5. My winning [certainly] surprised everyone, _you_, _her_, (Me, I, My)
   him, and especially _me_ . (I, her, he, you, me, she, him)

6. Our neighbors _themselves_ had heard (the) shattering (of glass). (theirselves, themselves)

7. My sister and _I_ (I, my sister, me) play tennis [as (often)] [as _you_ and _he_] ,(you, him, he) but you two win (more) games [than _she_ and _I_] . (I, her, me, she)

8. Was (their) volunteering (a) surprise (to _you_ and _her_)? (them, their, they)   (her, you, she)

9. Did _you_ and (your) brother buy _yourselves_ (that) (expensive) camera? (your brother, you)   (yourselves, yourselfs)

10. (The) suspect _himself_ had given (the) (incriminating) evidence. (hisself, himself)

11. Is either girl, _Beth_ or _she_ , [as] tall [as _you_ or _I_] ? (I, you, me) (Beth, her, she)

REVIEW: Nominative and Objective Personal Pronouns

Name _____

Date _____

Instructions: In the blanks, write in polite order the correct pronouns or nouns in parentheses. Mark or label all sentence parts as usual, including **Subj. Cl.** (subject of clause), **Int. Appos.** (intensive appositive), **Refl.** (reflexive pronoun), and **Poss. Ger.** (possessive before gerund); draw an arrow from **Appos.** to the identified word. Insert necessary commas.

1. _____ and _____ must have seen _____ girls
   (them, he, him, they)   (we, us)
   _____ _____ and _____ . (I, Michelle, me, you)

2. My parents just bought _____ _____ _____ and
   (my sister, theirselves, me, Sally, themselves, I)
   _____ in-line skates.

3. Possibly there could be four winners of the contest _____ and
   _____ . (us, they, we, them)

4. _____ two usually get better grades than _____ and
   (Us, We)
   _____ . (her, she, him, he)

5. _____ winning certainly surprised everyone _____ _____
   (Me, I, My)
   _____ and especially _____ . (I, her, he, you, me, she, him)

6. Our neighbors _____ had heard the shattering of glass.
   (theirselves, themselves)

7. _____ and _____ (I, my sister, me) play tennis as often as
   _____ and _____ (you, him, he) but you two win more
   games than _____ and _____ . (I, her, me, she)

8. Was _____ volunteering a surprise to _____ and _____ ?
   (them, their, they)   (her, you, she)

9. Did _____ *and* _____ buy _____ that expensive
   (your brother, you)   (yourselves, yourselfs)
   camera?

10. The suspect _____ had given the incriminating evidence.
    (hisself, himself)

11. Is either girl _____ or _____ as tall as _____ or
    (Beth, her, she)
    _____ ? (I, you, me)

TEST: Nominative and Objective Personal Pronouns

All sentences on this Test have been taken or adapted from sentences on the practice sheets, pages 101–119. Check only students' written words and related marking and labeling.

Sentence	Choice	Order	Label	Points		Sentence	Choice	Order	Label	Points
1	3	3	2	8		8	2	1	3	6
2	3	3	1	7		9	2	0	1	3
3	2	2	2	6		10	2	0	2	4
4	2	0	1	3		11	2	2	1	5
5	2	3	1	6		12	*2	2	1	5
6	3	2	2	7		13	3	4	2	9
7	1	0	1	2		(1.4% each)		Total points:		71

Grading scale:

–1, 99	–6, 92	–11, 85	–16, 78	–21, 71	–26, 64
–2, 97	–7, 90	–12, 83	–17, 76	–22, 69	–27, 62
–3, 96	–8, 89	–13, 82	–18, 75	–23, 68	–28, 61
–4, 94	–9, 87	–14, 80	–19, 73	–24, 66	–29, 59
–5, 93	–10, 86	–15, 79	–20, 72	–25, 65	–30, 58

Suggestion: Highlight on the Answer Key the items you will be correcting.

1. We ← choice   you, she, I ← label / order   Appos.   } = Points/8
   Subj. label   choice

2. your, Pat's, my ← label / order   Poss. Ger.   } = 7
   choice

TEST: Nominative and
Objective Personal Pronouns

Instructions: In the blanks, write in polite order the correct pronouns or nouns in parentheses. Mark or label those sentence parts as usual, including **Subj. Cl.** (subject of clause), **Int. Appos.** (intensive appositive), **Refl.** (reflexive pronoun), and **Poss. Ger.** (possessive before gerund). Draw one line under a subject; label: **LCV–N, D.O., O.P., Appos.**

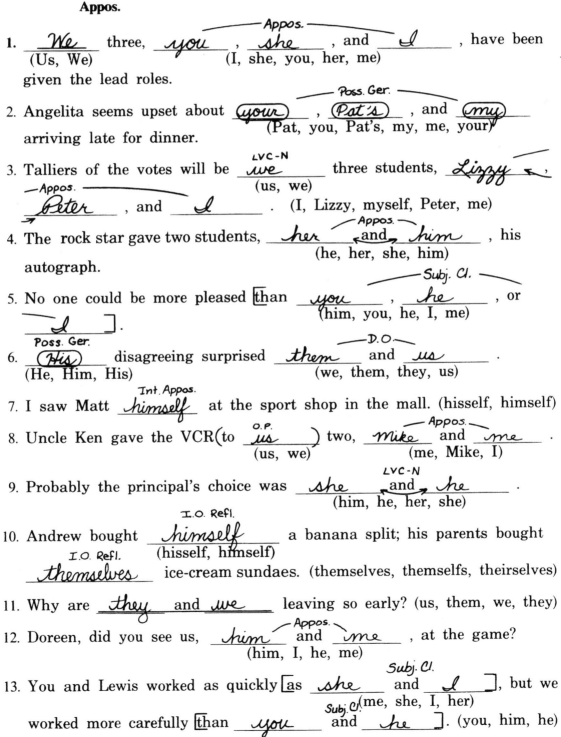

1. *We* three, *you*, *she*, and *I*, have been
   (Us, We)   (I, she, you, her, me)
   given the lead roles.

2. Angelita seems upset about *your*, *Pat's*, and *my*
   arriving late for dinner.   (Pat, you, Pat's, my, me, your)

3. Talliers of the votes will be *we* three students, *Lizzy*,
   (us, we)
   Peter, and *I*. (I, Lizzy, myself, Peter, me)

4. The rock star gave two students, *her* and *him*, his
   (he, her, she, him)
   autograph.

5. No one could be more pleased than *you*, *he*, or
   I.   (him, you, he, I, me)

6. *His* disagreeing surprised *them* and *us*.
   (He, Him, His)   (we, them, they, us)

7. I saw Matt *himself* at the sport shop in the mall. (hisself, himself)

8. Uncle Ken gave the VCR (to *us*) two, *Mike* and *me*.
   (us, we)   (me, Mike, I)

9. Probably the principal's choice was *she* and *he*.
   (him, he, her, she)

10. Andrew bought *himself* a banana split; his parents bought
    (hisself, himself)
    themselves ice-cream sundaes. (themselves, themselfs, theirselves)

11. Why are *they* and *we* leaving so early? (us, them, we, they)

12. Doreen, did you see us, *him* and *me*, at the game?
    (him, I, he, me)

13. You and Lewis worked as quickly [as *she* and *I*], but we
    (me, she, I, her)
    worked more carefully [than *you* and *he*]. (you, him, he)

Name _____

Date _____

TEST: Nominative and Objective Personal Pronouns

Instructions: In the blanks, write in polite order the correct pronouns or nouns in parentheses. Mark or label those sentence parts as usual, including **Subj. Cl.** (subject of clause), **Int. Appos.** (intensive appositive), **Refl.** (reflexive pronoun), and **Poss. Ger.** (possessive before gerund). Draw one line under a subject; label: **LCV–N**, **D.O.**, **O.P.**, **Appos.**

1. _____ three, _____, _____, and _____, have been
   (Us, We)   (I, she, you, her, me)
   given the lead roles.

2. Angelita seems upset about _____, _____, and _____
   arriving late for dinner.   (Pat, you, Pat's, my, me, your)

3. Talliers of the votes will be _____ three students, _____,
                                  (us, we)
   _____, and _____. (I, Lizzy, myself, Peter, me)

4. The rock star gave two students, _____ and _____, his
   autograph.   (he, her, she, him)

5. No one could be more pleased than _____, _____, or
                                     (him, you, he, I, me)
   _____.

6. _____ disagreeing surprised _____ and _____.
   (He, Him, His)   (we, them, they, us)

7. I saw Matt _____ at the sport shop in the mall. (hisself, himself)

8. Uncle Ken gave the VCR to _____ two, _____ and _____.
                             (us, we)   (me, Mike, I)

9. Probably the principal's choice was _____ and _____.
                                        (him, he, her, she)

10. Andrew bought _____ a banana split; his parents bought
                  (hisself, himself)
    _____ ice-cream sundaes. (themselves, themselfs, theirselves)

11. Why are _____ and _____ leaving so early? (us, them, we, they)

12. Doreen, did you see us, _____ and _____, at the game?
                           (him, I, he, me)

13. You and Lewis worked as quickly as _____ and _____, but we
                                        (me, she, I, her)
    worked more carefully than _____ and _____. (you, him, he)

Understanding and Using Good Grammar

Uses of Who, Whom, Whose, Who's

Analyze all sentences with students.

The relative pronouns *which* and *that* are also used to introduce adjective clauses. Complete study of adjective clauses begins on page 286.

To help students to recognize adjective clauses, point out that a sentence that has an adjective clause has more than one verb; the clause begins with *who, whom*, or *whose*.

On the chalkboard or overhead write these example sentences:

Jim is the boy ⟨who won the race.⟩ (Carefully demonstrate the analysis.)

    (a) is is one verb; won is another.

    (b) The main sentence: Jim is (the) boy.

    (c) The adjective clause: ⟨who won (the) race⟩ modifies boy.

Carri, the girl ⟨who just hurried past us,⟩ is our class president.

    (a) hurried is one verb; is is another.

    (b) The main sentence: Carri is (our)(class) president.

    (c) Adjective clause: ⟨who [just] hurried (past us⟩ modifies girl.

Analyze in the same way all other sentences on this page which contain adjective clauses. Collect the worksheets, check the Practice sentences, record the scores, and return the papers to the students.

Uses of *Who, Whom, Whose, Who's*

A. Who is used in **subject** and **LVC positions**:

1. **Subject:** Who came first?   Jared and who delivered the package?
2. **LVC:** The winners were you and who?   The captain will be who?

3. **Subject of an adjective clause** used to describe a noun in the sentence.

KNOW: An **adjective clause** is a group of words which contains a verb and a subject and is used to modify a noun in the main sentence.

1. An **adjective clause** may be introduced by **who, whom,** or **whose.**

2. Use pointed brackets to identify an adjective clause; draw an arrow to the word modified.

Jim is the boy <who won the race.>
Carri, the girl <who just hurried past us> is our class president.

PRACTICE: Mark and label all sentence parts as in the examples above.

1. Who are your best friends?
2. The person on the phone was who?
3. I gave my cousin, <who is going away to college> a pen and pencil set.

4. Was it Tom <who called you?>
5. It was Mario <who called.>

B. Whom is used in **object** positions:

1. **Direct Object:** Whom will he choose?
2. **Object of Preposition:** Whom are you talking about? (About whom . . .)
3. **Indirect Object:** The police gave whom a bicycle?

4. In an **object position of an adjective clause:**

Ophelia is one girl <whom I can trust.>
Our neighbor is the man <whom> I am looking for.> (For whom . . .)

PRACTICE: Mark or label all sentence parts as in the examples above.

1. Whom do you like?
2. From whom did Christine borrow the pencil?
3. Ann is one girl <whom everyone likes.>
4. Whom are you thinking about?
5. Could Omar have been the one <whom the teacher saw in the library?>

6. The girl <whom> I was telling you about> just came in.
7. The girl <who just came in> is my neighbor.

Uses of *Who, Whom, Whose, Who's*

Name _____

Date _____

A. Who is used in **subject** and **LVC positions:**

1. **Subject:** Who came first?   Jared and who delivered the package?

2. **LVC:** The winners were you and who?   The captain will be who?

3. **Subject of an adjective clause** used to describe a noun in the sentence.

KNOW: An **adjective clause** is a group of words which contains a verb and a subject and is used to modify a noun in the main sentence.

1. An **adjective clause** may be introduced by **who, whom,** or **whose.**

2. Use pointed brackets to identify an adjective clause; draw an arrow to the word modified.

Jim is the boy ⟨who won the race.⟩

Carri, the girl ⟨who [just] hurried (past us)⟩ is our class president.

PRACTICE: Mark and label all sentence parts as in the examples above.

1. Who are your best friends?

2. The person on the phone was who?

3. I gave my cousin, who is going away to college, a pen and pencil set.

4. Was it Tom who called you?

5. It was Mario who called.

B. Whom is used in **object** positions:

1. **Direct Object:** Whom will he choose?

2. **Object of Preposition:** Whom) are you talking (about? (About whom . . .)

3. **Indirect Object:** The police gave whom a bicycle?

4. In an **object position of an adjective clause:**

Ophelia is one girl ⟨whom I can trust.⟩

Our neighbor is the man ⟨whom) I am looking (for.⟩ (For whom . . .)

PRACTICE: Mark or label all sentence parts as in the examples above.

1. Whom do you like?

2. From whom did Christine borrow the pencil?

3. Ann is one girl whom everyone likes.

4. Whom are you thinking about?

5. Could Omar have been the one whom the teacher saw in the library?

6. The girl whom I was telling you about just came in.

7. The girl who just came in is my neighbor.

Understanding and Using Good Grammar

Uses of Who, Whom, Whose, Who's
(continued)

In example 2 under the **Whose** section, the clause, "whose report you are reading," is not necessary to understand that "Cleo is a good student," the main sentence. It is set off with commas.

In sentence 6 in the first Practice, the clause, "whose bike is lying on the curb," is not set off with commas because it gives added information to the main sentence, "The girl has injured her knee." The same is true of the clauses in sentences 7 and 8.

Under **Know**:

Example 1: When the interrupter is left out, the main sentence is structured in logical order.

2: When "do you think" is left out, the main sentence must be restructured: "Whom will the teacher believe?"

Uses of *Who, Whom, Whose, Who's*
(continued)

C. Whose, besides being a possessive pronoun, is often used to introduce a dependent adjective clause. Distinguish between **whose** and **who's**, the contraction of **who is** or **who has**.

Examples: 1. Whose house is the one on the corner?
2. Cleo, whose report you are reading, is a good student.
3. Who's your date?

PRACTICE: In sentences 1–4, write your choice of **whose** or **who's** in the blanks; mark and label sentence parts as in the examples, including pointed brackets around adjective clauses.

1. _Who's_ been selected for the position?

2. _Whose_ petition did you sign?

3. _Whose_ basketball is that?

4. _Who's_ turning in a report today?

5. My eccentric aunt, whose cat is a Maltese, had named her pet, Falcon.

6. The girl whose bike is lying on the curb has injured her knee.

7. We should talk to the chef whose rice pudding we're eating!

8. This is Nels Larson whose father is the new coach.

D. KNOW: Expressions like *did you say, does he think,* and *do they believe* are sentence interrupters; to separate them from the main sentence, draw a wavy line under them. Do not consider them when you decide between using **who** or **whom**.

1. **Subject:** Who did the audience think sang best?
2. **Object:** Whom do you think the teacher will believe?

PRACTICE: Mark or label all sentence parts as in the examples. Draw a wavy line under the sentence interrupter.

1. Who did the instructor say will be playing in the tournament?

2. Whom did Marcy say she was going with to the dance?

3. Whom did Xavier think he had seen at the mall?

4. Who did you say sent you that valentine?

5. Who did you say called me yesterday?

6. Whom do you think Francesca will invite?

7. Whom did Mia say she would write a report about?

Name _____

Date _____

Uses of *Who, Whom, Whose*
Who's (continued)

C. Whose, besides being a possessive pronoun, is often used to introduce a dependent adjective clause. Distinguish between **whose** and **who's**, the contraction of **who is** or **who has**.

Examples: 1. Whose house is the one on the corner?

2. Cleo, whose report you are reading, is a good student.

3. Who's your date?

PRACTICE: In sentences 1–4, write your choice of **whose** or **who's** in the blanks; mark and label sentence parts as in the examples, including pointed brackets around adjective clauses.

1. _____ been selected for the position?

2. _____ petition did you sign?

3. _____ basketball is that?

4. _____ turning in a report today?

5. My eccentric aunt, whose cat is a Maltese, had named her pet, Falcon.

6. The girl whose bike is lying on the curb has injured her knee.

7. We should talk to the chef whose rice pudding we're eating!

8. This is Nels Larson whose father is the new coach.

D. *KNOW:* Expressions like *did you say*, *does he think*, and *do they believe* are sentence interrupters; to separate them from the main sentence, draw a wavy line under them. Do not consider them when you decide between using **who** or **whom**.

1. **Subject:** Who did the audience think sang best?

2. **Object:** Whom do you think the teacher will believe?

PRACTICE: Mark or label all sentence parts as in the examples. Draw a wavy line under the sentence interrupter.

1. Who did the instructor say will be playing in the tournament?

2. Whom did Marcy say she was going with to the dance?

3. Whom did Xavier think he had seen at the mall?

4. Who did you say sent you that valentine?

5. Who did you say called me yesterday?

6. Whom do you think Francesca will invite?

7. Whom did Mia say she would write a report about?

Uses of Who, Whom, Whose, Who's

Understanding the use of *who*, *whom*, and *whose* requires advanced analytical thinking. This study was not included in *Steps to Good Grammar*.

Point out the following concerning the use of commas with adjective clauses:

1. A clause should not be set off with commas if the information it contains is essential to the thought expressed in the main sentence.

2. A clause should be set off with commas if it contains only additional, interesting information about the thought being expressed in the main sentence. If the term *incidentally* can sensibly be inserted in the clause, set the clause off with commas.

Sentence 5: Uncle Ted, whose plane, incidentally, will arrive soon, is my favorite uncle.

It certainly isn't necessary to know that "his plane will arrive soon" to understand that "Uncle Ted is my favorite uncle"!

This is the only sentence on this Practice sheet that requires commas to set off the clause.

Uses of *Who, Whom, Whose, Who's*

PRACTICE: Mark or label as usual all sentence parts, including the parts of a clause. Draw pointed brackets around an adjective clause and an arrow to the word it modifies. In the blanks, write **who**, **whom**, **whose**, or **who's**. Under an interrupter, draw a wavy line. Remember that a sentence with two verbs contains either an interrupter or a clause.

1. *Whom* has Julia added (to her guest list)?

2. {*Who* / *Who's*} finished the test?

3. The Joneses gave you and *whom* a ride (to school)?

4. *Whom* were you waving (at?

5. Uncle Ted, ⟨whose plane will arrive soon⟩, is my favorite uncle.

6. The volunteers are you, Alex, and *who* ?

7. *Whose* book are you using?

8. *Who* do you suppose is making all that noise?

9. Was Steffi the girl ⟨who won the tournament?⟩

10. *Whom* did you say you had seen (near the fire alarm)?

11. My little brother Maro is the one ⟨for *whom* I bought this book.⟩

12. Mr. Ryder is the man ⟨whose car we washed [yesterday]⟩

13. The woman ⟨who lives (in this house)⟩ is [not] Ms. Greene.

14. *Whom* are you thinking (about?

15. Did you know the woman ⟨who honked (at us?)⟩

16. *Whom* do you think Nat will invite (to the dance)?

17. A man ⟨whom I respect [very] much⟩ is my dad.

18. *Who* do the police think was the burglar?

19. The person ⟨whose coat this is⟩ [probably] needs it.

20. Was Janel the one ⟨whom the class chose?⟩

21. The man (beside the car) is *who* ?

22. *Whom* has Gary been tutoring [today]?

23. The boy ⟨who's fishing (off the pier)⟩ is my cousin.

24. *Whose* suggestion did most (of the students) like [best]?

Uses of *Who, Whom, Whose, Who's*

Name _____

Date _____

PRACTICE: Mark or label as usual all sentence parts, including the parts of a clause. Draw pointed brackets around an adjective clause and an arrow to the word it modifies. In the blanks, write **who, whom, whose,** or **who's.** Under an interrupter, draw a wavy line. Remember that a sentence with two verbs contains either an interrupter or a clause.

1. _____ has Julia added to her guest list?

2. _____ finished the test?

3. The Joneses gave you and _____ a ride to school?

4. _____ were you waving at?

5. Uncle Ted, _____ plane will arrive soon, is my favorite uncle.

6. The volunteers are you, Alex, and _____ ?

7. _____ book are you using?

8. _____ do you suppose is making all that noise?

9. Was Steffi the girl _____ won the tournament?

10. _____ did you say you had seen near the fire alarm?

11. My little brother Maro is the one for _____ I bought this book.

12. Mr. Ryder is the man _____ car we washed yesterday.

13. The woman _____ lives in this house is not Ms. Greene.

14. _____ are you thinking about?

15. Did you know the woman _____ honked at us?

16. _____ do you think Nat will invite to the dance?

17. A man _____ I respect very much is my dad.

18. _____ do the police think was the burglar?

19. The person _____ coat this is probably needs it.

20. Was Janel the one _____ the class chose?

21. The man beside the car is _____ ?

22. _____ has Gary been tutoring today?

23. The boy _____ fishing off the pier is my cousin.

24. _____ suggestion did most of the students like best?

Understanding and Using Good Grammar

FINAL PRACTICE:
Who, Whom, Whose, Who's

Sentence 1:   *Armando* is a "close" appositive to brother and does not need to be set off with commas.

The clause "who never stops trying" explains why Armando is admired.

The gerund "trying" functions as the direct object in the clause.

Sentences 5, 8, and 14:   Clauses in these sentences should be set off with commas because the information they contain is not essential to understanding the thought expressed in the main sentence.

Sentence 17:   Commas set off the prepositional phrase simply to clarify the question being asked. Some students may quite reasonably decide that the commas are unnecessary.

FINAL PRACTICE:
Who, Whom, Whose, Who's

PRACTICE: Mark or label as usual all sentence parts, including the parts of a clause. Draw pointed brackets around an adjective clause and an arrow to the word it modifies. In the blanks, write **who, whom, whose,** or **who's**. Under an interrupter, draw a wavy line. Insert commas in the three sentences that require them. Remember that a sentence with two verbs contains either an interrupter or a clause.

1. I [really] admire (my) brother Armando ⟨who [never] stops trying.⟩

2. (Sunny) weather was predicted (by (the) forecaster (to whom) we listened.⟩

3. (The) man ⟨whose car was [only] [slightly] damaged⟩ is [not] filing charges.

4. Whom are (the) Boy Scouts helping?

5. Mom and Dad have bought Patty, ⟨who is [only] (three years) old,⟩ (a) pair (of (ice) skates).

6. Who do you think (the) (guest) speaker will be?

7. (The) man ⟨who's wearing (the) raincoat⟩ is (my) uncle.

8. Mrs. Allen, ⟨whom we hadn't met [before]⟩ gave us girls (a) (large) donation.

9. (My) aunt is (the) woman ⟨whose dog won (the) (blue) ribbon.⟩

10. (The) winners were you and who ?

11. (The) woman ⟨who lives (in (that) house)⟩ has (five) dogs.

12. We've been talking (to (the) man) ⟨who's laying (our) (new) tile.⟩

13. Whom) did Kimmy say she was going (with (to (the) dance?⟩

14. (Our) (newspaper) girl, ⟨whom everyone admires⟩ [recently] won (a) ($500) scholarship.

15. Coach is (a) man ⟨whose (fine) reputation is well-deserved.⟩

16. I had been sitting (with students) ⟨who were (complete) strangers (to me.)⟩

17. Who , (besides Myla), is (on (the) committee?)

18. (Most) students like (the) teacher ⟨whom) I was telling you (about.⟩

19. I spoke (to (the) judge) ⟨whose decision seemed fair (to all.)⟩

Name _____

Date _____

FINAL PRACTICE:
Who, Whom, Whose, Who's

PRACTICE: Mark or label as usual all sentence parts, including the parts of a clause. Draw pointed brackets around an adjective clause and an arrow to the word it modifies. In the blanks, write **who**, **whom**, **whose**, or **who's**. Under an interrupter, draw a wavy line. Insert commas in the three sentences that require them. Remember that a sentence with two verbs contains either an interrupter or a clause.

1. I really admire my brother Armando _____ never stops trying.

2. Sunny weather was predicted by the forecaster to _____ we listened.

3. The man _____ car was only slightly damaged is not filing charges.

4. _____ are the Boy Scouts helping?

5. Mom and Dad have bought Patty _____ is only three years old a pair of ice skates.

6. _____ do you think the guest speaker will be?

7. The man _____ wearing the raincoat is my uncle.

8. Mrs. Allen _____ we hadn't met before gave us girls a large donation.

9. My aunt is the woman _____ dog won the blue ribbon.

10. The winners were you and _____ ?

11. The woman _____ lives in that house has five dogs.

12. We've been talking to the man _____ laying our new tile.

13. _____ did Kimmy say she was going with to the dance?

14. Our newspaper girl _____ everyone admires recently won a $500 scholarship.

15. Coach is a man _____ fine reputation is well-deserved.

16. I had been sitting with students _____ were complete strangers to me.

17. _____ besides Myla is on the committee?

18. Most students like the teacher _____ I was telling you about.

19. I spoke to the judge _____ decision seemed fair to all.

Understanding and Using Good Grammar

TEST: Who, Whom, Whose, Who's

To assist students in determining the use of the pronouns, they are instructed to mark or label all sentence parts. However, they should be informed that their grade will be based on five points: (1) choice of pronoun, (2) use of pronoun, (3) placement of pointed brackets, (4) wavy line under interrupter, (5) insertion of commas. You may prefer to have them show only those markings, 46 points total. To facilitate grading you may wish to highlight the five items on the Answer Key.

Sentences 6 and 11: Commas set off clauses containing only additional, interesting information.

Sentence 9: Some students may reason that the clause is essential to the meaning of the main sentence and that commas are not necessary. Either with or without commas may be accepted as correct.

Notice that the half-page test on page 146 is composed of simple sentences which cover the concepts presented on pages 134, 137, and 140. Students may use page 143 as a self-test with each one correcting his or her own paper under your instruction and taking the paper home to review for the Test on page 146.

Grading scale: 46 points

−1, 98	−5, 89	−9, 80	−13, 72	−17, 63
−2, 96	−6, 87	−10, 78	−14, 70	−18, 61
−3, 93	−7, 85	−11, 76	−15, 67	−19, 59
−4, 91	−8, 82	−12, 74	−16, 65	−20, 57

TEST:
Who, Whom, Whose, Who's

Instructions: In the blanks, mark or label as usual all parts of the main sentence and of an adjective clause if there is one. Put pointed brackets around each clause and draw an arrow to the word modified. In the blanks, write **who**, **whom**, **whose**, **who's** where appropriate. Under an interrupter, draw a wavy line. Insert necessary commas.

1. _Who_ (among all the contestants) do you think has the best chance?

2. Was it Brian <whom you were calling?>

3. Mr. Lee has sold his car (to the man <from whom he had bought it.>

4. _Whom_ has Mother invited (for Thanksgiving dinner)?

5. We have an estimate (from a contractor) <who's Dad's long-time friend.>

6. The children, <who had applauded [continuously] [really] enjoyed the circus.

7. (For whom) are most (of the students) voting?

8. (Whose) turn did she say is next?

9. The sad-looking child, <whom I had been watching> [suddenly] gave me a radiant smile.

10. That is the student <who won $500 (for his essay)>

11. Uncle Bob, <who [always] gives strange presents, gave me a six-foot-tall stuffed frog.

12. Grandpa attended a reunion (of army officers) <with whom) he had served (in World War II)>

13. The two officers <(whose) signatures are necessary (on the club's checks) are absent.

14. _Who's_ planning the Christmas dance?

15. The child received a generous reward (from the man) <who had lost the money.>

TEST: *Who, Whom, Whose, Who's*

Name _____

Date _____

Instructions: In the blanks, mark or label as usual all parts of the main sentence and of an adjective clause if there is one. Put pointed brackets around each clause and draw an arrow to the word modified. In the blanks, write **who, whom, whose, who's** where appropriate. Under an interrupter, draw a wavy line. Insert necessary commas.

1. _____ among all the contestants do you think has the best chance?

2. Was it Brian _____ you were calling?

3. Mr. Lee has sold his car to the man from _____ he had bought it.

4. _____ has Mother invited for Thanksgiving dinner?

5. We have an estimate from a contractor _____ Dad's long-time friend.

6. The children _____ had applauded continuously really enjoyed the circus.

7. For _____ are most of the students voting?

8. _____ turn did she say is next?

9. The sad-looking child _____ I had been watching suddenly gave me a radiant smile.

10. That is the student _____ won $500 for his essay.

11. Uncle Bob _____ always gives strange presents gave me a six-foot-tall stuffed frog.

12. Grandpa attended a reunion of army officers with _____ he had served in World War II.

13. The two officers _____ signatures are necessary on the club's checks are absent.

14. _____ planning the Christmas dance?

15. The child received a generous reward from the man _____ had lost the money.

TEST: Who, Whom, Whose, Who's

> The next reproducible page contains two copies of one half-page Test. Cut each duplicated page in half; give each student one half-page.

As on the preceding Test, students are instructed to mark or label all sentence parts. Their grade will be based on four points: (1) choice of pronoun, (2) use of pronoun, (3) placement of pointed brackets, (4) wavy line under interrupter. You may wish to highlight on the Answer Key the four items that will be graded.

Grading scale:

−1, 97	−4, 87	−7, 78	−10, 68	−13, 58
−2, 94	−5, 84	−8, 74	−11, 65	−14, 55
−3, 90	−6, 81	−9, 71	−12, 62	−15, 51

Notice that no sentence on this Test requires commas. You may want to write this sentence on the chalkboard and offer students 1% extra credit for each correct mark:

Ileane _____ loves reading has finished her fourth book report.

Ileane, ⟨who loves reading⟩ has finished (her)(fourth)(book) report.

Ileane, ⟨who loves reading⟩ has finished her fourth book report.

Points:

1 = choice of *who*
1 = subject underline
1 = both brackets
2 = 1 for each comma
―
5

TEST:
Who, Whom, Whose, Who's

Instructions: Mark or label all sentence parts as usual. Put pointed brackets around each clause. In the blanks, write **who**, **whom**, **whose**, or **who's**. Under an interrupter, draw a wavy line.

1. (The) boy ⟨*who* [just] walked by⟩ is Julio.

2. *Whom*) are you riding (with?

3. Liz is (one) girl ⟨*whom* everyone likes.⟩

4. Was it Dean ⟨*whose*) book was lost?⟩

5. *Who* do you think will be elected?

6. You and *who* are writing (the) report?

7. *Who's* planning (the)(assembly) program?

8. *Whom* did you say you had seen (in (the) hall?)

9. Was it Trudi ⟨*who* called you?⟩

10. Martina was (the) girl ⟨*whom*) I was looking (for.⟩

11. (The) woman could have been *who*?

12. *Whom* are you expecting?

Name _____

Date _____

TEST: *Who, Whom, Whose, Who's*

Instructions: Mark or label all sentence parts as usual. Put pointed brackets around each clause. In the blanks, write **who**, **whom**, **whose**, or **who's**. Under an interrupter, draw a wavy line.

1. The boy _____ just walked by is Julio.

2. _____ are you riding with?

3. Liz is one girl _____ everyone likes.

4. Was it Dean _____ book was lost?

5. _____ do you think will be elected?

6. You and _____ are writing the report?

7. _____ planning the assembly program?

8. _____ did you say you had seen in the hall?

9. Was it Trudi _____ called you?

10. Martina was the girl _____ I was looking for.

11. The woman could have been _____ ?

12. _____ are you expecting?

TEST: *Who, Whom, Whose, Who's*

Name _____

Date _____

Instructions: Mark or label all sentence parts as usual. Put pointed brackets around each clause. In the blanks, write **who**, **whom**, **whose**, or **who's**. Under an interrupter, draw a wavy line.

1. The boy _____ just walked by is Julio.

2. _____ are you riding with?

3. Liz is one girl _____ everyone likes.

4. Was it Dean _____ book was lost?

5. _____ do you think will be elected?

6. You and _____ are writing the report?

7. _____ planning the assembly program?

8. _____ did you say you had seen in the hall?

9. Was it Trudi _____ called you?

10. Martina was the girl _____ I was looking for.

11. The woman could have been _____ ?

12. _____ are you expecting?

Correct Usage:
Clear Reference; Possessive
Pronouns; Indefinite Pronouns

Emphasize the fact that pronouns should refer clearly to nouns used earlier. This concept was not included in *Steps to Good Grammar*. In the Practice either of the nouns used in the first part of the sentence could correctly replace the pronoun.

The material on possessive personal pronouns was covered in *Steps to Good Grammar*. Remind students that ancient grammarians had established these possessive pronouns before they ever devised punctuation. A possessive pronoun needs no apostrophe!

Emphasize that the apostrophe used in verb contractions replaces letters left out of the verb. The pronoun subject remains the same.

The apostrophe is, of course, used with nouns to show possession, as well as with indefinite pronouns.

Correct Usage: Clear Reference;
Possessive Pronouns; Indefinite Pronouns

REMEMBER: A **pronoun** may be used to replace a noun. The noun that is replaced is called the **antecedent** of the pronoun.

A pronoun should refer clearly to a noun used earlier.

1. *Confusing:* While Luca was running to help the woman, she tripped.

   The pronoun *she* could refer to *Luca* or to *woman.*

   Clear: While Luca was running to help the woman, ⟨ Luca tripped.
   the woman tripped.

2. *Confusing:* Scott's dad is a carpenter, so he chose it as a career.

   Neither *he* nor *it* has a clear antecedent.

   Clear: Scott's dad is a carpenter, so Scott chose carpentry as . . . .

PRACTICE: Make changes so the meaning of each sentence is clear.

1. Rick hasn't written his cousin since ~~he~~ joined the army. *Rick/his cousin*
2. When the clerk approached the customer, ~~he~~ seemed apprehensive. *the clerk/the customer*
3. Shortly after Mel passed the strange man, ~~he~~ got on the bus. *Mel/the strange man*
4. When Ms. Lynn saw the teacher, ~~she~~ was leaving the school. *Ms. Lynn/the teacher*

Possessive Personal Pronouns: my, mine, your, yours, his, her, hers, its, our, ours, their, theirs *never* use an apostrophe.

1. Our parakeet likes **its** cage.   2. Is this plan **yours, hers,** or **ours**?

REMEMBER: A **contraction of a helping verb** with a pronoun subject uses an apostrophe to replace letters left out of the verb.

1. You're (~~a~~re) right.   2. She's (~~i~~s) coming.   3. We'd (~~would~~) go.

Indefinite Pronouns do not refer to a definite noun: **anyone, no one, everyone, someone, one, somebody, everybody,** etc.

1. Use apostrophe to show possession: somebody's coat; no one's book.
2. When **else** (meaning *different*) is added (*anybody else*), the possessive form is written: **anybody else's.**

PRACTICE: Above any errors, write the correct form.

1. ~~Its~~ *It's* snowing again; wear ~~you're~~ *your* boots.
2. The kitten is on ~~it's~~ *its* pillow.
3. ~~Someones~~ *Someone's* lunch ticket was turned in.

4. ~~Everybodys~~ *Everybody's* report is due.
   ~~Your's isnt~~ *Yours isn't* ready?
   Is anyone ~~elses~~ *else's* not ready?

Correct Usage: Clear Reference;
Possessive Pronouns;
Indefinite Pronouns

Name _____

Date _____

REMEMBER: A **pronoun** may be used to replace a noun. The noun that is replaced is called the **antecedent** of the pronoun.

A pronoun should refer clearly to a noun used earlier.

1. *Confusing:* While Luca was running to help the woman, she tripped.

   The pronoun *she* could refer to *Luca* or to *woman.*

   Clear: While Luca was running to help the woman, < ~Luca tripped.
   ~the woman tripped.

2. *Confusing:* Scott's dad is a carpenter, so he chose it as a career.

   Neither *he* nor *it* has a clear antecedent.

   Clear: Scott's dad is a carpenter, so Scott chose carpentry as . . . .

PRACTICE: Make changes so the meaning of each sentence is clear.

1. Rick hasn't written his cousin since he joined the army.

2. When the clerk approached the customer, he seemed apprehensive.

3. Shortly after Mel passed the strange man, he got on the bus.

4. When Ms. Lynn saw the teacher, she was leaving the school.

Possessive Personal Pronouns: my, mine, your, yours, his, her, hers, its, our, ours, their, theirs *never* use an apostrophe.

1. Our parakeet likes **its** cage.   2. Is this plan **yours, hers,** or **ours**?

REMEMBER: A **contraction of a helping verb** with a pronoun subject uses an apostrophe to replace letters left out of the verb.

1. You're (~~a~~re) right.   2. She's (~~i~~s) coming.   3. We'd (~~would~~) go.

Indefinite Pronouns do not refer to a definite noun: **anyone, no one, everyone, someone, one, somebody, everybody,** etc.

1. Use apostrophe to show possession: somebody's coat; no one's book.
2. When **else** (meaning *different*) is added (*anybody else*), the possessive form is written: **anybody else's.**

PRACTICE: Above any errors, write the correct form.

1. Its snowing again; wear you're boots.

2. The kitten is on it's pillow.

3. Someones lunch ticket was turned in.

4. Everybodys report is due.

   Your's isnt ready?

   Is anyone elses not ready?

Understanding and Using Good Grammar

Correct Usage:
Pronoun-Verb Agreement

Point out to students that even though *some* and *every* have a plural connotation the words *one* and *body* are singular in spelling, they are not *ones* or *bodies*. *Someone* and *everybody* are singular words that take a singular verb and a singular possessive pronoun.

In the Practice all the sentences use the listed singular and plural words as *subjects* preceding prepositional phrases with plural objects of the preposition. This is an extension of the material covered in *Steps to Good Grammar*.

Correct Usage:
Pronoun-Verb Agreement

REMEMBER: **She**, **he, it,** and singular nouns are singular (just one) in meaning; they take singular verbs, verbs that end in -*s*:   She is. He does. It was. Hank walks. Shawna writes.

Other singular words: any, each, either, neither, another, none

no { one / body }   any { one / body }   some { one / body }   every { one / body }

  1. These words take singular verbs, verbs that end in -*s*.
  2. Possessive pronouns used as adjectives which refer to these words should be singular:

  Example: Each (of the firefighters) (was, ~~were~~) commended (for (his/her) ~~their~~) bravery).

REMEMBER: **You, we, they,** and plural nouns take plural verbs, verbs that do not end in -*s*:
You are. We do. They have. Boys play.

Other plural words: several, most, both, all, few, many, some

  1. These words take plural verbs, verbs that do *not* end in -*s*.
  2. Possessive pronouns that refer to these words should be plural.

  Example: (A few (~~wasn't,~~ weren't) working (on (his/her, their) projects.)

PRACTICE: Mark or label all sentence parts as in the examples above. Cross out the incorrect choice in parentheses.

  1. Each (of the teams) [always] (~~win,~~ wins) (~~their,~~ its) share (of trophies).
  2. Some (of the little boys) (~~wasn't,~~ weren't) putting [on] (~~his,~~ their) shoes.
  3. (Is, ~~Are~~) either (of the women) driving (her) ~~their~~ car?
  4. Few (of the girls) (forget, ~~forgets~~) (~~her,~~ their) gym clothes (on Monday).
  5. (~~Do,~~ Does) everyone (among the students) have (his/her, ~~their~~) schedule?
  6. Both (of my parents) (~~has,~~ have) attended (~~his/her,~~ their) class reunions.
  7. Neither (of those two) [ever] (~~change,~~ changes) (his/her, their) mind.
  8. (Was, ~~Were~~) any (of the suspects) questioned (about (~~their,~~ his/her) alibis?)
  9. None (of the witnesses) (~~have,~~ has) taken (the) stand [yet].
  10. Many (of the boys) [usually] (listen, ~~listens~~) (to (their) ~~his~~) parents.)
  11. (Has, ~~Have~~) anyone forgotten (his/her) ~~their~~) homework?

Name _____

Date _____

Correct Usage: Pronoun-Verb Agreement

REMEMBER: **She**, **he**, **it**, and singular nouns are singular (just one) in meaning; they take singular verbs, verbs that end in *-s*:   She is̲. He doe̲s̲. It wa̲s̲. Hank walk̲s̲. Shawna write̲s̲.

Other singular words: any, each, either, neither, another, none

no $\left\{ \begin{array}{l} \textbf{one} \\ \textbf{body} \end{array} \right.$ any $\left\{ \begin{array}{l} \textbf{one} \\ \textbf{body} \end{array} \right.$ some $\left\{ \begin{array}{l} \textbf{one} \\ \textbf{body} \end{array} \right.$ every $\left\{ \begin{array}{l} \textbf{one} \\ \textbf{body} \end{array} \right.$

  1. These words take singular verbs, verbs that end in *-s*.
  2. Possessive pronouns used as adjectives which refer to these words should be singular:

> *Example:* Each (of the firefighters) (was, ~~were~~) commended (for (his/her, ~~their~~) bravery.)

REMEMBER: **You**, **we**, **they**, and plural nouns take plural verbs, verbs that do not end in *-s*: You are̲. We do̲. They have̲. Boys play̲.

Other plural words: several, most, both, all, few, many, some

  1. These words take plural verbs, verbs that do *not* end in *-s*.
  2. Possessive pronouns that refer to these words should be plural.

> *Example:* (A) few (~~wasn't~~, weren't) working (on (~~his/her~~, their) projects.)

PRACTICE: Mark or label all sentence parts as in the examples above. Cross out the incorrect choice in parentheses.

1. Each of the teams always (win, wins) (their, its) share of trophies.

2. Some of the little boys (wasn't, weren't) putting on (his, their) shoes.

3. (Is, Are) either of the women driving (her, their) car?

4. Few of the girls (forget, forgets) (her, their) gym clothes on Monday.

5. (Do, Does) everyone among the students have (his/her, their) schedule?

6. Both of my parents (has, have) attended (his/her, their) class reunions.

7. Neither of those two ever (change, changes) (his/her, their) mind.

8. (Was, Were) any of the suspects questioned about (their, his/her) alibis?

9. None of the witnesses (have, has) taken the stand yet.

10. Many of the boys usually (listen, listens) to (their, his) parents.

11. (Has, Have) anyone forgotten (his/her, their) homework?

Understanding and Using Good Grammar

Correct Usage: Compound Subject-Verb-Possessive Pronoun Agreement

The material presented here was covered in *Steps to Good Grammar*. However, many students have difficulty in understanding it. Point out that *and* always means "more than one" and that *or/nor* always means "one *or* the other." Clarify the analysis of boxing the conjunctions and drawing the arrows.

Concerning Rule 2: emphasize that students should edit their own papers to avoid writing an awkward, though correct, sentence like Example sentence *a*. Practice sentence 4 is an example.

Correct Usage: Compound Subject-Verb-Possessive Pronoun Agreement

Rule 1. When you write a compound subject joined by **and**, think "they" or "we" in selecting the correct verb and the correct possessive pronoun to follow it.

(a) (Has, Have) Gail and Alexa brought (her, their) lunch?   D.O.

(b) He and I (am, are) writing (my, our) report.   D.O.

Rule 2. When you write a compound subject joined by **or/nor**, the verb and the possessive pronoun should agree with the part of the subject that is *nearer* the verb.

(a) My sisters or my brother
They   or   he   (has, have) forgotten (his, their) books.

(Correct, but awkward; think ahead and, instead, write:)

(b) My brother or my sisters
He   or   they   (has, have) forgotten (his, their) books.

PRACTICE: Mark or label all sentence parts as in the examples above. Draw a box around the conjunction **and**, and above it write **they** or **we**. From **they** or **we** draw an arrow to the correct verb; from the correct verb draw an arrow to the correct possessive pronoun. Draw a box around the conjunction **or/nor** and draw an arrow from the part of the subject nearer the verb to the correct verb; draw an arrow from the correct verb to the correct possessive pronoun.

1. Emily and he (is, are) writing (his, their) applications.   D.O.

2. (Do, Does) she and he always bring (his, their) lunch?   D.O.

3. Neither he nor they (have, has) invited (his, their) friends.   D.O.

4. Either her brothers or she (are, is) bringing (their, her) camera.   D.O.

5. They and I (was, were) riding (our, their) bikes (to school.)   D.O.   prep. O.P.

6. Bianca and she usually (does, do) (her, their) homework promptly.   D.O.

7. (Has, Have) they or Alice finished (her, their) report yet?   D.O.

8. Either she or he (are, is) playing (her or his, their) tennis match now.   D.O.

9. (Is, Are) Luke and he finishing (his, their) homework now?   D.O.

10. Neither he nor she (memorize, memorizes) (his or her, their) part easily.   D.O.

Correct Usage: Compound Subject-Verb-Possessive Pronoun Agreement

Name _____

Date _____

Rule 1. When you write a compound subject joined by **and**, think "they" or "we" in selecting the correct verb and the correct possessive pronoun to follow it.

(a) (~~Has~~, Have) Gail and Alexa brought (~~her~~, their) lunch? → they   D.O.

(b) He and I (~~am~~, are) writing (~~my~~, our) report. we   D.O.

Rule 2. When you write a compound subject joined by **or/nor**, the verb and the possessive pronoun should agree with the part of the subject that is *nearer* the verb.

(a) My sisters or my brother
    They   or   he   (has, ~~have~~) forgotten (his ~~their~~) books.

(Correct, but awkward; think ahead and, instead, write:)

(b) My brother or my sisters
    He   or   they   (~~has~~, have) forgotten (~~his~~, their) books.

PRACTICE: Mark or label all sentence parts as in the examples above. Draw a box around the conjunction **and**, and above it write **they** or **we**. From **they** or **we** draw an arrow to the correct verb; from the correct verb draw an arrow to the correct possessive pronoun. Draw a box around the conjunction **or/nor** and draw an arrow from the part of the subject nearer the verb to the correct verb; draw an arrow from the correct verb to the correct possessive pronoun.

1. Emily and he (is, are) writing (his, their) applications.

2. (Do, Does) she and he always bring (his, their) lunch?

3. Neither he nor they (have, has) invited (his, their) friends.

4. Either her brothers or she (are, is) bringing (their, her) camera.

5. They and I (was, were) riding (our, their) bikes to school.

6. Bianca and she usually (does, do) (her, their) homework promptly.

7. (Has, Have) they or Alice finished (her, their) report yet?

8. Either she or he (are, is) playing (her or his, their) tennis match now.

9. (Is, Are) Luke and he finishing (his, their) homework now?

10. Neither he nor she (memorize, memorizes) (his or her, their) part easily.

      Understanding and Using Good Grammar

FINAL PRACTICE:
Correct Pronoun Usage

Suggest that students box the conjunctions and draw arrows in the sentences containing compound subjects to assist them in recognizing the correct verbs and possessive pronouns.

Since this is the Final Practice before the Test on this unit, encourage students to work carefully on it so they will have a correct study sheet to take home to review in preparation for the Test.

FINAL PRACTICE:
Correct Pronoun Usage

Instructions: Where a choice is given, draw two lines under the verb, one under the subject, circle the possessive pronoun, and cross out the incorrect forms. In other sentences, write the correct form above errors.

1. (Has, ~~Have~~) Dora or she already received (~~their~~, her) book orders?

2. When Clint saw Lonnie, ~~he~~ was walking up the stairs. *Clint/Lonnie*

3. Somebody among the boys (is, ~~are~~) forgetting (his, ~~their~~) lunch!

4. Dad or one of my uncles (visits, ~~visit~~) Grandmother during (his, ~~their~~) lunch hour.

5. Either Jim or he always (hits, ~~hit~~) our window when (he, ~~they~~) (~~throw~~, throws) our newspaper.

6. Ann and she (~~is~~, are) inviting (~~her~~, their) parents. *they*

7. ~~Your~~ inviting ~~your's~~ ~~arent~~ you? *you're yours aren't*

8. Is that watch ~~her's~~ or his? It must be ~~someones~~! *hers someone's*

9. Not ~~everybodies~~ project can be chosen; hopefully, ~~your's~~ or ~~our's~~ will be! *everybody's yours ours*

10. Seth hasn't played tennis with Marco since ~~he~~ broke his tennis racket. *Seth/Marco*

11. Of the five books, this ~~ones~~ his and ~~thats~~ hers. Is ~~your's~~ this one? The others must be someone ~~elses~~. *one's that's yours else's*

12. (Do, ~~Does~~) he and his brother ride (~~his~~, their) motorcycles very often? *they*

13. Damone and he (~~has~~, have) come for (their, ~~his~~) package. *they*

14. Neither he nor either of his brothers often (~~play~~, plays) (his, ~~their~~) saxophone.

15. Diane and one of the twins (~~has~~, have) forgotten (their, ~~her~~) report. *they*

16. Few of the students (~~has~~, have) remembered (~~his/her~~, their) money.

17. Each of the books (was, ~~were~~) put in (its, ~~their~~) proper place.

18. (Has, ~~Have~~) another of the students misplaced (her/his, ~~their~~) pen?

Name _____

Date _____

FINAL PRACTICE: Correct Pronoun Usage

Instructions: Where a choice is given, draw two lines under the verb, one under the subject, circle the possessive pronoun, and cross out the incorrect forms. In other sentences, write the correct form above errors.

1. (Has, Have) Dora or she already received (their, her) book orders?

2. When Clint saw Lonnie, he was walking up the stairs.

3. Somebody among the boys (is, are) forgetting (his, their) lunch!

4. Dad or one of my uncles (visits, visit) Grandmother during (his, their) lunch hour.

5. Either Jim or he always (hits, hit) our window when (he, they) (throw, throws) our newspaper.

6. Ann and she (is, are) inviting (her, their) parents.

7. Your inviting your's arent you?

8. Is that watch her's or his?   It must be someones!

9. Not everybodies project can be chosen; hopefully, your's or our's will be!

10. Seth hasn't played tennis with Marco since he broke his tennis racket.

11. Of the five books, this ones his and thats hers. Is your's this one?

    The others must be someone elses.

12. (Do, Does) he and his brother ride (his, their) motorcycles very often?

13. Damone and he (has, have) come for (their, his) package.

14. Neither he nor either of his brothers often (play, plays) (his, their) saxophone.

15. Diane and one of the twins (has, have) forgotten (their, her) report.

16. Few of the students (has, have) remembered (his/her, their) money.

17. Each of the books (was, were) put in (its, their) proper place.

18. (Has, Have) another of the students misplaced (her/his, their) pen?

Understanding and Using Good Grammar

TEST:
Correct Pronoun Usage

> The next reproducible page contains two copies of one half-page Test. Cut each duplicated page in half; give each student one half-page.

Suggested Grading:

Give five points each for sentences 1 through 6:

- 1 point for subject underlined
- 2 points for verb choice and underline
- 2 points for pronoun choice and circle

For sentences 7 and 8 count 1 point for each correct form written above an error.

Total points: 38

Grading scale:

−1, 97	−5, 87	−9, 76	−13, 66
−2, 95	−6, 84	−10, 74	−14, 63
−3, 92	−7, 82	−11, 71	−15, 61
−4, 89	−8, 79	−12, 68	−16, 58

TEST:
Correct Pronoun Usage

Instructions: Where a choice is given, draw two lines under the verb, one under the subject, circle the possessive pronoun, and cross out the incorrect form. In other sentences, write the correct form above errors.

1. Both of the girls (was, were) doing (their) her) share.

2. Jenny or one of those two other girls always (finish, finishes) (her) their) test first.

3. (Do, Does) he and his brother start (their) his) homework promptly?

4. Neither his brother nor he (are, is) selling (his) their) mountain bike.

5. Everybody among the guests (want, wants) (their, (his or her) dessert now.

6. Most of the players on both teams (has, have) played (their) her or his) best.

7. *She's* Shes sure these ~~arent~~ *aren't* ~~her's~~ *hers.* If ~~their~~ *they're* not ~~your's~~ *yours,* his, or ~~our's~~ *ours,* they must be somebody ~~elses~~ *else's.*

8. When Lee saw her aunt, *Lee/her aunt* ~~she~~ was living in Texas.

TEST: Correct Pronoun Usage

Name _____

Date _____

Instructions: Where a choice is given, draw two lines under the verb, one under the subject, circle the possessive pronoun, and cross out the incorrect form. In other sentences, write the correct form above errors.

1. Both of the girls (was, were) doing (their, her) share.

2. Jenny or one of those two other girls always (finish, finishes) (her, their) test first.

3. (Do, Does) he and his brother start (their, his) homework promptly?

4. Neither his brother nor he (are, is) selling (his, their) mountain bike.

5. Everybody among the guests (want, wants) (their, his or her) dessert now.

6. Most of the players on both teams (has, have) played (their, her or his) best.

7. Shes sure these arent her's. If their not your's, his, or our's, they must be somebody elses.

8. When Lee saw her aunt, she was living in Texas.

TEST: Correct Pronoun Usage

Name _____

Date _____

Instructions: Where a choice is given, draw two lines under the verb, one under the subject, circle the possessive pronoun, and cross out the incorrect form. In other sentences, write the correct form above errors.

1. Both of the girls (was, were) doing (their, her) share.

2. Jenny or one of those two other girls always (finish, finishes) (her, their) test first.

3. (Do, Does) he and his brother start (their, his) homework promptly?

4. Neither his brother nor he (are, is) selling (his, their) mountain bike.

5. Everybody among the guests (want, wants) (their, his or her) dessert now.

6. Most of the players on both teams (has, have) played (their, her or his) best.

7. Shes sure these arent her's. If their not your's, his, or our's, they must be somebody elses.

8. When Lee saw her aunt, she was living in Texas.

Understanding and Using Good Grammar

Recognizing Transitive Verbs

Understanding the uses of verbs in active and passive voice is helpful to students in improving the effectiveness of their written expression. It is helpful, too, to those who study foreign languages.

Point out that a verb in passive voice always uses *is, am, are, was, were, be, being,* or *been* (forms of "to be") as a helping verb.

Work with students in identifying sentence parts. Remind them that this is an information page which they should keep for future reference.

Recognizing Transitive Verbs

LEARN: 1. Transitive is from the Latin *transire*, meaning "to go across."

2. The action of a **transitive verb** goes across to another word in the sentence.

3. A **transitive active** verb is said to have **active voice**.

   A **transitive passive** verb is said to have **passive voice**.

A. Transitive Active: A "doing" verb is transitive active (labeled **T.A.**) if *its action goes across to the direct object*. The subject is active, the subject "does" the verb. Active voice enlivens the sentence and emphasizes the action.

[Yesterday], (a)(reckless) driver [almost] hit (my) dog. T.A.   D.O.

B. Transitive Passive: A "doing" verb is transitive passive (labeled **T.P.**) if *its action goes back to the subject*. The subject is passive, it does nothing, it receives the action. The verb may be followed by a prepositional phrase beginning with *by*.

[Yesterday] (my) dog was [almost] hit (by (a)(reckless) driver). T.P.   prep.   O.P.

Reasons for using passive voice:

1. To emphasize that the subject receives the action.

2. To show that the doer of the action is unknown.

(The) package had been dropped (in (the)(trash) bin). T.P.   prep.   O.P.

PRACTICE: Mark verbs, subjects, adjectives, adverbs, and prepositional phrases; label **prep.**, **O.P.**, **D.O.**, and **Appos.** At the end of the sentence, write **T.A.** for transitive active and **T.P.** for transitive passive. Draw an arrow to the receiver of the action.

1. (That)(expensive) jacket was left (on (the) bleachers) (after (the) game.) T.P.   prep.   O.P.   prep.   O.P.

2. (The)(night) watchman had witnessed (the) break-in. T.A.   D.O.

3. (The)(old)(Victorian) house had been [completely] destroyed (by (the) fire). T.P.   prep.   O.P.

4. (My)(little) cousin Ted hit (a)(home) run (during (the) game) [yesterday] T.A.   Appos.   D.O.   prep.   O.P.

5. [Yesterday] (during (the) game), (a)(home) run had been hit (by (my) cousin) Ted. T.P.   prep.   O.P.   prep.   O.P.   Appos.

6. (The)(raging) floodwaters had carried (a)(large) section (of (the)(creek) bank) (down (the) stream.) T.A.   D.O.   prep.   O.P.   prep.   O.P.

7. (All)(the)(new) books have been shelved. T.P.

Recognizing Transitive Verbs

Name _____

Date _____

LEARN: 1. Transitive is from the Latin *transire,* meaning "to go across."

2. The action of a **transitive verb** goes across to another word in the sentence.

3. A **transitive active** verb is said to have **active voice.**
A **transitive passive** verb is said to have **passive voice.**

A. Transitive Active: A "doing" verb is transitive active (labeled **T.A.**) if *its action goes across to the direct object.* The subject is active, the subject "does" the verb. Active voice enlivens the sentence and emphasizes the action.

[Yesterday], a reckless driver [almost] hit my dog. T.A.

B. Transitive Passive: A "doing" verb is transitive passive (labeled **T.P.**) if *its action goes back to the subject.* The subject is passive, it does nothing, it receives the action. The verb may be followed by a prepositional phrase beginning with *by.*

[Yesterday] my dog was [almost] hit (by a reckless driver). T.P.

Reasons for using passive voice:

1. To emphasize that the subject receives the action.
2. To show that the doer of the action is unknown.

The package had been dropped (in the trash bin). T.P.

PRACTICE: Mark verbs, subjects, adjectives, adverbs, and prepositional phrases; label **prep.,** **O.P., D.O.,** and **Appos.** At the end of the sentence, write **T.A.** for transitive active and **T.P.** for transitive passive. Draw an arrow to the receiver of the action.

1. That expensive jacket was left on the bleachers after the game.

2. The night watchman had witnessed the break-in.

3. The old Victorian house had been completely destroyed by the fire.

4. My little cousin Ted hit a home run during the game yesterday.

5. Yesterday during the game, a home run had been hit by my cousin Ted.

6. The raging floodwaters had carried a large section of the creek bank down the stream.

7. All the new books have been shelved.

Understanding and Using Good Grammar

Transitive and Intransitive Verbs

As students rewrite the sentences in the first Practice, help them to use the same verb tense as the one used in the given sentence.

1. (Several) fingerprints were found (by (the) detective). T.P.

2. (My) (always-hungry) (teenage) brother had eaten (the) (whole) pie. T.A.

3. (The) owner has [recently] remodeled (the) house (beside ours). T.A.
   (The) owner (of (the) house) (beside ours) has [recently] remodeled (his) house. T.A.

(The use of *it* instead of *his house* would not be really clear.)

4. (A) (large) sum (of money) had been embezzled (by (the) (trusted) employee.) T.P.

To refresh the students' memory, write the list of linking verbs on the chalkboard or overhead: *is, am, are, was, were, be, being, been, become, seem, appear, feel, taste, smell, sound, grow, look.*

Transitive and Intransitive Verbs

PRACTICE: **Using active and passive voice verbs.** Mark verbs, subjects, adjectives, adverbs, and prepositional phrases; label **prep.**, **O.P.**, and **D.O.** Draw an arrow to the word that receives that action; write **T.A.** for transitive active or **T.P.** for transitive passive at the end of the sentence. On the reverse side, rewrite the sentence, changing the voice of the verb.

(The) raccoon bit (the) boy. ᴰ·ᴼ· T.A.   (The) boy was bitten (by (the) raccoon). T.P.

1. (The) detective found (several) fingerprints. ᴰ·ᴼ· T.A.

2. (The) (whole) pie had been eaten (by (my) (always-hungry) (teenage) brother.) T.P.

3. (The) house (beside ours) has [recently] been remodeled (by (the) owner). T.P.

4. (The) (trusted) employee had embezzled (a) (large) sum (of money.) T.A.

LEARN: **Intransitive** means "does *not* go across."

1. A "doing" verb is intransitive if the subject *does* it, but no word receives the action. (Label: **Intr-C**—intransitive complete)

   (The) man shouted [loudly]. Intr-C (*Man* did it; no word received the action)

2. **Linking verbs** are always intransitive; they express *no* action. (Label **Intr-L**—intransitive linking)

   Today has been beautiful. Intr-L   Gold is (a) (valuable) element. Intr-L

PRACTICE: **Recognizing intransitive verbs.** Mark verbs, subjects, adjectives (except **LVC–A**), adverbs, and prepositional phrases; label **LV, LVC–N, LVC–A, prep.,** and **O.P.** At the end of the sentence, label the verb **Intr-C** or **Intr-L**.

1. (The) sky [certainly] looks threatening. Intr-L

2. (My) (brother's) (favorite) sports are baseball, track, and golf. Intr-L

3. (Sean's) phone has been ringing [constantly]. Intr-C

4. (Their) (new) neighbors moved [in] [recently]. Intr-C

5. (His) story sounds strange, but it might be true. Intr-L

6. Caroline has become (an) (electrical) engineer. Intr-L

7. [How] has (the) team been playing? Intr-C

8. Did[n't] Dan look concerned? Intr-L

9. (The) children had [already] eaten. Intr-C

10. (The) days (since (the) accident) have been [very] difficult (for them.) Intr-L

11. (The) clouds have [finally] drifted [away]. Intr-C

Name _____

Date _____

Transitive and Intransitive Verbs

PRACTICE: Using active and passive voice verbs. Mark verbs, subjects, adjectives, adverbs, and prepositional phrases; label **prep.**, **O.P.**, and **D.O.** Draw an arrow to the word that receives that action; write **T.A.** for transitive active or **T.P.** for transitive passive at the end of the sentence. On the reverse side, rewrite the sentence, changing the voice of the verb.

(The) raccoon bit (the) boy. ^{D.O.} T.A.   (The) boy was bitten (by (the) raccoon.) T.P.

1. The detective found several fingerprints.

2. The whole pie had been eaten by my always-hungry teenage brother.

3. The house beside ours has recently been remodeled by the owner.

4. The trusted employee had embezzled a large sum of money.

LEARN: Intransitive means "does *not* go across."

1. A "doing" verb is intransitive if the subject *does* it, but no word receives the action. (Label: **Intr-C**—intransitive complete)

    (The) man shouted [loudly].   (*Man* did it; no word received the action) Intr. C.

2. **Linking verbs** are always intransitive; they express *no* action. (Label **Intr-L**—intransitive linking)

    Today has been beautiful. Intr-L   Gold is (a (valuable) element. Intr-L

PRACTICE: Recognizing intransitive verbs. Mark verbs, subjects, adjectives (except **LVC–A**), adverbs, and prepositional phrases; label **LV, LVC–N, LVC–A, prep.,** and **O.P.** At the end of the sentence, label the verb **Intr-C** or **Intr-L.**

1. The sky certainly looks threatening.
2. My brother's favorite sports are baseball, track, and golf.
3. Sean's phone has been ringing constantly.
4. Their new neighbors moved in recently.
5. His story sounds strange, but it might be true.

6. Caroline has become an electrical engineer.
7. How has the team been playing?
8. Didn't Dan look concerned?
9. The children had already eaten.
10. The days since the accident have been very difficult for them.
11. The clouds have finally drifted away.

Understanding and Using Good Grammar

FINAL PRACTICE and TEST:
Transitive and Intransitive Verbs

> The next reproducible page contains one half-page Final Practice and one half-page Test. Before passing out the page, cut it in two to remove the Test.

Final Practice

Encourage students to do the marking and labeling carefully so they will have a totally correct study sheet to review before the Test.

Sentence 10: This is an example of a transitive passive verb not followed by a prepositional phrase beginning with *by*.

Test

Sentence 12: Some student may suggest that *are* is a linking verb with *amused* as its **LVC–A**. Point out that *by Al* implies that Al is "doing" the amusing. The verb is **T.P.**

Grading Scale: All marks/labels, 80 points

–1, 99	–6, 92	–11, 86	–16, 80	–21, 74	–26, 67	–31, 61
–2, 97	–7, 91	–12, 85	–17, 79	–22, 72	–27, 66	–32, 60
–3, 96	–8, 90	–13, 84	–18, 77	–23, 71	–28, 65	–33, 59
–4, 95	–9, 89	–14, 82	–19, 76	–24, 70	–29, 64	–34, 57
–5, 94	–10, 87	–15, 81	–20, 75	–25, 69	–30, 62	

Quicker grading: On the Answer Key, highlight the markings in each sentence that pertain specifically to recognizing the verb types:

1, 8, 12: ____ **T.P.** = 4 pts. each = 12
2, 6, 9: ____ **D.O., T.A.** = 5 pts. each = 15
3, 5, 7: ____ **Intr-L** = 4 pts. each = 12
4, 10, 11: ___ ___ **Intr-C** = 3 pts. each = _9_
                                             48

–1, 98	–8, 83	–14, 71
–2, 96	–9, 81	–15, 69
–3, 94	–10, 79	–16, 67
–4, 92	–11, 77	–17, 65
–5, 90	–12, 75	–18, 63
–6, 88	–13, 73	–19, 60
–7, 85		

FINAL PRACTICE: Transitive
and Intransitive Verbs

Instructions: Mark verbs, subjects, adjectives (except **LVC–A**), adverbs, prepositional phrases; label **LV, LVC–N, LVC–A, prep., O.P., D.O.** At the end of each sentence, label the verb **T.A.** or **T.P.** (draw an arrow to the receiver), or **Intr-C** or **Intr-L.**

1. The dark clouds appeared blacker. Intr-L

2. It was a completely miserable night. Intr-L

3. Father gives generously to the local charity. Intr-C

4. The cake and cookies were brought by Rob. T.P.

5. The old car stopped suddenly on the bridge. Intr-C

6. The wrecked car stopped all traffic. T.A.

7. The new books have been placed on the table by the librarian. T.P.

8. Vandals had destroyed many fine antiques in the old house. T.A.

9. The captain should have been Kurt. Intr-L

10. The letter was delivered. T.P.

TEST: Transitive and
Intransitive Verbs

Instructions: Mark verbs, subjects, adjectives (except **LVC–A**), adverbs, prepositional phrases; label **LV, LVC–N, LVC–A, prep., O.P., D.O.** At the end of each sentence, label the verb **T.A.** or **T.P.** (draw an arrow to the receiver), or **Intr-C** or **Intr-L.**

1. Applicants were being interviewed by the manager. T.P.

2. Voters will cast their ballots tomorrow. T.A.

3. Sue had certainly become upset. Intr-L

4. Our team won! Intr-C

5. The man by the elevator is a well-known lawyer. Intr-L

6. Dad hadn't seen us. T.A.

7. The suspect was not being very cooperative. Intr-L

8. The package had been left on the bottom step. T.P.

9. Nick has correctly answered the question. T.A.

10. The team stormed onto the field. Intr-C

11. Everyone was yelling and whistling. Intr-C

12. We are amused by Al. T.P.

FINAL PRACTICE: Transitive and Intransitive Verbs

Name _____

Date _____

Instructions: Mark verbs, subjects, adjectives (except **LVC–A**), adverbs, prepositional phrases; label **LV**, **LVC–N**, **LVC–A**, **prep.**, **O.P.**, **D.O.** At the end of each sentence, label the verb **T.A.** or **T.P.** (draw an arrow to the receiver), or **Intr-C** or **Intr-L**.

1. The dark clouds appeared blacker.

2. It was a completely miserable night.

3. Father gives generously to the local charity.

4. The cake and cookies were brought by Rob.

5. The old car stopped suddenly on the bridge.

6. The wrecked car stopped all traffic.

7. The new books have been placed on the table by the librarian.

8. Vandals had destroyed many fine antiques in the old house.

9. The captain should have been Kurt.

10. The letter was delivered.

TEST: Transitive and Intransitive Verbs

Name _____

Date _____

Instructions: Mark verbs, subjects, adjectives (except **LVC–A**), adverbs, prepositional phrases; label **LV**, **LVC–N**, **LVC–A**, **prep.**, **O.P.**, **D.O.** At the end of each sentence, label the verb **T.A.** or **T.P.** (draw an arrow to the receiver), or **Intr-C** or **Intr-L**.

1. Applicants were being interviewed by the manager.

2. Voters will cast their ballots tomorrow.

3. Sue had certainly become upset.

4. Our team won!

5. The man by the elevator is a well-known lawyer.

6. Dad hadn't seen us.

7. The suspect was not being very cooperative.

8. The package had been left on the bottom step.

9. Nick has correctly answered the question.

10. The team stormed onto the field.

11. Everyone was yelling and whistling.

12. We are amused by Al.

Understanding and Using Good Grammar

PRETEST:
Irregular Verbs—List 1

Warn students to read the entire sentence before filling any blanks; the tense of the verb in the first blank may be made clear by a helping verb used with the verb to be written in the second blank:

Sentence 5: *Hadn't* before the second blank indicates a past tense; the tense of the verb to be written in the first blank should be simple past.

Sentence 7: *Is* before the second blank indicates present tense; the tense of the verb to be written in the first blank should be present.

Suggested Grading:

Pretest scores do not affect report card grades. A misspelled word is given half credit. there are 46 items—see page 141 for % scores. Give students Irregular Verbs—List 1 before returning their graded Pretests.

PRETEST:
Irregular Verbs—List 1

Instructions: In the blank, write the correct form of the verb shown in parentheses.

1. Judy is _beating_ Kay in this game; Kay had _beaten_ her yesterday. (beat)
2. Lou was _beginning_ (begin) to worry; just then we _drove_ (drive) up.
3. Terry had _become_ (become) discouraged when she hadn't been _chosen_ (choose).
4. Because we were _eating_ , and the others had already _eaten_ , Lenore _ate_ . (eat)
5. I _did_ the dishes since Greg hadn't _done_ them. (do)
6. Had Brad _known_ (know) that he had already _begun_ (begin) the job?
7. Brent usually _did / does_ his homework promptly; he is _doing_ it now. (do)
8. I _hid_ Phil's books because he had _hidden_ mine. (hide)
9. We had _driven_ (drive) slowly because many rocks had _fallen_ (fall) on the highway.
10. The water in the ponds has _frozen_ (freeze) solidly, and the geese have _flown_ (fly) south.
11. The boys had _gone_ (go) up the path, had _gotten_ (get) a huge log, and had _dragged_ (drag) it to camp.
12. I _brought_ a pencil for you, but you've _brought_ your own! (bring)
13. Franco certainly _grew_ this summer. How much has he _grown_? (grow)
14. Jill _catches_ fly balls so well! She has just _caught_ another one. (catch)
15. Tom hadn't _broken_ the sugar bowl; Sid _broke_ it. (break)
16. The Scouts had _drunk_ (drink) their cocoa slowly after they _dragged_ (drag) themselves to the camp fire.
17. Our dog has never _bitten_ anyone seriously, but he just playfully _bit_ me. (bite)
18. The wind _blew_ hard this morning but has _blown_ even harder this afternoon. (blow)
19. Mom _came_ home from work shortly after we had _come_ home. (come)
20. Later the boys _became_ (become) tired of waiting and _went_ (go) home.
21. I just _gave_ my report. Have you _given_ yours yet? (give)
22. Jess _drew_ your name. Whose name have you _drawn_ ? (draw)

Name _____

Date _____

Instructions: In the blank, write the correct form of the verb shown in parentheses.

1. Judy is _____ Kay in this game; Kay had _____ her yesterday. (beat)

2. Lou was_____(begin) to worry; just then we_____ (drive) up.

3. Terry had_____(become) discouraged when she hadn't been_____(choose).

4. Because we were_____ , and the others had already_____ , Lenore _____ . (eat)

5. I _____ the dishes since Greg hadn't _____ them. (do)

6. Had Brad _____ (know) that he had already _____ (begin) the job?

7. Brent usually _____ his homework promptly; he is _____ it now. (do)

8. I _____ Phil's books because he had _____ mine. (hide)

9. We had_____(drive) slowly because many rocks had_____(fall) on the highway.

10. The water in the ponds has ___(freeze) solidly, and the geese have___ (fly) south.

11. The boys had _____ (go) up the path, had _____ (get) a huge log, and had _____ (drag) it to camp.

12. I _____ a pencil for you, but you've _____ your _____ own! (bring)

13. Franco certainly_____ this summer. How much has he_____? (grow)

14. Jill _____ fly balls so well! She has just _____ another one. (catch)

15. Tom hadn't _____ the sugar bowl; Sid _____ it. (break)

16. The Scouts had _____ (drink) their cocoa slowly after they _____ (drag) themselves to the camp fire.

17. Our dog has never __anyone seriously, but he just playfully _ me. (bite)

18. The wind ___ hard this morning but has ___even harder this afternoon. (blow)

19. Mom _____ home from work shortly after we had _____ home. (come)

20. Later the boys _____ (become) tired of waiting and _____ (go) home.

21. I just _____ my report. Have you _____ yours yet? (give)

22. Jess _____ your name. Whose name have you _____? (draw)

Understanding and Using Good Grammar

Irregular Verbs—List 1

Distribute the list before you return the Pretest.

Point out the column labeled **Present Participle**. This verb form is used in advanced sentence structure. One use is as a **gerund**, the verb form ending in *-ing* that is used as a noun.

Eating is [probably] (that) (child's) (favorite) pastime.

The **Remember** column items contain important information. As you read them aloud (students read silently), relate items 1, 2, 2a, and 2b to headings of the columns.

Many students have found the sound differences described in items 3a and 3b to be especially helpful in using correctly the simple past and the past participle of the irregular verbs. Students hear the difference between the sharp sound of the simple past (beg**an**) and the softer sound of the past participle (beg**un**) which takes a helping verb (have beg**un**). With most irregular verbs, the sound difference is between the past participle which ends in an *n* sound—go**ne**, which takes a helping verb (have go**ne**), and the simple past that does not end in an *n* sound—went, which never uses a helper.

Many students master irregular verbs simply by memorizing the forms, saying the helping verbs with the participles:

> begin   is beginning   began   has begun

Only *brought-brought* and *caught-caught* do not fall into one of the two sound categories, but obviously, no choice needs to be made.

After students have perused the list, return the Pretests so that they can use the list to correct the mistakes you marked. They should keep the corrected Pretest to study since there will be only one practice sheet before the final Test. They should know correct spelling.

Name _____   **Irregular Verbs—List 1**

Date _____

Regular verbs form the past and past participle by adding **-d** or **-ed** to the present form.

Irregular verbs change the spelling to form the past and past participle.

Present	Present Participle	Past	Past Participle	
(Say: "Today I . . .")	(Use forms of *to be*.)	(Say: "Yesterday I . . .")	(Use forms of *to have*.)	***REMEMBER***
beat	beating	beat	beaten	1. *Participle* means "part of the expression."
become	becoming	became	become	
begin	beginning	began	begun	2. Participles use *helping verbs*:
bite	biting	bit	bitten	
blow	blowing	blew	blown	a. **Present participle:**
break	breaking	broke	broken	is, am, are, was, were, be, being, been
		(not "busted!")		
bring	bringing	brought	brought	b. **Past participle:**
		(not "brang" or "brung")		have/has, had, shall/will have
catch	catching	caught	caught	
choose	choosing	chose	chose	3. Sound differences between past and past participle of a verb:
come	coming	came	come	
do	doing	did	done	a. **Past**: sharp sound, uses no helper:
*drag	dragging	dragged	dragged	began, came, drank
		(not "drug")		
draw	drawing	drew	drawn	**Past participle**: softer sound, uses a helper
drink	drinking	drank	drunk	
drive	driving	drove	driven	have begun, have come, have drunk
eat	eating	ate	eaten	
fall	falling	fell	fallen	b. **Past**: no *n* ending sound, no helper:
fly	flying	flew	flown	
freeze	freezing	froze	frozen	bit, blew, chose
get	getting	got	gotten	
give	giving	gave	given	**Past participle**: *n*-ending sound, uses helper:
go	going	went	gone	
grow	growing	grew	grown	have bitten, have blown, have chosen
hide	hiding	hid	hidden	
know	knowing	knew	known	

*Drag is a regular verb. It is included in this list to emphasize the correct forms: *dragged* and *have dragged*.

Understanding and Using Good Grammar

PRACTICE:
Irregular Verbs—List 1

Since participles use helping verbs, students should underline helping verbs and the subject to help them write the correct irregular verb form.

Have volunteers complete sentences 1–10, with you confirming their correct answers. Other students should correct their own work. In sentence 6 the subject of all the verbs is *we*. Therefore, *had*, the helping verb before *done*, carries over in meaning to the next verb, *go*; (had) *gone* is the correct form. The meaning of *had* also carries over to *drag*, but *dragged* is the correct form with or without a helping verb.

Ask the students to complete sentences 11–20 on their own. They should correct any errors when you read the sentences with the correct forms. Have them take the worksheet home to study in preparation for the Test.

PRACTICE: Irregular Verbs—List 1

Instructions: Draw two lines under helping verbs, one under the subject. In the blanks, write the correct form of the verb in parentheses.

1. Dad hadn't _known_ (know) that we had already _dragged_ (drag) a log to the camp fire.
2. Tim has _begun_ his homework; Amy is just _beginning_ hers. (begin)
3. I had _bitten_ into my apple, so Joanie _bit_ into hers. (bite)
4. I _chose_ to stay home, but I wish I had _chosen_ to go. (choose)
5. The others had _drunk_ their milk shakes, so Bev _drank_ hers quickly. (drink)
6. After we _ate_ (eat) dinner, we had _done_ (do) the dishes, _gone_ (go) into the living room, and _dragged_ (drag) out the old family album.
7. I had _fallen_ on the ice right after my sister _fell_ . (fall)
8. Verna _got_ to class on time even though she had _gotten_ up late. (get)
9. Had he already _given_ you a present when you _gave_ him one? (give)
10. Jill had _gone_ home, so I _went_ home, too. (go)
11. Jo _grew_ two inches last summer. Have you _grown_ very much? (grow)
12. Shortly after the game _began_ (begin) it seemed obvious that our team would be _beaten_ . (beat)
13. Yesterday the wind _blew_ (blow) wildly, branches were _broken_ (break) off trees, and several trees were _blown_ (blow) down.
14. Have you ever _flown_ to Hawaii? Last summer Dad and I _flew_ there. (fly)
15. The teacher had _become_ (become) annoyed because so many students had _come_ (come) in late and had not _brought_ (bring) their books.
16. My brother had _eaten_ (eat) the leftovers or Mom would have _frozen_ (freeze) them.
17. The police had found where the money was _hidden_ (hide) and had _caught_ (catch) the thief.
18. On our vacation we _drove_ 10,000 miles; we had never before _driven_ so far. (drive)
19. I _brought_ my lunch money. Have you _brought_ yours? (bring)
20. I had _drawn_ a lucky ticket; then Megan _drew_ one. (draw)

PRACTICE: Irregular Verbs— List 1

Name _____

Date _____

Instructions: Draw two lines under helping verbs, one under the subject. In the blanks, write the correct form of the verb in parentheses.

1. Dad hadn't _____ (know) that we had already _____ (drag) a log to the camp fire.
2. Tim has _____ his homework; Amy is just _____ hers. (begin)
3. I had _____ into my apple, so Joanie _____ into hers. (bite)
4. I _____ to stay home, but I wish I had _____ to go. (choose)
5. The others had _____ their milk shakes, so Bev _____ hers quickly. (drink)
6. After we _____ (eat) dinner, we had _____ (do) the dishes, _____ (go) into the living room, and _____ (drag) out the old family album.
7. I had _____ on the ice right after my sister _____ . (fall)
8. Verna _____ to class on time even though she had _____ up late. (get)
9. Had he already _____ you a present when you _____ him one? (give)
10. Jill had _____ home, so I _____ home, too. (go)
11. Jo _____ two inches last summer. Have you _____ very much? (grow)
12. Shortly after the game _____ (begin) it seemed obvious that our team would be _____ . (beat)
13. Yesterday the wind _____ (blow) wildly, branches were _____ (break) off trees, and several trees were _____ (blow) down.
14. Have you ever _____ to Hawaii? Last summer Dad and I _____ there. (fly)
15. The teacher had _____ (become) annoyed because so many students had _____ (come) in late and had not _____ (bring) their books.
16. My brother had _____ (eat) the leftovers or Mom would have _____ (freeze) them.
17. The police had found where the money was _____ (hide) and had _____ (catch) the thief.
18. On our vacation we _____ 10,000 miles; we had never before _____ so far. (drive)
19. I _____ my lunch money. Have you _____ yours? (bring)
20. I had _____ a lucky ticket; then Megan _____ one. (draw)

Understanding and Using Good Grammar

TEST: Irregular Verbs—List 1

Correct spelling is required on final tests of irregular verbs. You may want to review some points of spelling.

1. In writing the present participle:

   (a) With verbs ending in silent *e*, drop the *e* and add *-ing*.

   become, *becoming*; bite, *biting*

   (b) With *begin*, *drag*, and *get*, to keep a short sound in the root word, double the final consonant and add *-ing*:

   begin, beginning (not "begining")

   drag, dragging (not "draging")

   get, getting (not "geting")

2. In writing the past participle of *bite*, *get*, and *hide*:

   Write the simple past: *bit*, *got*, and *hid*; double the final consonant to keep the short sound

   and add *-en*: *bitten*, *gotten*, and *hidden* (not "biten", "goten, "hiden").

   Students are instructed to underline the helping verbs and subject to aid them in determining the correct verb to write. Only the 43 written words should be graded.

Grading scale:

–1, 98	–4, 91	–7, 84	–10, 77	–13, 70	–16, 63
–2, 95	–5, 88	–8, 81	–11, 74	–14, 67	–17, 60
–3, 93	–6, 86	–9, 79	–12, 72	–15, 65	–18, 58

TEST: Irregular Verbs—List 1

Instructions: Draw two lines under helping verbs, one under the subject. In the blanks, write the correct form of the verb in parentheses.

1. I *became* concerned because Sis had *become* so pale. (become)

2. We had *begun* to cheer before the team *began* to play. (begin)

3. Flo *brought* some cheese; Diana had *brought* some crackers. (bring)

4. I *fell* asleep in class! Have you ever *fallen* asleep in school? (fall)

5. Jed has *chosen* a shirt like the one Dad *chose* ; which one are you *choosing* ? (choose)

6. Today my little brother *caught* more fish than I; he often *catches* more! (catch)

7. I could have *driven* the car, but my brother *drove* . (drive)

8. Their team is *beating* ours, but ours has often *beaten* theirs. (beat)

9. I had *gotten* bored, so I *got* up and left. (get)

10. Ken *went* to the parade because everyone else had *gone* . (go)

11. My little sisters *dragged* one log to the camp fire; I had *dragged* one earlier. (drag)

12. Those bushes have *grown* more this year than they *grew* last year. (grow)

13. I *came* on time; Travis had *come* earlier; Pedro is *coming* now. (come)

14. Teddy had *drunk* (drink) his orange juice; then he *ate* (eat) his cereal.

15. Our neighbor had *flown* to Paris in a *Concorde*; she is *flying* back in one. (fly)

16. I was *hiding* Lewis's book because he has often *hidden* mine. (hide)

17. We could have *frozen* (freeze) the leftovers; however, my brother and I had *eaten* (eat) them.

18. Eddie hadn't *known* (know) that the test hadn't been *given* (give) yesterday.

19. The little girl had *broken* (break) the vase, but she had *done* (do) it accidentally.

20. Billy had *drawn* (draw) attention to himself when he had *blown* (blow) a huge bubble of gum.

21. The child had *bitten* a chunk out of the cookie. (bite)

Name _____

Date _____

TEST: Irregular Verbs— List 1

Instructions: Draw two lines under helping verbs, one under the subject. In the blanks, write the correct form of the verb in parentheses.

1. I _____ concerned because Sis had _____ so pale. (become)

2. We had _____ to cheer before the team _____ to play. (begin)

3. Flo _____ some cheese; Diana had _____ some crackers. (bring)

4. I _____ asleep in class! Have you ever _____ asleep in school? (fall)

5. Jed has _____ a shirt like the one Dad _____ ; which one are you _____ ? (choose)

6. Today my little brother _____ more fish than I; he often _____ more! (catch)

7. I could have _____ the car, but my brother _____ . (drive)

8. Their team is _____ ours, but ours has often _____ theirs. (beat)

9. I had _____ bored, so I _____ up and left. (get)

10. Ken _____ to the parade because everyone else had _____ . (go)

11. My little sisters _____ one log to the camp fire; I had _____ one earlier. (drag)

12. Those bushes have _____ more this year than they _____ last year. (grow)

13. I _____ on time; Travis had _____ earlier; Pedro is _____ now. (come)

14. Teddy had _____ (drink) his orange juice; then he _____ (eat) his cereal.

15. Our neighbor had _____ to Paris in a *Concorde*; she is _____ back in one.

16. I was _____ Lewis's book because he has often _____ mine. (hide)

17. We could have _____ (freeze) the leftovers; however, my brother and I had _____ (eat) them.

18. Eddie hadn't _____ (know) that the test hadn't been _____ (give) yesterday.

19. The little girl had _____ (break) the vase, but she had _____ (do) it accidentally.

20. Billy had _____ (draw) attention to himself when he had _____ (blow) a huge bubble of gum.

21. The child had _____ a chunk out of the cookie. (bite)

Understanding and Using Good Grammar

PRACTICE: Irregular Verbs—
To Lie *and* To Lay

Students seem to have a strong resistance to learning the correct use of *lie* and *lay*. To overcome this, it might be helpful to have the class read in unison, several times, the underlined words in the lists:

"I lie—I rest; Dad lies—Dad rests; Mom is lying—Mom is resting," etc.

Lie

1. Emphasize the spelling of *lie, lies, lying.*

2. The long-*a* sound in the simple past, *lay*, and in the past participle, *lain*, is the cause for the confusion. There is no explanation! Students should simply memorize the forms.

Lay

The forms are really simple, all having the long-*a* sound and logical spelling: *lay, lays, laying, laid, laid.*

Emphasize the meaning: *Lay, lays* (*present* tense) mean only *put, puts; am laying, have laid* mean only *am putting, have put.*

Warn students to save and study this paper! They will have only one page of sentence practice before the Test!

PRACTICE: Irregular Verbs,
To Lie and *To Lay*

MEMORIZE THE PRINCIPAL PARTS OF TO LIE (*To lie* means "to rest."):

Present: { I <u>lie</u> down to rest.
<u>Dad</u> <u>lies</u> down every day at noon.   *Think:* { "I <u>rest</u>."
"Dad <u>rests</u>."

Present Participle: <u>Mom</u> <u>is lying</u> on the couch.   *Think:* "Mom <u>is resting</u>."

Past: Yesterday <u>I</u> <u>lay</u> in the sun.   *Think:* "I <u>rested</u>."

Past Participle: <u>I</u> <u>have lain</u> in the sun often.   *Think:* "I <u>have rested</u>."

PRACTICE: In the blanks, write the correct form of *lie*.

1. (You) *Lie* down if you're tired.
2. My dog often { *lies* / *lay* } on the front porch.
3. The child { *lies* / *lay* } there, fast asleep.
4. Whose coat is *lying* on that chair?
5. My sister *lies* in bed until Mom yells at her.

6. We had *lain* in the sun too long.
7. I tan easily when I *lie* on the beach.
8. Frightened, I *lay* there without moving.
9. The coins had *lain* there several days.

MEMORIZE THE PRINCIPAL PARTS OF TO LAY (*To lay* means "to put."):

Present: { Every day <u>I</u> <u>lay</u> my books here.
<u>Bud</u> <u>lays</u> his books here often.   *Think:* { "I <u>put</u>."
"Bud <u>puts</u>."

Present Participle: <u>I</u> <u>am laying</u> my books here.   *Think:* "I <u>am putting</u>."

Past: Yesterday <u>Carrie</u> <u>laid</u> her books there.   *Think:* "Carrie <u>put</u>."

Past Participle: Now <u>Joe</u> <u>has laid</u> his books there.   *Think:* "Joe <u>has put</u>."

PRACTICE: In the blanks, write the correct form of *lay*.

1. Mother is *laying* the baby in the crib.
2. Sharon, don't *lay* your skates there.
3. Every day he { *laid* / *lays* } the newspaper here.
4. Yesterday, Marie *laid* her bike on the driveway.
5. Rosa has *laid* her report on the teacher's desk.

6. The money must have been *laid* on the table by someone.
7. Ian was *laying* the puppy in its box.
8. *Lay* this blanket over the baby, please.
9. Dom always *lays* his keys here.

Use *lie* or *lay*.

1. Dad { *lays* / *laid* } his newspaper down and then { *lies* / *lay* } down himself.

2. Your book has *lain* there ever since you *laid* it there.

PRACTICE: Irregular Verbs—
To Lie and *To Lay*

Name _____

Date _____

***MEMORIZE THE PRINCIPAL PARTS OF* TO LIE (*To lie* means "to rest."):**

Present: { I <u>lie</u> down to rest.   *Think:* { "I <u>rest</u>."
             { <u>Dad</u> <u>lies</u> down every day at noon.   { "<u>Dad</u> <u>rests</u>."

Present Participle: <u>Mom</u> is <u>lying</u> on the couch.   *Think:* "<u>Mom</u> is <u>resting</u>."

Past: Yesterday <u>I</u> <u>lay</u> in the sun.   *Think:* "<u>I</u> <u>rested</u>."

Past Participle: <u>I</u> <u>have lain</u> in the sun often.   *Think:* "<u>I</u> <u>have rested</u>."

PRACTICE: In the blanks, write the correct form of *lie*.

1. _____ down if you're tired.

2. My dog often _____ on the front porch.

3. The child _____ there, fast asleep.

4. Whose coat is _____ on that chair?

5. My sister _____ in bed until Mom yells at her.

6. We had _____ in the sun too long.

7. I tan easily when I _____ on the beach.

8. Frightened, I _____ there without moving.

9. The coins had _____ there several days.

***MEMORIZE THE PRINCIPAL PARTS OF* TO LAY (*To lay* means "to put."):**

Present: { Every day <u>I</u> <u>lay</u> my books here.   *Think:* { "I <u>put</u>."
             { <u>Bud</u> <u>lays</u> his books here often.   { "<u>Bud</u> <u>puts</u>."

Present Participle: <u>I</u> am <u>laying</u> my books here.   *Think:* "<u>I</u> am <u>putting</u>."

Past: Yesterday <u>Carrie</u> <u>laid</u> her books there.   *Think:* "<u>Carrie</u> <u>put</u>."

Past Participle: Now <u>Joe</u> <u>has laid</u> his books there.   *Think:* "<u>Joe</u> <u>has put</u>."

PRACTICE: In the blanks, write the correct form of *lay*.

1. Mother is _____ the baby in the crib.

2. Sharon, don't _____ your skates there.

3. Every day he _____ the newspaper here.

4. Yesterday, Marie _____ her bike on the driveway.

5. Rosa has _____ her report on the teacher's desk.

6. The money must have been _____ on the table by someone.

7. Ian was _____ the puppy in its box.

8. _____ this blanket over the baby, please.

9. Dom always _____ his keys here.

Use *lie* or *lay*.

1. Dad _____ his newspaper down and then _____ down himself.

2. Your book has _____ there ever since you _____ it there.

Understanding and Using Good Grammar

PRACTICE: *Irregular Verbs,*
To Lie *and* To Lay *(continued)*

Encourage students to follow the instructions. As they write the partial sentences, they should spell the verb aloud and say the meaning.

Today I L-I-E—rest, etc.

Often I have L-A-I-N—have rested

Use this system with all tenses of *lie* and with *lay*.

Point out that this method of study involves the use of seeing, hearing, speaking, writing, and above all, thinking!

Answer Key—Simple Past and Past Participle of *lay*.

1. Yesterday I laid
2. Yesterday you laid
3. Yesterday he/she/it laid
4. Yesterday we laid
5. Yesterday you laid
6. Yesterday they laid

1. Often I have laid
2. Often you have laid
3. Often he/she/it has laid
4. Often we have laid
5. Often you have laid
6. Often they have laid

PRACTICE: Irregular Verbs,
To Lie and *To Lay (continued)*

Instructions: Conjugate each tense, using the beginning of the sentence that is given. As you write, spell the verb aloud (*example:* L-I-E) and say its meaning (*example:* rest).

Lie   **Simple Present:** *lie/lies* (rest/rests)
     Today I lie on the patio.

1. *Today I lie -- rest*
2. *Today you lie -- rest*
3. *Today he/she/it lies -- rests*
4. *Today we lie -- rest*
5. *Today you lie -- rest*
6. *Today they lie -- rest*

Present Participle: *lying* (resting)
     Today I am lying on the patio.

1. *Today I am lying -- resting*
2. *Today you are lying -- resting*
3. *Today he/she/it is lying -- resting*
4. *Today we are lying -- resting*
5. *Today you are lying -- resting*
6. *Today they are lying -- resting*

Simple Past: *lay* (rested)
     Yesterday ...

1. *Yesterday I lay -- rested*
2. *Yesterday you lay -- rested*
3. *Yesterday he/she/it lay -- rested*
4. *Yesterday we lay -- rested*
5. *Yesterday you lay -- rested*
6. *Yesterday they lay -- rested*

Past Participle: *have lain* (have rested)
     Often I have ...

1. *Often I have lain -- have rested*
2. *Often you have lain -- have rested*
3. *Often he/she/it has lain -- has rested*
4. *Often we have lain -- have rested*
5. *Often you have lain -- have rested*
6. *Often they have lain -- have rested*

Lay   **Simple Present:** *lay/lays* (put/puts)
     Every day I lay a book here.

1. *Every day I lay -- put*
2. *Every day you lay -- put*
3. *Every day he/she/it lays -- put*
4. *Every day we lay -- put*
5. *Every day you lay -- put*
6. *Every day they lay -- put*

Present Participle: *laying* (putting)
     Today I am laying one here.

1. *Today I am laying -- putting*
2. *Today you are laying -- putting*
3. *Today he/she/it is laying -- putting*
4. *Today we are laying -- putting*
5. *Today you are laying -- putting*
6. *Today they are laying -- putting*

Simple Past: *laid* (put)
     Yesterday I laid ...

Past Participle: *have laid* (have put)
     Often I have ...

On the reverse side, write the six sentences for **simple past** form and for **past participle** of **lay**.

Name _____

Date _____

Instructions: Conjugate each tense, using the beginning of the sentence that is given. As you write, spell the verb aloud (*example:* L-I-E) and say its meaning (*example:* rest).

Lie   **Simple Present:** *lie/lies* (rest/rests)
 Today I lie on the patio.

1. _____
2. _____
3. _____
4. _____
5. _____
6. _____

Present Participle: *lying* (resting)
 Today I am lying on the patio.

1. _____
2. _____
3. _____
4. _____
5. _____
6. _____

Simple Past: *lay* (rested)
 Yesterday . . .

1. _____
2. _____
3. _____
4. _____
5. _____
6. _____

Past Participle: *have lain* (have rested)
 Often I have . . .

1. _____
2. _____
3. _____
4. _____
5. _____
6. _____

Lay   **Simple Present:** *lay/lays* (put/puts)
 Every day I lay a book here.

1. _____
2. _____
3. _____
4. _____
5. _____
6. _____

Present Participle: *laying* (putting)
 Today I am laying one here.

1. _____
2. _____
3. _____
4. _____
5. _____
6. _____

Simple Past: *laid* (put)
 Yesterday I laid . . .

Past Participle: *have laid* (have put)
 Often I have . . .

On the reverse side, write the six sentences for **simple past** form and for **past participle** of **lay**.

Understanding and Using Good Grammar

FINAL PRACTICE and TEST:
Irregular Verbs, To Lie *and* To Lay

> The next reproducible page contains one half-page Final Practice and one half-page Test. Before passing out the page, cut it in two to remove the Test.

Final Practice

After students have completed the Final Practice, have volunteers read their answers. Confirm their correct answers. Remind other students to make careful corrections in order to have a perfect paper to review before the Test.

Sentence 1: *You* is the understood subject in a request.

Sentence 8: *Grandpa* is the subject for both verbs; therefore, *has,* the helping verb for *laid,* carries over to (*has*) *lain.*

Test

Grade only the 20 written words. Subtract 5% for each error.

Sentence 8: Before students begin the Test, point out that the verb part of *won't,* the contraction of *will not,* should be underlined, <u>won</u>'t.

Sentence 4: *Had,* the helping verb for the first blank carries over to (*had*) as a helping verb for the second blank.

FINAL PRACTICE: Irregular Verbs, *To Lie* and *To Lay*

Instructions: Draw two lines under helping verbs used with **lie** or **lay**. In the blanks, write the correct form of **lie** or **lay**.

1. *Lay* your books on the hall table; Lizzy *lays* hers there sometimes.

2. His wallet <u>had</u> *lain* on the store counter ever since he *laid* it there.

3. <u>Don't</u> *lie* in the sun very long; yesterday you *lay* there too long.

4. Dad always *lays* his keys on the mantle, but he <u>hasn't</u> *laid* them there tonight.

5. Uncle Greg <u>will</u> *lay* the rest of the patio bricks now; he *laid* most of them yesterday.

6. See! Our farm *lies* there in the valley.

7. Many leaves *lay* on the ground yesterday, but many more <u>are</u> *lying* there now.

8. Grandpa <u>has</u> *laid* his magazine down and *lain* back in his chair for a short rest.

9. I found Vic's fishing rod *lying* near the plank he <u>had</u> *laid* across the stream.

TEST: Irregular Verbs, *To Lie* and *To Lay*

Instructions: Draw two lines under helping verbs used with **lie** or **lay**. In the blanks, write the correct form of **lie** or **lay**.

1. I saw Vic's fishing rod *lying* near the plank he <u>had</u> *laid* across the stream.

2. Why <u>are</u> you *laying* your coat on the floor? Elsa's coat <u>is</u> *lying* on the chair. *Lay* yours there, too.

3. Before he <u>will</u> *lie* down for a nap, my little cousin *lays* his toys away carefully.

4. I <u>had</u> *laid* out my sleeping bag, crawled in, and *lain* there, looking up at the stars.

5. Yesterday, Grandpa *laid* the saw there before he *lay* down to rest.

6. Dad *laid* the paper down, went to his room, and *lay* down.

7. When you return, *lay* Lee's keys where she usually *lays* them.

8. I <u>won't</u> *lie* in the sun today; I *lay* there too long yesterday.

9. Vicky <u>had been</u> *laying* the beach towel down smoothly; now she <u>is</u> *lying* on it.

10. The old letter <u>had</u> *lain* on the attic floor for years.

FINAL PRACTICE:
Irregular Verbs, *To Lie* and *To Lay*

Name _____

Date _____

Instructions: Draw two lines under helping verbs used with **lie** or **lay**. In the blanks, write the correct form of **lie** or **lay**.

1. _____ your books on the hall table; Lizzy_____ hers there sometimes.
2. His wallet had _____ on the store counter ever since he _____ it there.
3. Don't _____ in the sun very long; yesterday you _____ there too long.
4. Dad always _____ his keys on the mantle, but he hasn't _____ them there tonight.
5. Uncle Greg will _____ the rest of the patio bricks now; he _____ most of them yesterday.
6. See! Our farm _____ there in the valley.
7. Many leaves _____ on the ground yesterday, but many more are _____ there now.
8. Grandpa has _____ his magazine down and _____ back in his chair for a short rest.
9. I found Vic's fishing rod _____ near the plank he had _____ across the stream.

TEST: Irregular Verbs,
To Lie and *To Lay*

Name _____

Date _____

Instructions: Draw two lines under helping verbs used with **lie** or **lay**. In the blanks, write the correct form of **lie** or **lay**.

1. I saw Vic's fishing rod _____ near the plank he had _____ across the stream.
2. Why are you _____ your coat on the floor? Elsa's coat is _____ on the chair. _____ yours there, too.
3. Before he will _____ down for a nap, my little cousin _____ his toys away carefully.
4. I had _____ out my sleeping bag, crawled in, and _____ there, looking up at the stars.
5. Yesterday, Grandpa _____ the saw there before he _____ down to rest.
6. Dad _____ the paper down, went to his room, and _____ down.
7. When you return, _____ Lee's keys where she usually _____ them.
8. I won't _____ in the sun today; I _____ there too long yesterday.
9. Vicky had been _____ the beach towel down smoothly; now she is _____ on it.
10. The old letter had _____ on the attic floor for years.

Understanding and Using Good Grammar

PRETEST:
Irregular Verbs—List 2

Pretest scores do not affect students' report card grades. Students should underline helping verbs to aid them in writing the correct verb.

Sentence 4: *Student* is the subject for three verbs; the helping verb, *had*, with *taken* carries over to (*had*) *torn* and (*had*) *thrown*.

Percent scores for 38 points are found on page 159.

PRETEST:
Irregular Verbs—List 2

Instructions: In the blank, write the correct form of the verb shown in parentheses.

1. I had *ridden* (ride) my bike to school and arrived before the tardy bell had *rung* . (ring)

2. Yesterday Pam *said* (say), "I *saw* (see) him when he *sneaked* (sneak) out of the library."

3. We had *run* (run) toward the stranger, and yelled, or he might have *stolen* (steal) your bicycle.

4. Clay has *sworn* (swear) that another student had *taken* (take) his paper, *torn* (tear) it in two, and *thrown* (throw) it into the wastebasket.

5. Tad *swam* faster than he has ever *swum* before. (swim)

6. That person has *sat* (sit) there for an hour and hasn't *spoken* (speak) to anyone.

7. Geno must have *seen* (see) the boat when it *sank* . (sink)

8. Coach had *sprung* (spring) back just in time when Gil *swung* (swing) the bat wildly.

9. I had *written* (write) my sister a note telling her that I had *worn* (wear) her coat.

10. I am sure the chorus had previously *sung* the song they *sang* today. (sing)

11. The child had *shrunk* (shrink) back in terror when the huge dog had *risen* (rise) to its feet.

12. 12. After Jess had *shown* (show) Dad his report card, Dad had been visibly *shaken* (shake).

13. My brother had *tried* (try) to remove the stinger after the wasp *stung* (sting) him.

14. Claire had been *riding* (ride) her bike; now she is *swimming* (swim).

In these sentences, select the correct word in parentheses and write the correct form of that word in the blank.

15. The bank must *have* (of/have) *lent* (loan/lend) Deb the money.

16. If your mom *brings* you to my house, my dad will *take* us to school. (bring/take)

17. That teacher has *taught* (teach/learn) us well.

18. Our dog *sat* on the pad we had *set* out for him. (sit/set)

Name _____

Date _____

PRETEST: Irregular Verbs—
List 2

Instructions: In the blank, write the correct form of the verb shown in parentheses.

1. I had _____ (ride) my bike to school and arrived before the tardy bell had _____ . (ring)
2. Yesterday Pam _____ (say), "I _____ (see) him when he _____ (sneak) out of the library."
3. We had _____ (run) toward the stranger, and yelled, or he might have _____ (steal) your bicycle.
4. Clay has _____ (swear) that another student had _____ (take) his paper, _____ (tear) it in two, and _____ (throw) it into the wastebasket.
5. Tad _____ faster than he has ever _____ before. (swim)
6. That person has _____ (sit) there for an hour and hasn't _____ (speak) to anyone.
7. Geno must have _____ (see) the boat when it _____ . (sink)
8. Coach had _____ (spring) back just in time when Gil _____ (swing) the bat wildly.
9. I had _____ (write) my sister a note telling her that I had _____ (wear) her coat.
10. I am sure the chorus had previously _____ the song they _____ today. (sing)
11. The child had _____ (shrink) back in terror when the huge dog had _____ (rise) to its feet.
12. 12. After Jess had _____ (show) Dad his report card, Dad had been visibly _____ (shake).
13. My brother had _____ (try) to remove the stinger after the wasp _____ (sting) him.
14. Claire had been _____ (ride) her bike; now she is _____ (swim).

In these sentences, select the correct word in parentheses and write the correct form of that word in the blank.

15. The bank must _____ (of/have) _____ (loan/lend) Deb the money.
16. If your mom _____ you to my house, my dad will _____ us to school. (bring/take)
17. That teacher has _____ (teach/learn) us well.
18. Our dog _____ on the pad we had _____ out for him. (sit/set)

Understanding and Using Good Grammar

Irregular Verbs—List 2

The **Remember** items 1 through 5 are review. Items 6 through 9 contain added information which students should assimilate.

Point out that *sneak* is a regular verb to which *-ed* is added to form the past and past participle. *Snuck* is not a word!

After you have gone over the list, return the Pretests so the students can correct any errors they may have made. They should save the paper to have a study sheet to review before the Test.

Students may say they have seen *loan* used as a verb. Undoubtedly they have. Give them this quote from *The American Heritage Dictionary*, 1981: "*Loan* has long been established as a verb, especially in business usage. *Lend* is considered to be preferable to *loan* in general usage, particularly in formal writing." In this study, *loan* will be considered to be a noun, *lend*, a verb.

Name _____

Date _____

Irregular Verbs—List 2

Present	Present Participle	Past	Past Participle
(Say: "Today I . . .")	(Use forms of *to be*.)	(Say: "Yesterday I . . .")	(Use forms of *to have*.)
ride	riding	rode	ridden
ring	ringing	rang	rung
rise	rising	rose	risen
run	running	ran	run
say	saying	said	said
see	seeing	saw	seen
set (to put)	setting	set	set
shake	shaking	shook	shaken
show	showing	showed	shown
shrink	shrinking	shrank	shrunk
sing	singing	sang	sung
sink	sinking	sank	sunk
sit (to rest)	sitting	sat	sat
sneak	sneaking	sneaked	sneaked
		(never "snuck")	
speak	speaking	spoke	spoken
spring	springing	sprang	sprung
steal	stealing	stole	stolen
sting	stinging	*stung*	*stung*
swear	swearing	swore	sworn
swim	swimming	swam	swum
swing	swinging	*swung*	*swung*
take	taking	took	taken
tear	tearing	tore	torn
throw	throwing	threw	thrown
try	trying	tried	tried
wear	wearing	wore	worn
write	writing	wrote	written

REMEMBER

1. *Participle* means "part of the expression."

2. Use helping verbs with participles.

3. **Present participle:**
   is, am, are, was, were, be, being, been

4. **Past participle:**
   have/has, had, shall/will have

5. Sound differences:

Sharp (Use *no* helper.)	*Softer* (Use helper.)
rang	have rung
sank	have sunk
swam	have swum

   With ending *n*-sound words, use helper.

rode	have ridden
saw	have seen
took	have taken

6. *Learn* means "get knowledge."

   Teach means "give instruction."

   <u>We</u> <u>learned</u> what <u>she</u> <u>was teaching</u>.

7. *Bring*: motion toward speaker.

   Take: motion away from speaker.

   (You) <u>Bring</u> your books with you; <u>take</u> them when you leave.

8. *Loan* is a noun: The bank gave me a loan. [I.O.] [D.O.]

   Lend is a verb: The bank lent me the money. [I.O.] [D.O.]

   | lend | lending | lent | have lent |

9. Be alert! <u>You</u> (should of) (<u>should have</u>) <u>come</u>, too. *Of* is not a helping verb!

Understanding and Using Good Grammar

PRACTICE:
Irregular Verbs—List 2

This is the only Practice for List II. Students should work carefully to have a perfect paper to take home to review before the Test.

Sentence 7: *Child* is the subject of two verbs. *Had*, the helping verb for *shrunk*, carries over to (*had*) *run*.

Irregular Verbs—List 2

PRACTICE: Draw two lines under helping verbs. In the blanks, write the correct form of the verb shown in parentheses.

1. Pete <u>had</u> *ridden* his bike to my house, so we *rode* our bikes to school. (ride)
2. The tardy bell *rang* early. <u>Has</u> it ever *rung* early before? (ring)
3. The river <u>is</u> *rising* fast; <u>has</u> it *risen* this high before? (rise)
4. Nicole *saw* Tami at the mall; I <u>hadn't</u> *seen* either of them. (see)
5. The man *set* down his toolbox and then *sat* down with us. (sit/set)
6. He <u>had</u> *shown* me his report, so I *showed* him mine. (show)
7. As the snarling dog *rose* (rise) to its feet, the child <u>had</u> *shrunk* (shrink) back and *run* (run) away.
8. The chorus *sang* better than it <u>had</u> *sung* during the rehearsal. (sing)
9. We <u>could have</u> *stolen* (steal) out as they *sneaked* (sneak) in.
10. Rashidi thought the boat <u>had</u> *sunk* yesterday, but it *sank* today. (sink)
11. Mr. Hunt <u>had</u> *shaken* Tomas's hand; then he *shook* mine. (shake)
12. He <u>had</u> *spoken* to us, so we *spoke* to him. (speak)
13. The boy <u>had</u> *sprung* (spring) up suddenly when the bee *stung* (sting) him.
14. Tom and Huck <u>had</u> already *sworn* not to tell, but they *swore* again. (swear)
15. <u>Have</u> you *swum* in their pool? We *swam* in it yesterday. (swim)
16. He <u>hadn't</u> *taken* any pictures, but I *took* some. (take)
17. This page <u>has been</u> *torn*. Who *tore* it? (tear)
18. That little rascal *threw* the only rock that <u>was</u> *thrown*. (throw)
19. One monkey *swung* to a lower branch and the others <u>had</u> *swung* right after him. (swing)
20. Your sister <u>should</u> *have* (of/have) *worn* her new dress before you *wore* it! (wear)
21. My brother <u>is</u> *teaching* (learn/teach) me to play chess.
22. I just *wrote* my application; <u>have</u> you *written* yours? (write)
23. They <u>had</u> *brought* their books when they came and <u>had</u> *taken* them when they left. (take/bring)
24. Leon <u>might</u> *lend* you his backpack; he *lent* it to me once. (loan/lend)

Irregular Verbs—List 2

Name _____

Date _____

PRACTICE: Draw two lines under helping verbs. In the blanks, write the correct form of the verb shown in parentheses.

1. Pete had _____ his bike to my house, so we _____ our bikes to school. (ride)
2. The tardy bell _____ early. Has it ever _____ early before? (ring)
3. The river is _____ fast; has it _____ this high before? (rise)
4. Nicole _____ Tami at the mall; I hadn't _____ either of them. (see)
5. The man _____ down his toolbox and then _____ down with us. (sit/set)
6. He had _____ me his report, so I _____ him mine. (show)
7. As the snarling dog _____ (rise) to its feet, the child had _____ (shrink) back and _____ (run) away.
8. The chorus _____ better than it had _____ during the rehearsal. (sing)
9. We could have _____ (steal) out as they _____ (sneak) in.
10. Rashidi thought the boat had _____ yesterday, but it _____ today. (sink)
11. Mr. Hunt had _____ Tomas's hand; then he _____ mine. (shake)
12. He had _____ to us, so we _____ to him. (speak)
13. The boy had _____ (spring) up suddenly when the bee _____ (sting) him.
14. Tom and Huck had already _____ not to tell, but they _____ again. (swear)
15. Have you _____ in their pool? We _____ in it yesterday. (swim)
16. He hadn't _____ any pictures, but I _____ some. (take)
17. This page has been _____ . Who _____ it? (tear)
18. That little rascal _____ the only rock that was _____ . (throw)
19. One monkey _____ to a lower branch and the others had _____ right after him. (swing)
20. Your sister should _____ (of/have) _____ her new dress before you _____ it! (wear)
21. My brother is _____ (learn/teach) me to play chess.
22. I just _____ my application; have you _____ yours? (write)
23. They had _____ their books when they came and had _____ them when they left. (take/bring)
24. Leon might _____ you his backpack; he _____ it to me once. (loan/lend)

Understanding and Using Good Grammar

TEST:
Irregular Verbs—List 2

Again, students are instructed to underline helping verbs to aid them in determining the correct form of the verb to write. Only the 41 written words should be graded.

Sentence 3: The helping verb, *had*, in *had worn* carries over to (*had*) *stolen* and (*had*) *run*.

Grading scale:

–1, 98	–4, 90	–7, 83	–10, 76	–13, 68	–16, 61
–2, 95	–5, 88	–8, 80	–11, 73	–14, 66	–17, 58
–3, 93	–6, 85	–9, 78	–12, 71	–15, 63	–18, 56

TEST:
Irregular Verbs—List 2

Instructions: Draw two lines under helping verbs. In the blanks, write the correct form of the verb shown in parentheses.

1. Dad *sat* (sit) down after he <u>had</u> *shaken* (shake) the speaker's hand.
2. After Abe <u>had</u> *worn* (wear) my ski jacket, I discovered it <u>was</u> *torn* . (tear)
3. The little boy <u>had</u> *sprung* (spring) out of his chair, *stolen* (steal) quietly down the hall, and *run* (run) home.
4. We <u>had</u> *risen* (rise) to our feet when the aerialist *swung* (swing) out on the trapeze.
5. The magician *showed* me how to do the trick; earlier he <u>had</u> *shown* me several others. (show)
6. The team's spirit *sank* even lower than it <u>had</u> already *sunk* . (sink)
7. Olga *wrote* a letter yesterday; she <u>had</u> *written* one the day before; now she <u>is</u> *writing* another. (write)
8. Paul said he *swam* across the lake. <u>Could</u> he <u>have</u> *swum* so far? (swim)
9. The mysterious man *shrank* (shrink) back and *sneaked* (sneak) away.
10. Rachel and I *saw* him; he didn't know anyone <u>had</u> *seen* him. (see)
11. Hope <u>is</u> *riding* my horse. I <u>have</u> often *ridden* hers. (ride)
12. How often <u>have</u> I *lent* (loan/lend) you a pencil?
13. The little scouts *sang* with more spirit than they <u>had</u> ever *sung* before. (sing)
14. When John <u>had</u> *thrown* (throw) the newspaper carelessly the man <u>had</u> *spoken* (speak) to him about it.
15. I *took* (take) my jeans back to the store because they <u>had</u> *shrunk* (shrink) six inches.
16. I <u>had</u> *tried* (try) to remove the stinger after the wasp *stung* (sting) me.
17. The chairs <u>had been</u> *set* on the stage and the candidates <u>had</u> *sat* down. (sit/set)
18. When the neighbor's phone *rang* , I thought ours <u>had</u> *rung* . (ring)
19. Erik <u>should</u> *have* (of/have) *taken* the books to the library, but he <u>had</u> *brought* them to my room. (bring/take)
20. Ms. Land <u>has</u> *taught* (learn/teach) us to tap dance.

Name _____

Date _____

TEST: Irregular Verbs— List 2

Instructions: Draw two lines under helping verbs. In the blanks, write the correct form of the verb shown in parentheses.

1. Dad _____ (sit) down after he had _____ (shake) the speaker's hand.

2. After Abe had _____ (wear) my ski jacket, I discovered it was _____ . (tear)

3. The little boy had _____ (spring) out of his chair, _____ (steal) quietly down the hall, and _____ (run) home.

4. We had _____ (rise) to our feet when the aerialist _____ (swing) out on the trapeze.

5. The magician _____ me how to do the trick; earlier he had _____ me several others. (show)

6. The team's spirit _____ even lower than it had already _____ . (sink)

7. Olga _____ a letter yesterday; she had _____ one the day before; now she is _____ another. (write)

8. Paul said he _____ across the lake. Could he have _____ so far? (swim)

9. The mysterious man _____ (shrink) back and _____ (sneak) away.

10. Rachel and I _____ him; he didn't know anyone had _____ him. (see)

11. Hope is _____ my horse. I have often _____ hers. (ride)

12. How often have I _____ (loan/lend) you a pencil?

13. The little scouts _____ with more spirit than they had ever _____ before. (sing)

14. When John had _____ (throw) the newspaper carelessly the man had _____ (speak) to him about it.

15. I _____ (take) my jeans back to the store because they had _____ (shrink) six inches.

16. I had _____ (try) to remove the stinger after the wasp _____ (sting) me.

17. The chairs had been _____ on the stage and the candidates had _____ down. (sit/set)

18. When the neighbor's phone _____ , I thought ours had _____ . (ring)

19. Erik should _____ (of/have) _____ the books to the library, but he had _____ them to my room. (bring/take)

20. Ms. Land has _____ (learn/teach) us to tap dance.

Understanding and Using Good Grammar

Principal Parts of Verbs

This worksheet turns students' attention from merely understanding correct use of irregular verbs to focusing upon the principal parts of all verbs.

The written work is preparation for studying verb tenses and, later, for studying the various grammatical functions of participial forms.

In **Remember** item 2 point out:

1. Helping verbs used with the present participle are forms of *to be*: *is, am, are, was, were, be, being, been,* and

2. helping verbs used with the past participle are forms of *to have*: *have/has, had, shall/will have.*

You may wish to give students credit for completing the first Practice.

When you return the paper to the students, remind them to add it to their collection of information sheets.

Principal Parts of Verbs

REMEMBER:

1. All verbs have four principal parts: **present**, **present participle**, **past**, and **past participle**.

2. *Participle* roughly means "part of the expression." Helping verbs are always used with the participles of verbs. Helping verbs are the other "part of the expression."

3. **Regular verbs** form the past and past participle by adding **-d** or **-ed** to the present form:

> erase, am erasing, eras**ed**, have eras**ed**
> call, am calling, call**ed**, have call**ed**

4. **Irregular verbs** change the spelling to form the past and past participle:

> go, am going, went, have gone
> sing, am singing, sang, have sung

PRACTICE: Write the principal parts of these verbs, as in the example; label *Regular* or *Irregular*.

	Present	Present Participle	Past	Past Participle	Regular/Irregular
Example:	jump	am jumping	jumped	have jumped	Regular
	grow	am growing	grew	have grown	Irregular
1.	excel	am excelling	excelled	have excelled	Reg.
2.	come	am coming	came	have come	Irreg.
3.	change	am changing	changed	have changed	Reg.
4.	bring	am bringing	brought	have brought	Irreg.
5.	proceed	am proceeding	proceeded	have proceeded	Reg.
6.	precede	am preceding	preceded	have preceded	Reg
7.	take	am taking	took	have taken	Irreg.
8.	drink	am drinking	drank	have drunk	Irreg.

Notice: Helping verbs combined with participles of the main verb allow us to express various specific meanings.

PRACTICE: Write at least two helping verbs in the blank before the participle to express specific meaning.

Example: Elaine _had been_ planning this surprise for several days.

1. I ___should not have___ signed up for the drama.

2. Dad ___could have___ taken that exit.

3. Sally ___might have been___ buying new shoes.

4. No one in the class ___had been___ auditioning for the part.

5. These books ___must have been___ borrowed from the library.

Principal Parts of Verbs

Name _____

Date _____

REMEMBER:

1. All verbs have four principal parts: **present**, **present participle**, **past**, and **past participle**.

2. *Participle* roughly means "part of the expression." Helping verbs are always used with the participles of verbs. Helping verbs are the other "part of the expression."

3. **Regular verbs** form the past and past participle by adding **-d** or **-ed** to the present form:

    erase, am erasing, eras**ed**, have eras**ed**
    call, am calling, call**ed**, have call**ed**

4. **Irregular verbs** change the spelling to form the past and past participle:

    go, am going, went, have gone
    sing, am singing, sang, have sung

PRACTICE: Write the principal parts of these verbs, as in the example; label *Regular* or *Irregular*.

	Present	Present Participle	Past	Past Participle	Regular/Irregular
Example:	jump	am jumping	jumped	have jumped	Regular
	grow	am growing	grew	have grown	Irregular

1. excel _____

2. come _____

3. change _____

4. bring _____

5. proceed _____

6. precede _____

7. take _____

8. drink _____

Notice: Helping verbs combined with participles of the main verb allow us to express various specific meanings.

PRACTICE: Write at least two helping verbs in the blank before the participle to express specific meaning.

Example: Elaine *must have been* planning this surprise for several days.

1. I _____ signed up for the drama.

2. Dad _____ taken that exit.

3. Sally _____ buying new shoes.

4. No one in the class _____ auditioning for the part.

5. These books _____ borrowed from the library.

Understanding and Using Good Grammar

Verbs—Simple Tenses

For sentences 1–4, work with students as volunteers provide the required subjects and verb tenses.

For sentences 5–9, have each student complete his or her own sentences. Read the correct forms while students correct any errors they may have made. Have them hand in their papers to receive credit for work completed.

The distinction between *shall* or *will* is another fine point in semantics which many students enjoy thinking about and understanding.

As you go over the chart with the students, emphasize the logic of designating the speaker as the first person, the person spoken to as the second person, and the person spoken of as the third person. Relate *today* to present; *yesterday* to past; *tomorrow* to future. Singular means *one*; plural means *more than one*.

Verbs—Simple Tenses

REMEMBER:

1. **Tense** in grammar means "time."
2. The tense of the verb tells when the action takes place, in the **present** (today), **past** (yesterday) **future** (tomorrow).
3. There are two main tenses: **simple tense** and **perfect tense**. Tenses are conjugated, arranged for understanding, according to nominative (subject) pronouns.

SIMPLE TENSES

Singular	Present	Past	Future
1st person (speaker):	I call	I called	I shall call
2nd person (spoken to):	You call	You called	You will call
3rd person (spoken of):	He/She/It/ Sue calls	He/She/It/ Sue called	He/She/It/ Sue will call
Plural			
1st person (speaker):	We call	We called	We shall call
2nd person (spoken to):	You call	You called	You will call
3rd person (spoken of):	They/People call	They/People called	They/People will call

Notice: *Shall* and *will* are used as helping verbs with **simple future**.

(a) With **first** person singular and plural, use *shall* to express a statement of fact; use *will* to express determination.

(b) With **second** and **third** person singular and plural, use *will* to express a statement of fact; use *shall* to express determination.

PRACTICE: In the blank provided, write the subject and verb tense indicated for the verbs listed. Abbreviations: **Pres.**, present; **Past**; **Fut.**, future; **pers.**, person; **sing.**, singular; **pl.**, plural.

Example: Resent: Pres., 3rd person. sing. *He/She/It/Sue resents*

1. *expect:* Past, 1st pers. pl. *We expected*

2. *direct:* Fut. (fact), 1st pers. sing. *I shall direct*

3. *interrupt:* Pres., 2nd pers. pl. *You interrupt*

4. *locate:* Past, 3rd pers. pl. *They/People located*

5. *translate:* Fut. (fact), 3rd pers. sing. *He/She/It/Sue will translate*

6. *trim:* Past, 2nd pers. sing. *You trimmed*

7. *remit:* Fut. (determination), 1st pers. pl. *We will remit*

8. *simplify:* Pres., 3rd pers. sing. *He/She/It/Sue simplifies*

9. *occupy:* Fut. (determination), 2nd pers. pl. *You shall occupy*

Name _____

Verbs—Simple Tenses

Date _____

REMEMBER:

1. **Tense** in grammar means "time."

2. The tense of the verb tells when the action takes place, in the **present** (today), **past** (yesterday) **future** (tomorrow).

3. There are two main tenses: **simple tense** and **perfect tense**. Tenses are conjugated, arranged for understanding, according to nominative (subject) pronouns.

SIMPLE TENSES

Singular	Present	Past	Future
1st person (speaker):	I call	I called	I shall call
2nd person (spoken to):	You call	You called	You will call
3rd person (spoken of):	He/She/It/	He/She/It/	He/She/It/
	Sue calls	Sue called	Sue will call
Plural			
1st person (speaker):	We call	We called	We shall call
2nd person (spoken to):	You call	You called	You will call
3rd person (spoken of):	They/People call	They/People called	They/People will call

Notice: *Shall* and *will* are used as helping verbs with **simple future**.

(a) With **first** person singular and plural, use *shall* to express a statement of fact; use *will* to express determination.

(b) With **second** and **third** person singular and plural, use *will* to express a statement of fact; use *shall* to express determination.

PRACTICE: In the blank provided, write the subject and verb tense indicated for the verbs listed. Abbreviations: **Pres.**, present; **Past**; **Fut.**, future; **pers.**, person; **sing.**, singular; **pl.**, plural.

Example: Resent: Pres., 3rd person. sing. *He/She/It/Sue resents* _____

1. *expect*: Past, 1st pers. pl. _____

2. *direct*: Fut. (fact), 1st pers. sing. _____

3. *interrupt*: Pres., 2nd pers. pl. _____

4. *locate*: Past, 3rd pers. pl. _____

5. *translate*: Fut. (fact), 3rd pers. sing. _____

6. *trim*: Past, 2nd pers. sing. _____

7. *remit*: Fut. (determination), 1st pers. pl. _____

8. *simplify*: Pres., 3rd pers. sing. _____

9. *occupy*: Fut. (determination), 2nd pers. pl. _____

Understanding and Using Good Grammar

Verbs—Perfect Tenses

Before studying the perfect tenses students should be able to conjugate the simple tenses of *to have*.

The class should work together in doing this entire page. Determining the correct pronoun equivalent of a noun or of a compound subject will be a challenge:

Sentence 3: *All* (of us)—*we*, 1st pl.
Sentence 5: *relatives—they*, 3rd pl.
Sentence 6: *you and she—you*, 2nd pl.
Sentence 7: *he and I—we*, 1st pl.
Sentence 8: *they and we—we*, 1st pl.
Sentence 9: *Mom and Dad—they*, 3rd pl.
Sentence 12: *You* officers—*You*, 2nd pl.
Sentence 13: *team—it/they*, 3rd sing./pl.

To relieve some of the tedium of checking the students' work, check only sentences 8–14. They contain examples of all the persons, singular and plural, and all the tenses.

Verbs—Perfect Tenses

REMEMBER:

1. **Perfect tenses** express completed (perfected) action, action completed at the present time, in the past, or in the future.

2. Perfect tenses use forms of the helping verb *have* with the past participle, the **-d** or **-ed** form, of the main verb.

SIMPLE TENSES OF *HAVE*

Present		Past		Future	
Singular	**Plural**	**Singular**	**Plural**	**Singular**	**Plural**
1st: I have	We have	I had	We had	I shall have	We shall have
2nd: You have	You have	You had	You had	You will have	You will have
3rd: He/She/It/ Sue has	They/People have	He/She/It/ Sue had	They/People had	He/She/It/Sue will have	They/People will have

PRACTICE: **Recognizing the person and tense of the verb *have*.** Mark verbs, subjects, adjectives, adverbs, and prepositional phrases; label **D.O.**, **prep.**, **O.P.**, and **Appos.** In the blank following each sentence, write the person and tense of the verb; write **(Deter.)** or **(Fact)** after future tense. Abbreviations: **Pres.**, present; **Past**; **Fut.**, future; **pers.**, person; **s.**, singular; **pl.**, plural; **Deter.**, determination; **Fact.**

Example: The hikers will have an early breakfast. ___3rd pl., Fut. (Fact)___

1. I have my lunch in my locker. ___1st s., Pres.___
2. Jenny has plenty of time. ___3rd s., Pres.___
3. All of us will have lunch there. ___1st pl., Fut. (Deter.)___
4. You already had your turn. ___2nd s., Past___
5. Will your friends have dinner with us? ___3rd pl., Fut. (Fact)___
6. You and she have the lead roles. ___2nd pl., Pres.___
7. He and I will have our registration money. ___1st pl., Fut. (Deter.)___
8. They and we had a good doubles match. ___1st pl., Past___
9. Both Mom and Dad have several siblings. ___3rd pl., Pres.___
10. I will have my report tomorrow. ___1st s., Fut., (Deter.)___
11. At present, I have no solution to the problem. ___1st s., Pres.___
12. You officers had no suspicions? ___2nd pl., Past___
13. Won't the team have a game on that day? ___3rd s./pl., Fut. (Fact)___
14. Had he any choice in the matter? ___3rd s., Past___

Verbs—Perfect Tenses

Name _____

Date _____

REMEMBER:

1. **Perfect tenses** express completed (perfected) action, action completed at the present time, in the past, or in the future.

2. Perfect tenses use forms of the helping verb *have* with the past participle, the **-d** or **-ed** form, of the main verb.

SIMPLE TENSES OF *HAVE*

	Present		Past		Future	
	Singular	**Plural**	**Singular**	**Plural**	**Singular**	**Plural**
1st:	I have	We have	I had	We had	I shall have	We shall have
2nd:	You have	You have	You had	You had	You will have	You will have
3rd:	He/She/It/ Sue has	They/People have	He/She/It/ Sue had	They/People had	He/She/It/Sue will have	They/People will have

PRACTICE: **Recognizing the person and tense of the verb *have*.** Mark verbs, subjects, adjectives, adverbs, and prepositional phrases; label **D.O.**, **prep.**, **O.P.**, and **Appos.** In the blank following each sentence, write the person and tense of the verb; write **(Deter.)** or **(Fact)** after future tense. Abbreviations: **Pres.**, present; **Past**; **Fut.**, future; **pers.**, person; **s.**, singular; **pl.**, plural; **Deter.**, determination; **Fact.**

Example: (The) hikers will have (an) (early) breakfast. 3ʳᵈ pl., Fut. (Fact) ____

1. I have my lunch in my locker. _____

2. Jenny has plenty of time. _____

3. All of us will have lunch there. _____

4. You already had your turn. _____

5. Will your friends have dinner with us? _____

6. You and she have the lead roles. _____

7. He and I will have our registration money. _____

8. They and we had a good doubles match. _____

9. Both Mom and Dad have several siblings. _____

10. I will have my report tomorrow. _____

11. At present, I have no solution to the problem. _____

12. You officers had no suspicions? _____

13. Won't the team have a game on that day? _____

14. Had he any choice in the matter? _____

Using Perfect Tenses of Verbs

Emphasize the following:

1. The *present*, *past*, and *future* of the perfect tenses refer to the present, past, and future of the *helping verb*.

2. *Perfect* refers to the *-d* or *-ed* form, the past participle, of the *main verb*.

If needed, write this explanation on the chalkboard or overhead:

Present	Today I <u>have</u> the book.	Today I <u>have returned</u> the book.
"Today"	(Present)	(Present Perfect)
Past	Yesterday I <u>had</u> the book.	Yesterday I <u>had returned</u> the book.
"Yesterday"	(Past)	(Past Perfect)
Future	Tomorrow I <u>shall have</u> the book.	By tomorrow I <u>shall have returned</u> the book.
"Tomorrow"	(Future)	(Future Perfect)

In Practice A point out that in the Future Perfect column, the typed verbs, *left*, *eaten*, *written*, and *tried*, are irregular verbs in the past participle form.

Answers to Practices A and B may vary.

Using Perfect Tenses of Verbs

REMEMBER:

1. **Perfect tenses** express completed (perfected) action, action completed at this time, in the past, or in the future.

2. **Perfect tenses** use tenses of the helping verb **have** with the past participle, the **-d** or **-ed** form, of the main verb.

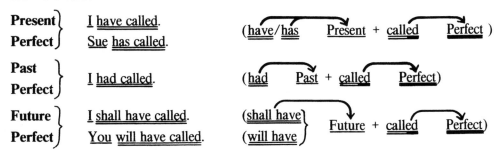

Present **Perfect**	I <u>have called</u>. Sue <u>has called</u>.	(have/has Present + called Perfect)
Past **Perfect**	I <u>had called</u>.	(had Past + called Perfect)
Future **Perfect**	I <u>shall have called</u>. You <u>will have called</u>.	(shall have) (will have) Future + called Perfect)

PRACTICE A: In the blank in each line, write the correct tense of the helping verb or the past participle of your choice of a main verb.

Present Perfect (action completed *at this time*)		**Past Perfect** (action completed in the *past*)		**Future Perfect** (action completed in the *future*)	
Helper	*Main Verb*	*Helper*	*Main Verb*	*Helper*	*Main Verb*
I have	gone.	I had	suggested.	I shall have	moved.
You *have*	pretended.	You *had*	suspected.	You *will have*	left.
She has	*(departed)* .	He had	*(regretted)* .	It will have	*(ceased)* .
John *has*	considered.	Kay *had*	finished.	Sue *will have*	eaten.
We have	*(returned)* .	We had	*(rejoiced)* .	We shall have	*(chosen)* .
You *have*	surmised.	You *had*	refused.	You *will have*	written.
They have	*(arrived)* .	They had	*(hiked)* .	They will have	*(gone)* .
Farmers *have*	plowed.	Everyone *had*	voted.	Some *will have*	tried.

PRACTICE B: Mark verbs, subjects, adjectives, adverbs, and prepositional phrases; label **D.O.**, **prep**, **O.P.**, and **Appos**. In the blank, write an appropriate perfect tense helping verb; at the end of the sentence, write the person and tense of the completed verb.

1. Jeremy ___*had*___ arrived [late][yesterday]. *3rd sing., Past Perfect*

2. [Surely] (the) plane ___*will have*___ landed (by now). *3rd sing., Future Perfect (fact)*

3. Mother and I ___*have*___ finalized (our) plans. *1st pl., Present Perfect*

4. ___*Have/Had*___ you girls received (your) awards? *2nd pl., Present/Past Perfect*

5. I ___*will have*___ made [up] (my) mind (by tomorrow). *1st sing., Future Perfect (deter)*

Name _____

Date _____

Using Perfect Tenses of Verbs

REMEMBER:

1. **Perfect tenses** express completed (perfected) action, action completed at this time, in the past, or in the future.

2. **Perfect tenses** use tenses of the helping verb **have** with the past participle, the **-d** or **-ed** form, of the main verb.

Present Perfect I have called. Sue has called. (have/has Present + called Perfect)

Past Perfect I had called. (had Past + called Perfect)

Future Perfect I shall have called. You will have called. (shall have) (will have) Future + called Perfect)

PRACTICE A: In the blank in each line, write the correct tense of the helping verb or the past participle of your choice of a main verb.

Present Perfect (action completed *at this time*)	Past Perfect (action completed in the *past*)	Future Perfect (action completed in the *future*)
Helper Main Verb	*Helper Main Verb*	*Helper Main Verb*
I have gone.	I had suggested.	I shall have moved.
You _____ pretended.	You _____ suspected.	You _____ left.
She has _____ .	He had _____ .	It will have _____ .
John ____ considered.	Kay _____ finished.	Sue _____ eaten.
We have _____ .	We had _____ .	We shall have_____ .
You _____ surmised.	You _____ refused.	You _____ written.
They have _____ .	They had _____ .	They will have_____ .
Farmers ____ plowed.	Everyone ____ voted.	Some _____ tried.

PRACTICE B: Mark verbs, subjects, adjectives, adverbs, and prepositional phrases; label **D.O.**, **prep**, **O.P.**, and **Appos**. In the blank, write an appropriate perfect tense helping verb; at the end of the sentence, write the person and tense of the completed verb.

1. Jeremy _____ arrived late yesterday. _____

2. Surely the plane _____ landed by now. _____

3. Mother and I _____ finalized our plans. _____

4. _____ you girls received your awards? _____

5. I _____ made up my mind by tomorrow. _____

Using Simple and Perfect Tenses of Verbs

Remind students:

Sentence 8: Think *they* in choosing the correct verb for a compound subject joined by *and*.

Sentence 14: With a compound subject joined by *or*, the part of the subject nearer the verb determines the correct verb form.

The material covered on pages 208, 211, and 214 had been studied in *Steps to Good Grammar*.

The class should work together carefully on page 217 so that each students has a completely correct paper to review, along with information pages 208, 211, and 214, to prepare for the Test on page 220.

Using Simple and Perfect
Tenses of Verbs

Instructions: Draw one line under the subject. In the blank(s), using the tense given, write the verb shown in parentheses. Abbreviations: **Pres.**, present; **Past**; **Fut.**, future; **S.**, simple; **Perf.**, perfect; **Fact**; **Deter.**, determination.

1. The girls *plan* to study computer science. (*plan*, S. Pres.)

2. Fran quickly *finished* the assignment. (*finish*, S. Past)

3. You *shall clean* your room! (*clean*, S. Fut. Deter.)

4. Finally, we *have completed* our project. (*complete*, Pres. Perf.)

5. Stu *had* carelessly *dropped* the dish. (*drop*, Past Perf.)

6. By then, you *will have landed* in Atlanta. (*land*, Fut. Perf. Fact)

7. I certainly *will play* in the tournament! (*play*, S. Fut. Deter.)

8. Mandy and she *want* dessert now. (*want*, S. Pres.)

9. *Had* both of you already *changed* into your costumes?
(*change*, Past Perf.)

10. We *will have decided* by noon tomorrow. (*decide*, Fut. Perf. Deter.)

11. *Has* the mail *arrived* yet? (*arrive*, Pres. Perf.)

12. The secretary *will* already *have distributed* the mail.
(*distribute*, Fut. Perf. Fact)

13. We *hiked* quickly up the trail. (*hike*, S. Past)

14. Mom or Dad usually *drives* us to school. (*drive*, S. Pres.)

15. The boys *had carried* the joke too far. (*carry*, Past Perf.)

16. We *will discuss* our plans after lunch. (*discuss*, S. Fut. Deter.)

17. Where *have* they *built* their cabin? (*build*, Pres. Perf.)

18. Probably you all *will have left* the school by then. (*leave*, Fut. Perf. Fact)

19. The storm *raged* violently outside. (*rage*, S. Past)

20. I *had* already *accepted* the invitation. (*accept*, Past Perf.)

Using Simple and Perfect Tenses of Verbs

Name _____

Date _____

Instructions: Draw one line under the subject. In the blank(s), using the tense given, write the verb shown in parentheses. Abbreviations: **Pres.**, present; **Past**; **Fut.**, future; **S.**, simple; **Perf.**, perfect; **Fact**; **Deter.**, determination.

1. The girls _____ to study computer science. (*plan*, S. Pres.)

2. Fran quickly _____ the assignment. (*finish*, S. Past)

3. You _____ your room! (*clean*, S. Fut. Deter.)

4. Finally, we _____ our project. (*complete*, Pres. Perf.)

5. Stu _____ carelessly _____ the dish. (*drop*, Past Perf.)

6. By then, you _____ in Atlanta. (*land*, Fut. Perf. Fact)

7. I certainly _____ in the tournament! (*play*, S. Fut. Deter.)

8. Mandy and she _____ dessert now. (*want*, S. Pres.)

9. _____ both of you already _____ into your costumes?
   (*change*, Past Perf.)

10. We _____ by noon tomorrow. (*decide*, Fut. Perf. Deter.)

11. _____ the mail _____ yet? (*arrive*, Pres. Perf.)

12. The secretary _____ already_____ the mail.
    (*distribute*, Fut. Perf. Fact)

13. We _____ quickly up the trail. (*hike*, S. Past)

14. Mom or Dad usually _____ us to school. (*drive*, S. Pres.)

15. The boys _____ the joke too far. (*carry*, Past Perf.)

16. We_____ our plans after lunch. (*discuss*, S. Fut. Deter.)

17. Where _____ they _____ their cabin? (*build*, Pres. Perf.)

18. Probably you all _____ the school by then. (*leave*, Fut. Perf. Fact)

19. The storm _____ violently outside. (*rage*, S. Past)

20. I _____ already _____ the invitation. (*accept*, Past Perf.)

Understanding and Using Good Grammar

TEST: Using Simple and Perfect Tenses of Verbs

Advise students to draw one line under the subject to help them to determine the correct verb words to write.

In grading the Tests give 1 point to helping verbs: *has, have, had, will/shall have*. There are 20 points which equal 5% each.

TEST: Using Simple and Perfect Tenses of Verbs

Instructions: In the blank(s), write, in the tense indicated, the verb shown in parentheses. Abbreviations: **Pres.**, present; **Past**; **Fut.**, future; **S.**, simple; **Perf.**, perfect; **Fact**; **Deter.**, Determination.

1. _Will_ the parade _proceed_ down Main Street? (*proceed*, S. Fut. Fact)

2. The noise _had interrupted_ my train of thought. (*interrupt*, Past Perf.)

3. Everyone _changes_ his or her mind occasionally. (*change*, S. Pres.)

4. Our problems in math _have become_ quite difficult. (*become*, Pres. Perf.)

5. Grandmother obviously _expected_ us for dinner. (*expect*, S. Past)

6. Before the end of the play, everyone in the cast _will have appeared_ on stage. (*appear*, Fut. Perf. Fact)

7. Fortunately, the class _took_ the warning seriously. (*take*, S. Past)

8. _Has_n't either of them _announced_ the date of the dance? (*announce*, Pres. Perf.)

9. I certainly _will study_ for the test. (*study*, S. Fut. Deter.)

10. A violent windstorm _had preceded_ the torrential downpour. (*precede*, Past Perf.)

11. According to Mom, my brothers _shall have cleaned_ their room before dinner! (*clean*, Fut. Perf. Deter.)

12. Actually, most teenagers _accept_ commonsense advice quite willingly. (*accept*, S. Pres.)

Name _____

Date _____

TEST: Using Simple and Perfect Tenses of Verbs

Instructions: In the blank(s), write, in the tense indicated, the verb shown in parentheses. Abbreviations: **Pres.**, present; **Past**; **Fut.**, future; **S.**, simple; **Perf.**, perfect; **Fact**; **Deter.**, Determination.

1. _____ the parade _____ down Main Street? (*proceed*, S. Fut. Fact)

2. The noise _____ my train of thought. (*interrupt*, Past Perf.)

3. Everyone _____ his or her mind occasionally. (*change*, S. Pres.)

4. Our problems in math _____ quite difficult. (*become*, Pres. Perf.)

5. Grandmother obviously _____ us for dinner. (*expect*, S. Past)

6. Before the end of the play, everyone in the cast _____ on stage. (*appear*, Fut. Perf. Fact)

7. Fortunately, the class _____ the warning seriously. (*take*, S. Past)

8. _____n't either of them_____ the date of the dance? (*announce*, Pres. Perf.)

9. I certainly _____ for the test. (*study*, S. Fut. Deter.)

10. A violent windstorm _____ the torrential downpour. (*precede*, Past Perf.)

11. According to Mom, my brothers_____ their room before dinner! (*clean*, Fut. Perf. Deter.)

12. Actually, most teenagers _____ commonsense advice quite willingly. (*accept*, S. Pres.)

Simple Progressive Forms
of Verb Tenses

IMPORTANT: Pages 221–238 present study of progressive and emphatic verb forms. You may decide to use this material only with very capable students who will find it to be an interesting challenge.

As students read silently, read aloud the instructional material which describes the progressive forms. Reiterate that the terms *present, past,* and *future* refer to the simple tenses of the helping verb *be*. Demonstrate this fact as you read the conjugations.

Students should know the conjugation of the simple tenses of *be*. For homework assign memorizing the forms. Tell students they will be required to write them perfectly the next day.

Emphasize using the days related to the tenses:

[Today] I am calling all my friends. (Simple present of *be*: *is, am, are*)

[Yesterday] I was calling . . . (Simple past of *be*: *was, were*)

[Tomorrow] I shall be calling . . . (Simple future of *be*: *shall/will be*)

In the Practice tell students to triple underline the helping verb and the *-ing* at the end of the main verb to focus attention on the makeup of the tenses.

This page should be added to the students' collection of information sheets.

Simple Progressive Forms of Verb Tenses

Progressive forms express **action in progress** at the time referred to—in the past, in the present, or in the future.

To form the **simple progressive**, use forms of the verb **be** as helpers before the present participle (the **-ing** form) of the main verb.

CONJUGATION—SIMPLE TENSES OF *BE*

	Present Today		**Past** Yesterday		**Future** Tomorrow	
Person	*Singular*	*Plural*	*Singular*	*Plural*	*Singular*	*Plural*
1st:	I am	We are	I was	We were	I shall be	We shall be
2nd:	You are	You are	You were	You were	You will be	You will be
3rd:	He is	They are	He was	They were	He will be	They will be

CONJUGATION OF *CALL*—SIMPLE PROGRESSIVE FORMS

Present Progressive	**Past Progressive**	**Future Progressive**
I am calling	I was calling	I shall be calling
You are calling	You were calling	I will be calling
He/She/It is calling	He was calling	He will be calling
We are calling	We were calling	We shall be calling
You are calling	You were calling	You will be calling
They/People are calling	They were calling	They will be calling

PRACTICE: Mark verbs, subjects, adjectives, adverbs, and prepositional phrases; label **D.O.**, **prep.**, **O.P.**, and **Appos.** At the end of each sentence, write the person (**1st, 2nd, 3rd, s., pl.**) and tense (**Pres. Prog., Past Prog., Future Prog.**); indicate the use of *shall* and *will* (**Fact**) or (**Deter.**), for determination.

Example: We will be attending (the) dance (on Friday) 1st pl., Fut. Prog. (Deter.)

1. I am enrolling (in (drama) class) today 1st s., Pres. Prog.

2. They will be walking [home] (after school) 3rd pl., Fut. Prog. (Fact)

3. Was Josh planning (an) (overnight) hike? 3rd s., Past Prog.

4. Gloria and I shall be auditioning [tomorrow] 1st pl., Fut. Prog. (Fact)

5. [Why] were you boys talking (to (the) principal)? 2nd pl., Past Prog.

6. I will, [indeed], be arriving (on time) [tomorrow] 1st s., Fut. Prog. (Deter)

7. You shall be improving (your) grades, or I shall be grounding you.
   2nd s., Fut. Prog. (Deter.)   1st s., Fut. Prog. (Fact)

Simple Progressive Forms of Verb Tenses

Name _____

Date _____

Progressive forms express **action in progress** at the time referred to—in the past, in the present, or in the future.

To form the **simple progressive**, use forms of the verb **be** as helpers before the present participle (the **-ing** form) of the main verb.

CONJUGATION—SIMPLE TENSES OF *BE*

	Present Today		**Past** Yesterday		**Future** Tomorrow	
Person	*Singular*	*Plural*	*Singular*	*Plural*	*Singular*	*Plural*
1st:	I am	We are	I was	We were	I shall be	We shall be
2nd:	You are	You are	You were	You were	You will be	You will be
3rd:	He is	They are	He was	They were	He will be	They will be

CONJUGATION OF *CALL*—SIMPLE PROGRESSIVE FORMS

Present Progressive	**Past Progressive**	**Future Progressive**
I am calling	I was calling	I shall be calling
You are calling	You were calling	I will be calling
He/She/It is calling	He was calling	He will be calling
We are calling	We were calling	We shall be calling
You are calling	You were calling	You will be calling
They/People are calling	They were calling	They will be calling

PRACTICE: Mark verbs, subjects, adjectives, adverbs, and prepositional phrases; label **D.O.**, **prep.**, **O.P.**, and **Appos.** At the end of each sentence, write the person (**1st, 2nd, 3rd, s., pl.**) and tense (**Pres. Prog., Past Prog., Future Prog.**); indicate the use of *shall* and *will* (**Fact**) or (**Deter.**), for determination.

Example: We will be attending the dance on Friday. 1st pl., Fut. Prog. (Deter.)

1. I am enrolling in drama class today. _____

2. They will be walking home after school. _____

3. Was Josh planning an overnight hike? _____

4. Gloria and I shall be auditioning tomorrow. _____

5. Why were you boys talking to the principal? _____

6. I will, indeed, be arriving on time tomorrow. _____

7. You shall be improving your grades, or I shall be grounding you.

_____   _____

Understanding and Using Good Grammar

Perfect Progressive Forms
of Verb Tenses

Write the following on the chalkboard if students need help in understanding the formation of perfect progressive forms:

1. Simple tenses of *have*	*Present* have/has	*Past* had	*Future* shall/will have
2. Principle parts of *be*	*Present* be	*Pres. Participle* being	*Past Participle* (used in perfect tenses) been
3. Perfect tenses of *be*	*Pres. Perf.* have been	*Past Perf.* had been	*Future Perf.* will have been
4. Perfect progressive of *call*	*Pres. Perf. Prog.* have been calli*ng*	*Past Perf. Prog.* had been calli*ng*	*Future Perf. Prog.* will have been calli*ng*

In sentences 7, 9, and 10 point out that the verbs are simple progressive, not perfect progressive.

Perfect Progressive Forms
of Verb Tenses

Perfect progressive forms express action going on at the time referred to. To form the perfect progressive use the past participle of *be* (**been**) before the present participle (the **-ing** form) of the main verb.

PERFECT TENSES OF *BE*

Present Perfect	Past Perfect	Future Perfect
have/has been	had been	shall/will have been

PERFECT PROGRESSIVE FORMS OF *CALL*

Present Perfect Prog.	Past Perfect Prog.	Future Perfect Prog.
have been calling (I/You/We/They/People)	had been calling (used with all persons, singular and plural)	shall have been calling (I/We)
has been calling (He/She/It/John)		will have been calling (You/He/She/It/John/They/People)

PRACTICE: Mark verbs, subjects, adjectives, adverbs, and prepositional phrases; label **D.O.**, **prep.**, **O.P.**, **Appos.**, and **N.A.** (noun of address). At the end of each sentence, write the person (**1st, 2nd, 3rd, s., pl.**) and tense (**S.** or **Pres. Perf. Prog., Past Prog.,** or **Fut. Prog.**); indicate the use of *shall* and *will* (**Fact**) or (**Deter.**), for determination.

Example: Had Mark [really] been washing (the) car? 3rd s., Past Perf. Prog.

1. We had been playing tennis [regularly]. 1st pl., Past Perf. Prog.

2. Have you girls been planning (a) party? 2nd pl., Pres. Perf. Prog.

3. (By noon), I shall have been practicing (for (two) hours) 1st s., Fut. Perf. Prog. (Fact)

4. Jeff has been wishing (for (a) car) 3rd s., Pres. Perf. Prog.

5. Had (the) (band) members been decorating (the) float? 3rd pl., Past Perf. Prog.

6. Dad will have been waiting (for us) (for (an) hour) 3rd s., Fut. Perf. Prog. (Fact)

7. Dylan and I shall be walking (to school) 1st pl., S Fut. Prog. (Fact)

8. Have you and Leonardo been baking cookies [today]? 2nd pl. Pres Perf. Prog

9. Jen and Chris, [why] are you looking (out (the) window)? 2nd pl., S Pres. Prog.

10. Were you talking (to him) (on (the) bus)? 2nd s., S. Past Prog.

Name _____

Date _____

Perfect Progressive Forms of Verb Tenses

Perfect progressive forms express action going on at the time referred to. To form the perfect progressive use the past participle of *be* (**been**) before the present participle (the **-ing** form) of the main verb.

PERFECT TENSES OF *BE*

Present Perfect	Past Perfect	Future Perfect
have/has been	had been	shall/will have been

PERFECT PROGRESSIVE FORMS OF *CALL*

Present Perfect Prog.	Past Perfect Prog.	Future Perfect Prog.
have been calling (I/You/We/They/People) has been calling (He/She/It/John)	had been calling (used with all persons, singular and plural)	shall have been calling (I/We) will have been calling (You/He/She/It/John/They/People)

PRACTICE: Mark verbs, subjects, adjectives, adverbs, and prepositional phrases; label **D.O.**, **prep.**, **O.P.**, **Appos.**, and **N.A.** (noun of address). At the end of each sentence, write the person (**1st, 2nd, 3rd, s., pl.**) and tense (**S.** or **Pres. Perf. Prog., Past Prog.,** or **Fut. Prog.**); indicate the use of *shall* and *will* (**Fact**) or (**Deter.**), for determination.

Example: Had Mark [really] been washing (the) car? 3rd sing., Past Perf. Prog.

1. We had been playing tennis regularly. _____

2. Have you girls been planning a party? _____

3. By noon, I shall have been practicing for two hours. _____

4. Jeff has been wishing for a car. _____

5. Had the band members been decorating the float? _____

6. Dad will have been waiting for us for an hour. _____

7. Dylan and I shall be walking to school. _____

8. Have you and Leonardo been baking cookies today? _____

9. Jen and Chris, why are you looking out the window? _____

10. Were you talking to him on the bus? _____

Understanding and Using Good Grammar

Verbs—Emphatic Forms and Unit Review

Point out that the emphatic form can be expressed only in the present and past simple tenses. "I do be calling" or "he did have run" are meaningless. Students easily understand the emphatic form; therefore, very little practice in recognizing its use is given.

As you confirm the sentence analysis given by volunteers, students should carefully check their work to be sure that they have a correct sheet to study from in preparing for a test on this unit. This is especially true of the Review section.

Verbs—Emphatic Forms and Unit Review

Emphatic forms are used to express emphasis or insistence regarding the verb. The helping verbs **do/does** are used before the main verb in the present tense. *Did* is used before the main verb to show past tense.

I/You/We/They <u>do call</u> frequently.   He/She/It/John <u>does call</u> frequently.

All persons, singular and plural, use *did* to show past tense.

I <u>did call</u> yesterday.   You <u>did call</u> yesterday.   People <u>did call</u>.

PRACTICE: Mark verbs, subjects, adjectives, and adverbs; label **D.O.** and **Appos.** At the end of each sentence, write the person and tense of the verb. Use abbreviations: **1st, 2nd, 3rd, s., pl., Pres., Past, Emph.** (emphatic).

1. Dad [certainly] <u>does walk</u> [fast].
   3ʳᵈ s., Pres. Emph.

2. [Usually], Jacob and Isaac <u>do</u>
   <u>finish</u> (their) homework. _3ʳᵈ pl., Pres._
   Emph.

REVIEW: Underline the verb twice and the subject once. At the end of each sentence, write the tense of the verb. Use abbreviations: **S.** (Simple), **Perf., Pres., Past, Fut., Prog. Emph.**; indicate **(Fact)** or **(Deter.)** for *shall* or *will*.

3. [Actually], I <u>didn't</u> <u>wait</u> [very]
   [long]. _1ˢᵗ s., Past Emph._

4. You boys [really] <u>do play</u> [very]
   [well]. _2ⁿᵈ pl., Pres. Emph._

5. She and I <u>did serve</u> (our)
   detention. _1ˢᵗ pl., Past Emph._

1. Marc <u>plays</u> chess.
   S. Pres.

2. Erika <u>drew</u> that picture.
   S. Past

3. She and I <u>will sign</u> the
   petition. _S. Fut._   _(Deter.)_

4. Jesse <u>has arrived</u> on time.
   Pres. Perf.

5. Several students <u>had</u> already
   <u>left</u>. _Past Perf._

6. Mother <u>will have prepared</u> lunch
   by now.
   Fut. Perf.   (Fact)

7. Are you <u>leaving</u> already?
   S. Pres. Prog.

8. Russell <u>will be handing</u> in his
   report.
   S. Fut. Prog. (Fact)

9. The dog <u>was</u> just <u>barking</u> at
   the moon.
   S. Past Prog.

10. That girl really <u>does enjoy</u>
    gymnastics.
    Pres. Emph.

11. Our team <u>did win</u>!
    Past Emph.

12. Do you <u>believe</u> him?
    Pres. Emph.

13. I <u>shall have finished</u> on time.
    Fut. Perf.   (Fact)

14. That family <u>has inherited</u> a
    fortune.
    Pres. Perf.

15. Art <u>answered</u> the question.
    S. Past

16. Alestra <u>had been writing</u>.
    Past Perf. Prog.

17. Paula <u>did finish</u> her essay.
    Past Emph.

18. Angela <u>was borrowing</u> a book.
    S. Past Prog.

19. Will Sara <u>change</u> her mind?
    S. Fut.   (Fact)

20. I <u>do like</u> dessert!
    Pres. Emph.

Verbs—Emphatic Forms and Unit Review

Name _____

Date _____

Emphatic forms are used to express emphasis or insistence regarding the verb. The helping verbs **do/does** are used before the main verb in the present tense. *Did* is used before the main verb to show past tense.

I/You/We/They <u>do call</u> frequently.   He/She/It/John <u>does call</u> frequently.

All persons, singular and plural, use *did* to show past tense.

I <u>did call</u> yesterday.   You <u>did call</u> yesterday.   People <u>did call</u>.

PRACTICE: Mark verbs, subjects, adjectives, and adverbs; label **D.O.** and **Appos.** At the end of each sentence, write the person and tense of the verb. Use abbreviations: **1st, 2nd, 3rd, s., pl., Pres., Past, Emph.** (emphatic).

1. Dad certainly does walk fast.
   _____

2. Usually, Jacob and Isaac do finish their homework. _____

3. Actually, I didn't wait very long. _____

4. You boys really do play very well. _____

5. She and I did serve our detention. _____

REVIEW: Underline the verb twice and the subject once. At the end of each sentence, write the tense of the verb. Use abbreviations: **S.** (Simple), **Perf., Pres., Past, Fut., Prog. Emph.**; indicate (**Fact**) or (**Deter.**) for *shall* or *will*.

1. Marc plays chess.
   _____

2. Erika drew that picture.
   _____

3. She and I will sign the petition. _____

4. Jesse has arrived on time.
   _____

5. Several students had already left. _____

6. Mother will have prepared lunch by now.
   _____

7. Are you leaving already?
   _____

8. Russell will be handing in his report. _____

9. The dog was just barking at the moon.
   _____

10. That girl really does enjoy gymnastics.
    _____

11. Our team did win!
    _____

12. Do you believe him?
    _____

13. I shall have finished on time.
    _____

14. That family has inherited a fortune.
    _____

15. Art answered the question.
    _____

16. Alestra had been writing.
    _____

17. Paula did finish her essay.
    _____

18. Angela was borrowing a book.
    _____

19. Will Sara change her mind?
    _____

20. I do like dessert!
    _____

Understanding and Using Good Grammar

REVIEW: Simple and Perfect Verb Tenses; Progressive and Emphatic Forms

Many students have difficulty in understanding the makeup of the perfect progressive form. Copy this analysis on the overhead or chalkboard. Explain each step carefully and instruct the students to copy it on the back of the worksheet. For some, this final demonstration may turn on the light of understanding.

PERFECT PROGRESSIVE

Simple Tenses of *have*	Past Participle of *be*: been	Present Participle of *call*: calling
PRESENT: – → have/has – – – – – –	PERFECT: → been – – – – – –	PROGRESSIVE: → calling
PAST: – – – → had – – – – – – – – –	PERFECT: → been – – – – – –	PROGRESSIVE: → calling
FUTURE: – → shall/will have – – –	PERFECT: → been – – – – – –	PROGRESSIVE: → calling

Say: Have/has makes it present; been makes it perfect; -ing makes it progressive.

   PRESENT PERFECT PROGRESSIVE: have/has been calling

REVIEW: Simple and Perfect Verb Tenses; Progressive and Emphatic Forms

Simple tenses have helpers only with the future tense:

Pres.: call, calls
Past: call<u>ed</u>
Fut.: shall/will call

Perfect tenses: Simple tenses of *have* are used before past participle *called*:

Pres. Perf.: have/has call<u>ed</u>
Past Perf.: had call<u>ed</u>
Fut. Perf.: shall/will have call<u>ed</u>

Simple Progressive: Simple tenses of *be* are used before present participle:

Pres. Prog.: is/am/are call*ing*
Past Prog.: was/were call*ing*
Fut. Prog.: shall/will be call*ing*

Perfect Progressive: Tenses of *have* are used before the past participle *been*, which is followed by the present participle:

Pres. Perf. Prog.: have/has *been* call*ing*
Past Perf. Prog.: had *been* call*ing*
Fut. Perf. Prog.: shall/will have *been* call*ing*

Emphatic forms are used to show emphasis or insistence.

Pres. Emph.: *do/does* call | *Past Emph.*: *did* call

PRACTICE: In the following sentences, underline the verb twice and subject once; above the verb, write the tense. Following each sentence, in the blank provided, write the verb in the required tense.

Example: My <u>grandparents</u> <u>live</u> nearby. [S. Pres.] Pres. Perf. _have lived_

Pres. Emph. _do live_   Pres. Prog. _are living_

Pres. Perf. Prog. _have been living_

1. <u>I</u> <u>wax</u> the floors. [S. Pres.] S. Fut. Deter. _will wax_   Pres. Emph. _do wax_

   Past Prog. _was waxing_   Past Perf. _had waxed_   Fut. Perf.

   Prog. _shall have been waxing_   S. Past _waxed_

2. <u>You</u> <u>aimed</u> at the target. [S. Past] Past Emph. _did aim_   Past Perf.

   Prog. _had been aiming_   Pres. Perf. _have aimed_   Pres.

   Prog. _are aiming_   Fut. Perf. _will have aimed_

3. <u>Mom and Dad</u> <u>will be leaving</u>. [S. Fut. Prog.] Fut. Perf. _will have left_   Pres. Emph. _do_

   leave   S. Past _left_   Past Prog. _were leaving_

4. <u>Pete</u> <u>dreaded</u> this meeting. [S. Past] S. Pres. _dreads_   Pres. Perf. Prog. _has_

   been dreading Fut. Prog. _will be dreading_ Past Perf. _had dreaded_

5. <u>Lisa</u> <u>reviewed</u> two books. [S. Past] Past Emph. _did review_   Pres.

   Prog. _is reviewing_   S. Fut. _will review_

   Past Perf. _had reviewed_

Name _____

Date _____

REVIEW: Simple and Perfect Verb Tenses; Progressive and Emphatic Forms

Simple tenses have helpers only with the future tense:

Pres.: call, calls
Past: call<u>ed</u>
Fut.: shall/will call

Perfect tenses: Simple tenses of *have* are used before past participle *called*:

Pres. Perf.: have/has call<u>ed</u>
Past Perf.: had call<u>ed</u>
Fut. Perf.: shall/will have call<u>ed</u>

Simple Progressive: Simple tenses of *be* are used before present participle:

Pres. Prog.: is/am/are call<u>ing</u>
Past Prog.: was/were call<u>ing</u>
Fut. Prog.: shall/will be call<u>ing</u>

Perfect Progressive: Tenses of *have* are used before the past participle *been*, which is followed by the present participle:

Pres. Perf. Prog.: have/has *been* call<u>ing</u>
Past Perf. Prog.: had *been* call<u>ing</u>
Fut. Perf. Prog.: shall/will have *been* call<u>ing</u>

Emphatic forms are used to show emphasis or insistence.

Pres. Emph.: *do/does* call | *Past Emph.*: *did* call

PRACTICE: In the following sentences, underline the verb twice and subject once; above the verb, write the tense. Following each sentence, in the blank provided, write the verb in the required tense.

Example: My grandparents *(S. Pres.)* live nearby. Pres. Perf. *have lived*

Pres. Emph. *do live*   Pres. Prog. *are living*

Pres. Perf. Prog. *have been living*

1. I wax the floors. S. Fut. Deter. _____   Pres. Emph. _____

Past Prog. _____   Past Perf. _____   Fut. Perf.

Prog. _____   S. Past _____

2. You aimed at the target. Past Emph. _____   Past Perf.

Prog. _____   Pres. Perf. _____   Pres.

Prog. _____   Fut. Perf. _____

3. Mom and Dad will be leaving. Fut. Perf. _____   Pres. Emph. _____

_____ S. Past _____   Past Prog. _____

4. Pete dreaded this meeting. S. Pres. _____   Pres. Perf. Prog. _____

_____ Fut. Prog. _____   Past Perf. _____

5. Lisa reviewed two books. Past Emph. _____   Pres.

Prog. _____   S. Fut. _____

Past Perf. _____

Understanding and Using Good Grammar

FINAL PRACTICE:
Simple and Perfect Verb Tenses; Progressive and Emphatic Forms

Since this is the Final Practice, you may want to have the class work together on sentences 1–8. Students could complete, individually, 9–17 as a self-test. When you read the correct forms, each could write corrections of any errors he or she may have made.

Sentence 3: *Mick* is a noun of address; the subject, *you*, requires the use of the helping verb *were*.

Sentences 16 and 17: *Everyone* and *none* are singular subjects which use the helping verbs *does* and *has*.

Students should use this page and page 232 to review for the Test on page 238.

FINAL PRACTICE:
Simple and Perfect Verb Tenses;
Progressive and Emphatic Forms

Instructions: In the blank(s), write, in the tense indicated, the verb shown in parentheses. Abbreviations: **Pres.**, present; **Past**; **Fut.**, future; **S.**, simple; **Perf.**, perfect; **Prog.**, progressive; **Emph.**, emphatic; **Fact**; **Deter.**, determination.

1. Usually, I _do finish_ my assignments. (*finish*, Pres. Emph.)

2. Soon, I _shall have been waiting_ for an hour for Edy. (*wait*, Fut. Perf. Prog., Fact)

3. Mick, what _were_ you _thinking_ about? (*think*, Past. Prog.)

4. Dad _has altered_ the itinerary for our trip. (*alter*, Pres. Perf.)

5. A wild storm _had been raging_ during the night. (*rage*, Past Perf. Prog.)

6. Tony usually _arrives_ promptly. (*arrive*, S. Pres.)

7. _Did_ Lucy _enroll_ in computer science? (*enroll*, Past Emph.)

8. Probably Mom _will give_ me her permission. (*give*, S. Fut., Fact)

9. Shannon _is entering_ the singles tournament. (*enter*, Pres. Prog.)

10. Some of the students _have been dreading_ this test. (*dread*, Pres. Perf. Prog.)

11. You certainly _shall have completed_ your homework before dinner!
(*complete*, Fut. Perf., Deter.)

12. The students _walked_ quickly down the stairs. (*walk*, S. Past)

13. _Shall_ we _be auditioning_ after school? (*audition*, Fut. Prog., Fact)

14. _Had_ you _done_ your report on time? (*do*, Past Perf.)

15. In spite of your pleas, we _will have_ the test tomorrow. (*have*, S. Fut., Deter.)

16. _Does_ every one of the students _intend_ to go? (*intend*, Pres. Emph.)

17. _Has_ none of the students _brought_ the permission slip?
(*bring*, Pres. Perf.)

FINAL PRACTICE: Simple and Perfect Verb Tenses; Progressive and Emphatic Forms

Name _____

Date _____

Instructions: In the blank(s), write, in the tense indicated, the verb shown in parentheses. Abbreviations: **Pres.**, present; **Past**; **Fut.**, future; **S.**, simple; **Perf.**, perfect; **Prog.**, progressive; **Emph.**, emphatic; **Fact**; **Deter.**, determination.

1. Usually, I_____ my assignments. (*finish*, Pres. Emph.)

2. Soon, I _____ for an hour for Edy. (*wait*, Fut. Perf. Prog., Fact)

3. Mick, what _____ you _____ about? (*think*, Past. Prog.)

4. Dad _____ the itinerary for our trip. (*alter*, Pres. Perf.)

5. A wild storm _____ during the night. (*rage*, Past Perf. Prog.)

6. Tony usually_____ promptly. (*arrive*, S. Pres.)

7. _____ Lucy_____ in computer science? (*enroll*, Past Emph.)

8. Probably Mom_____ me her permission. (*give*, S. Fut., Fact)

9. Shannon _____ the singles tournament. (*enter*, Pres. Prog.)

10. Some of the students _____this test. (*dread*, Pres. Perf. Prog.)

11. You certainly _____ your homework before dinner!
    (*complete*, Fut. Perf., Deter.)

12. The students _____ quickly down the stairs. (*walk*, S. Past)

13. _____ we _____ after school? (*audition*, Fut. Prog., Fact)

14. _____ you _____ your report on time? (*do*, Past Perf.)

15. In spite of your pleas, we_____the test tomorrow. (*have*, S. Fut., Deter.)

16. _____ every one of the students _____ to go? (*intend*,
    Pres. Emph.)

17. _____ none of the students _____ the permission slip?
    (*bring*, Pres. Perf.)

Understanding and Using Good Grammar

TEST: Simple and Perfect Verb Tenses; Progressive and Emphatic Forms

Suggested Grading:

Give each helping verb 1 point; also, count as 1 point the two words required to express future tense in Sentences 7 (shall have); 13 (shall be); 15 (will have); 16 (shall be).

In all, count 17 helping verbs and 16 main verbs, a total of 33 points. Deduct 3% for each error.

TEST: Simple and Perfect
Verb Tenses; Progressive
and Emphatic Forms

Instructions: In the blank(s), write, in the tense indicated, the verb shown in parentheses. Abbreviations: **Pres.**, present; **Past; Fut.**, future; **S.**, simple; **Perf.**, perfect; **Prog.**, progressive; **Emph.**, emphatic; **Fact; Deter.**, determination.

1. I *have* already *finished* my chores. (*finish*, Pres. Perf.)

2. This torrential rain *has been falling* for hours. (*fall*, Pres. Perf. Prog.)

3. Devon *enrolled* in computer science yesterday. (*enroll*, S. Past)

4. We *will* probably *alter* the itinerary for our trip. (*alter*, S. Fut. Deter.)

5. Mick, what *had* you *been thinking* about? (*think*, Past Perf. Prog.)

6. *Does* Tony usually *arrive* promptly? (*arrive*, Pres. Emph.)

7. By noon, I *shall have been studying* for two hours. (*study*, Fut. Perf. Prog., Fact)

8. Fortunately, Mom *is giving* me her permission. (*give*, Pres. Prog.)

9. Every one of the students *was intending* to go. (*intend*, Past Prog.)

10. Some of the students *had dreaded* this test. (*dread*, Past Perf.)

11. I *will hand* in my report tomorrow. (*hand*, S. Fut., Deter.)

12. Most of the students *did enjoy* the concert. (*enjoy*, Past Emph.)

13. *Shall* they *be auditioning* after school? (*audition*, Fut. Prog., Deter.)

14. That girl always *wears* stylish clothes. (*wear*, S. Pres.)

15. The district office *will have closed* by now. (*close*, Fut. Perf., Fact)

16. Kirsten and I *shall be leaving* early. (*leave*, Fut. Prog., Fact)

Name _____

Date _____

TEST: Simple and Perfect Verb Tenses; Progressive and Emphatic Forms

Instructions: In the blank(s), write, in the tense indicated, the verb shown in parentheses. Abbreviations: **Pres.**, present; **Past**; **Fut.**, future; **S.**, simple; **Perf.**, perfect; **Prog.**, progressive; **Emph.**, emphatic; **Fact**; **Deter.**, determination.

1. I _____ already_____ my chores. (*finish*, Pres. Perf.)

2. This torrential rain _____ for hours. (*fall*, Pres. Perf. Prog.)

3. Devon_____ in computer science yesterday. (*enroll*, S. Past)

4. We_____ probably_____ the itinerary for our trip. (*alter*, S. Fut. Deter.)

5. Mick, what _____ you_____ about? (*think*, Past Perf. Prog.)

6. _____ Tony usually _____ promptly? (*arrive*, Pres. Emph.)

7. By noon, I _____ for two hours. (*study*, Fut. Perf. Prog., Fact)

8. Fortunately, Mom_____ me her permission. (*give*, Pres. Prog.)

9. Every one of the students _____ to go. (*intend*, Past Prog.)

10. Some of the students _____ this test. (*dread*, Past Perf.)

11. I _____ in my report tomorrow. (*hand*, S. Fut., Deter.)

12. Most of the students _____ the concert. (*enjoy*, Past Emph.)

13. _____ they _____ after school? (*audition*, Fut. Prog., Deter.)

14. That girl always _____ stylish clothes. (*wear*, S. Pres.)

15. The district office_____by now. (*close*, Fut. Perf., Fact)

16. Kirsten and I _____early. (*leave*, Fut. Prog., Fact)

Understanding and Using Good Grammar

Gerunds and Gerund Phrases

Emphasize strongly that possessive nouns and pronouns are correctly used before a gerund. People frequently use incorrectly an objective pronoun or a plain noun in that position:

Because of (~~Jon~~, Jon's) and (~~me~~, my) arriving so late . . . .

The possessives, *Jon's* and *my*, tell *whose* arriving was so late.

For part *B* inform students that because a gerund is a verbal, a noun derived from a verb, it may have complements or modifiers that make up a gerund phrase. In the example:

(Lisa's) winning (the) election) didn't surprise anyone.

The verb is did surprise; the one-word subject is winning; the direct object of the gerund, *winning*, is *election*; the adjective that tells "whose" about the gerund is (Lisa's). The gerund phrase, Lisa's winning the election, is the complete subject of the sentence. Point out to students that this is shown by the customary (subject) single line drawn under it.

Gerunds and Gerund Phrases

DEFINITION: A **gerund** is a verb form, the present participle ending in **-ing**, that is used as a noun. (To be labeled: **Ger.**)

A. A **gerund** may be used in the same sentence parts as a noun may be.

1. *Subject:* Snowboarding is a popular new sport.
2. *Direct Object:* I really enjoy snowboarding.
3. *Linking Verb Complement:* My favorite sport is snowboarding.
4. *Object of Preposition:* I give much of my time to snowboarding.
5. *Indirect Object:* Mother said, "You give snowboarding too much time."
6. *Appositive:* Do you enjoy the new sport, snowboarding?

Notice: In the case of a passive verb, where the subject receives the action of a "doing" verb, the participle is formed by the "helping" verb. Before a gerund, use a possessive pronoun or noun.

Example: My having been chosen and now Sue's being chosen pleases me.

PRACTICE: Mark verbs, subjects, adjectives (except **LVC–A**), adverbs, and prepositional phrases; label **LV, LVC–N, LVC–A, D.O., I.O., prep.,** and **O.P.** Label gerunds as in the examples above.

1. Listening is important in the classroom.
2. Alex's favorite pastime is cartooning.
3. This book has a surprising ending.
4. You Bring me some examples of your painting.
5. The islanders gave sandbagging all their energy.
6. Her leaving was unexpected.

B. A **gerund phrase (Ger. Ph.)**, made up of a gerund with modifiers or complements, functions the same as a simple gerund.

Example: (Lisa's winning the election) didn't surprise anyone.

PRACTICE: Mark and label sentence parts as in part *A*. Enclose gerund phrases in parentheses; label them **Ger. Ph.** and indicate their function; label the parts of the gerund phrases.

1. Dad's hobby, (playing golf) gives him much pleasure.
2. (Sewing a tailored garment) requires patience and skill.
3. That person's chief fault is (making derogatory remarks about others.)
4. (Listening and concentrating in class) can be very beneficial.
5. (Tying a shoelace) may be quite difficult for a small child.
6. (Your finishing your report on time) is mandatory.

Gerunds and Gerund Phrases

Name _____

Date _____

DEFINITION: A **gerund** is a verb form, the present participle ending in **-ing**, that is used as a noun. (To be labeled: **Ger.**)

A. A **gerund** may be used in the same sentence parts as a noun may be.

1. *Subject:* Snowboarding is a popular new sport.
2. *Direct Object:* I really enjoy snowboarding.
3. *Linking Verb Complement:* My favorite sport is snowboarding.
4. *Object of Preposition:* I give much of my time to snowboarding.
5. *Indirect Object:* Mother said, "You give snowboarding too much time."
6. *Appositive:* Do you enjoy the new sport, snowboarding?

Notice: In the case of a passive verb, where the subject receives the action of a "doing" verb, the participle is formed by the "helping" verb. Before a gerund, use a possessive pronoun or noun.

Example: My having been chosen and now Sue's being chosen pleases me.

PRACTICE: Mark verbs, subjects, adjectives (except **LVC–A**), adverbs, and prepositional phrases; label **LV, LVC–N, LVC–A, D.O., I.O., prep.,** and **O.P.** Label gerunds as in the examples above.

1. Listening is important in the classroom.

2. Alex's favorite pastime is cartooning.

3. This book has a surprising ending.

4.   Bring me some examples of your painting.

5. The islanders gave sandbagging all their energy.

6. Her leaving was unexpected.

B. A **gerund phrase (Ger. Ph.)**, made up of a gerund with modifiers or complements, functions the same as a simple gerund.

Example: Lisa's winning the election didn't surprise anyone.

PRACTICE: Mark and label sentence parts as in part *A*. Enclose gerund phrases in parentheses; label them **Ger. Ph.** and indicate their function; label the parts of the gerund phrases.

1. Dad's hobby, playing golf, gives him much pleasure.

2. Sewing a tailored garment requires patience and skill.

3. That person's chief fault is making derogatory remarks about others.

4. Listening and concentrating in class can be very beneficial.

5. Tying a shoelace may be quite difficult for a small child.

6. Your finishing your report on time is mandatory.

       Understanding and Using Good Grammar

Infinitives and Infinitive Phrases Used as Nouns

This page introduces infinitives and infinitive phrases. Students are given practice in recognizing these verb forms used as nouns.

Demonstrate the diagramming of infinitives/infinitive phrases. For part *A* use example sentence 5:

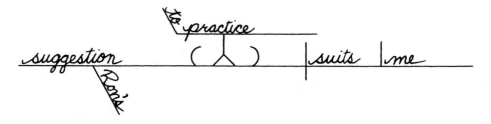

For part *B* use Practice sentence 3:

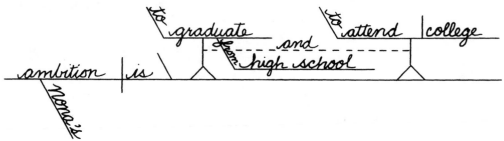

In the part *B* Practice note the following:

Sentence 4: *Come*, which is a contraction of *become*, is a linking verb.

Sentence 5: *To have left* is the infinitive form of *have left, have* plus the past participle of *leave*.

Page 243 contains important additional information regarding the use of infinitives.

Infinitives and Infinitive Phrases
Used as Nouns

An **infinitive**, a verbal made up of **to** and the plain form of the verb, may be used as a noun. It answers the question "what?" (To be labeled: **Inf.**)

Inf. Subj.　　LV　LVC-A
(To wait) would be wise.

Inf.　　D.O.
(Most) people like (to be praised.)
(Passive verb infinitive form)

A. An infinitive may be used in a sentence just as a noun may be.

1. *Subject*: (To win) was (Dena's (highest) hope.
   — Inf. Subj. — LV — LVC-N

2. *Direct Object*: (The) team [really] tried [hard] (to win.)
   — Inf. D.O.

3. *Linking Verb Complement*: (His) goal (in life) is (to succeed)
   — prep. O.P. — LV — Inf. LVC-N

4. *Object of Preposition*: We wanted nothing (except to eat.)
   — D.O. — prep. Inf. O.P.

5. *Appositive*: (Ron's) suggestion, (to practice), suits me.
   — Inf. Appos. — D.O.

Notice: In some instances, infinitives are written without using *to*; its use is understood.

I wanted [only] (to finish and (to) leave.)
— Inf. cd. D.O.

PRACTICE: Mark and label all sentence parts as in the examples above. Put parentheses around the infinitive and show its use in the sentence; insert **to** where it is understood. Write **Inf.** above the infinitive.

1. (To fly) was (the) (whole) (family's) idea.
   — Inf. Subj. — LV — LVC-N

2. Antonio volunteered (to help.)
   — Inf. D.O.

3. (Burt's) intention had been (to practice.)
   — LV — Inf. LVC-N

4. (Lynn's) suggestion, (to quit,) seemed [rather] foolish.
   — Inf. Appos. — LV — LVC-A

5. (The) (little) Cub Scouts wanted nothing (except to eat and ∧ sleep.)
   — D.O. — prep. Inf. cd. O.P. (to)

6. (At (the) assembly,) we [really] wanted (to see and ∧ hear.)
   — prep. O.P. — Inf. cd. D.O. (to)

B. An **infinitive phrase (Inf. Ph.)**, an infinitive with modifiers or complements, functions the same as a simple infinitive.

Chad plans (to complete (his) project [soon.])
— Inf. Ph. D.O. — D.O.

The entire phrase functions as the sentence **D.O.**

PRACTICE: Mark or label all sentence parts as in the examples above. Put parentheses around the infinitive phrase, label it **Inf. Ph.**, and show its use in the sentence.

1. (To stay after class) is [probably] (a) (good) idea.
   — Inf. Ph. Subj. — LV — LVC-N

2. [When] do you expect (to know (the) outcome?)
   — Inf. Ph. D.O. — D.O.

3. (Nona's) ambition is (to graduate from high school) and (to attend college.)
   — LV — Inf. Ph. LVC-N — Inf. Ph. LVC-N

4. (Mortisha's (greatest) wish, (to travel abroad,) may come true.
   — Inf. Ph. Appos. — LV — LVC-A

5. I had intended (to have left by now.)
   — Inf. Ph. D.O.

Name _____

Date _____

Infinitives and Infinitive Phrases Used as Nouns

An **infinitive**, a verbal made up of **to** and the plain form of the verb, may be used as a noun. It answers the question "what?" (To be labeled: **Inf.**)

Inf. Subj.   LV   LVC-A   Inf. D.O.
(To wait) would be wise.   (Most) people like (to be praised)

(Passive verb infinitive form)

A. An infinitive may be used in a sentence just as a noun may be.

                         Inf. Subj.   LV   LVC-N
1. *Subject*: (To win) was (Dena's)(highest) hope.
                                          Inf. D.O.
2. *Direct Object*: (The) team [really] tried [hard] (to win).
                               prep. O.P. LV Inf. LVC-N
3. *Linking Verb Complement*: (His) goal (in life) is (to succeed).
                                D.O.   prep. Inf. O.P.
4. *Object of Preposition*: We wanted nothing (except (to eat).)
                        Inf. Appos.   D.O.
5. *Appositive*: (Ron's) suggestion, (to practice), suits me.

Notice: In some instances, infinitives are written without using *to*; its use is understood.

                      Inf. cd. D.O.
   I wanted [only] (to finish and (to) leave)

PRACTICE: Mark and label all sentence parts as in the examples above. Put parentheses around the infinitive and show its use in the sentence; insert **to** where it is understood. Write **Inf.** above the infinitive.

1. To fly was the whole family's idea.

2. Antonio volunteered to help.

3. Burt's intention had been to practice.

4. Lynn's suggestion, to quit, seemed rather foolish.

5. The little Cub Scouts wanted nothing except to eat and sleep.

6. At the assembly, we really wanted to see and hear.

B. An **infinitive phrase** (**inf. ph.**), an infinitive with modifiers or complements, functions the same as a simple infinitive.

                 Inf. Ph. D.O.   D.O.
Chad plans (to complete (his) project [soon]).   The entire phrase functions as the sentence **D.O.**

PRACTICE: Mark or label all sentence parts as in the examples above. Put parentheses around the infinitive phrase, label it **Inf. Ph.**, and show its use in the sentence.

1. To stay after class is probably a good idea.

2. When do you expect to know the outcome?

3. Nona's ambition is to graduate from high school and to attend college.

4. Mortisha's greatest wish, to travel abroad, may come true.

5. I had intended to have left by now.

                                   Understanding and Using Good Grammar

Understanding and Using Infinitives

No Answer Key is necessary for this page since most of the material is self-explanatory. Point out to the students that the information it contains will help them to use infinitives effectively in their writing. Have students take notes on additional information you give them. You might quiz them as you go through the information.

As you go through the **Understand** section, discuss the meaning of the following terms:

person: (1st—speaker; 2nd—spoken to; 3rd—spoken of)
number: (singular, plural)
tense: (time of the action, present, past, future; simple, perfect)

Ask students to tell to what principal part of the verb *see* the following infinitives are related:

to see: (present or plain form)
to be seeing: (present participle)
to have seen: (past participle)
to be seen: (infinitive in passive voice where the action goes back to the subject)

In item 2 of the **Usage** section point out:

  (a) *Really* modifies *well*, not *spell*.

     "*To spell really well* is Mateo's goal" is correct structure.

  (b) Analyze the sentence parts:

     We hoped (to . . . finish). The modifying adverbs should follow the infinitive.

  (c) Splitting an infinitive with *not* is a common error. Point out that "Not *to continue* now . . ." expresses the idea clearly.

Tell students that they can add interest and variety to their writing by occasionally beginning sentences with an infinitive or infinitive phrase:

(To win this game,) we will [certainly] need (your) and (his) help.

(To assure our leaving on time,) Mom set (the alarm) clock (to awaken us early.)

(To convince your audience), you should speak [knowledgeably] and [sincerely].

This page may be duplicated and distributed to the students.

Name _____

Date _____

Understanding and Using Infinitives

UNDERSTAND:

1. **Infinite** means endless, not limited.

2. The infinitive form of a verb (*to arrive, to leave*) is not limited by person, number, or tense.

3. There are different forms of infinitives: *to see, to be seeing, to have seen, to be seen.*

4. Distinguish between *to* followed by a verb word as used in an **infinitive** (*to go*) and *to* followed by a noun or pronoun as used in a **prepositional phrase** (*to the mall, to you and him*).

5. An infinitive may be used as:

   (a) A *noun*: School policy requires us (to arrive on time.)

   (b) An *adjective*: Eight o'clock is the time (to arrive.)   To be studied

   (c) An *adverb*: I was [not] able (to arrive on time.)   in later units.

USAGE:
1. **Sometimes *to* is omitted:**

   (a) When using *to* sounds awkward:

      We heard someone (to) laugh.   Did you watch him (to) go?

   (b) After the verbs *dare*, and *help*:

      I did not dare (to) cross the stream on that plank.
      Studying would have helped me (to) be prepared for the test.

   (c) In compound sentence parts:

      The puppies seemed just to want to eat and (to) eat.

2. **Avoid "splitting" an infinitive** by using a word(s) between *to* and the verb word:

   (a) *Poor:*   To really spell well is Mateo's goal.
       Better: *To spell* really well is Mateo's goal.

   (b) *Poor:*   We hoped to quickly, carefully, and completely finish.
       Better: We hoped *to finish* quickly, carefully, and completely.

   (c) *Poor:*   To not continue now would be a mistake.
       Better: Not *to continue* now would be a mistake.

3. **Avoid using a "dangling" infinitive phrase**, a phrase that does not state clearly who does the action.

   (a) *Poor:*   To avoid the rush, leaving early would be necessary.
       Better: To avoid the rush, *we needed* to leave early.

   (b) *Poor:*   To see better, standing on our chairs was helpful.
       Better: To see better, *we stood* on our chairs.

4. **To develop concise expression**, replace longer groups of words with infinitives or infinitive phrases:

   (a) *Long:*   This is the river that Dad said that we should fish.
       More concise: This is the river Dad said to fish.

   (b) *Long:*   Joe planned that he would maintain an even pace.
       More concise: Joe planned to maintain an even pace.

Understanding and Using Good Grammar

Using Verbal Nouns

This type of practice is a worthwhile challenge to very able students. You may want to omit it for the less able and have them concentrate on analyzing the sentences to help them recognize and label the sentence parts on page 252.

Answers to this exercise will vary. The Answer Key gives sample sentences.

Using Verbal Nouns

Instructions: Write sentences using the underlined gerunds and infinitives in the given sentence positions. Use verb tenses you studied in the previous unit. Above the verbal noun in your sentences label appropriately **Ger., Ger. Ph., Inf., Inf. Ph.**, and its use in the sentence. Mark verbs, nouns, adjectives (except **LVC–A**), adverbs, prepositional phrases, gerunds and gerund phrases, and infinitives and infinitive phrases; label **LV, LVC–N, LVC–A, D.O., I.O., prep., O.P.**, and **Appos.** At the end indicate the verb tense.

Sample Sentences:

1. Use to go as the subject.

   (To go) was (an)(agreeable) idea.   **S. Past**

   (To go at that time) didn't seem [very] wise (to me.)   **Past Emph.**

2. Use to leave as the direct object.

   Scot wants (to leave.)   **S. Pres.**

   Leslie had wanted (to leave the puppy at the veterinarian's.)   **Past Perf.**

3. Use skiing as the subject.

   (Skiing) has [always] been (Lars's)(favorite)(winter) sport.   **Pres. Perf.**

   (Skiing at Aspen, Colorado,) is exhilarating.   **S. Pres.**

4. Use dancing as the **LVC–N.**

   (Karen's)(favorite)(social) activity is (dancing.)   **S. Pres.**

   (The) theme (of (our)(winter) dance) was ("Dancing Under the Stars.")
   S. Past

5. Use listening and concentrating as an appositive.

   Most (of (the) students) have been learning (two)(important) skills, (listening and concentrating in the classroom.)   **Pres. Perf. Prog.**

   (Most) students practice (two) skills, (listening and concentrating.)   **S. Pres.**

6. Use to win as the object of the preposition except.

   Jodie wanted nothing (except (to win.)   **S. Past**

   (The) team had entered (the) tournament (for (no) reason)(except (to win.)
   Past Perf.

7. Use to travel as an appositive.

   Grandmother retired (for [only] (one) reason)(to travel.)   **S. Past**

   She has (one)(big) dream, (to travel in space.)   **S. Pres.**

8. Use washing as the object of the preposition besides.

   (Besides washing (the) car,) I [really] did wax and polish it.   **Past Emph.**

   (Besides washing,) I shall dry and put [away](the) dishes.   **S. Fut.**

Using Verbal Nouns

Name _____

Date _____

Instructions: Write sentences using the underlined gerunds and infinitives in the given sentence positions. Use verb tenses you studied in the previous unit. Above the verbal noun in your sentences label appropriately **Ger.**, **Ger. Ph.**, **Inf.**, **Inf. Ph.**, and its use in the sentence. Mark verbs, nouns, adjectives (except **LVC–A**), adverbs, prepositional phrases, gerunds and gerund phrases, and infinitives and infinitive phrases; label **LV**, **LVC–N**, **LVC–A**, **D.O.**, **I.O.**, **prep.**, **O.P.**, and **Appos.** At the end indicate the verb tense.

1. Use <u>to go</u> as the subject.

2. Use <u>to leave</u> as the direct object.

3. Use <u>skiing</u> as the subject.

4. Use <u>dancing</u> as the **LVC–N**.

5. Use <u>listening and concentrating</u> as an appositive.

6. Use <u>to win</u> as the object of the preposition <u>except</u>.

7. Use <u>to travel</u> as an appositive.

8. Use <u>washing</u> as the object of the preposition <u>besides</u>.

Understanding and Using Good Grammar

Recognizing Gerunds, Gerund Phrases, Infinitives and Infinitive Phrases Used as Nouns

This is the Final Practice sheet before the Test on this unit. You may wish to have students work together on sentences 1–10 with volunteers analyzing the sentence parts. They could complete sentences 11–20 individually and correct their errors when you read the correct forms.

When examining the sample sentence, remind students that the entire phrase answers the question "what?" in relation to the verb:

What should enable? "Our careful saving now" is the subject.

Should enable what? "to afford a nice vacation" is the direct object.

"Who's going to get the vacation?" "Us" is the indirect object.

Inform students that several sentences on the Test have been taken from this worksheet. It would really be worth their time to study and understand fully the analysis of each sentence.

Recognizing Gerunds, Gerund Phrases, Infinitives and Infinitive Phrases Used as Nouns

Instructions: Enclose the verbals in parentheses and label them **Ger.**, **Ger. Ph.**, **Inf.**, or **Inf. Ph.**
Label their use in the sentence. Mark verbs, subjects, adjectives (except **LVC–A**),
adverbs, and prepositional phrases; label **LV**, **LVC–N**, **LVC–A**, **D.O.**, **I.O.**, **prep.**,
O.P., and **Appos.**

Example: (Our careful saving [now]) should enable us (to afford a nice vacation.)

1. (To smile) was (a) challenge (at (that) point.)

2. (My)(little) sister is learning (to tell time.)

3. (Careful reading of instructions) should become (a) habit.

4. (Her leaving) was (a) disappointment (to all)(of us.)

5. [Surely] (the) teacher plans (to return.)

6. Father enjoys (some) housework, (vacuuming and ironing.)

7. Did you forget (to do your homework?)

8. (Our) intention is (to play ball after school) and (to do our homework after dinner.)

9. (My) uncle devotes (much) time (to (his) hobby,) (sailing his boat.)

10. Emily regretted (losing that match); she had hoped (to win the tournament.)

11. (Constant showing off) may be (a) sign (of immaturity.)

12. I had [only] (one) option, (to agree.)

13. (Our) job is (counting the ballots) and (recording the results.)

14. (That person's greatest failing) is (leaving everything until the last minute.)

15. (The)(little) girl enjoys everything (except (doing the dishes).)

16. (To work hard for something) and [then] (to win it) gives anyone (a) (feeling of real satisfaction.)

17. (One) aspect (of maturity,) (behaving responsibly,) requires self-discipline.

18. (One) form (of immaturity) is (ridiculing another person) (for (making a slight mistake.)

19. (To save money) is hard (for some people.)

20. (Being awarded the trophy) was (a) "dream come true."

Name _____

Date _____

Recognizing Gerunds, Gerund Phrases, Infinitives and Infinitive Phrases Used as Nouns

Instructions: Enclose the verbals in parentheses and label them **Ger.**, **Ger. Ph.**, **Inf.**, or **Inf. Ph.** Label their use in the sentence. Mark verbs, subjects, adjectives (except **LVC–A**), adverbs, and prepositional phrases; label **LV**, **LVC–N**, **LVC–A**, **D.O.**, **I.O.**, **prep.**, **O.P.**, and **Appos.**

Example: (Our careful saving [now]) should enable us (to afford a nice vacation.)

    Ger. Ph. Subj.   *I.O.* *Inf. Ph. D.O.*

1. To smile was a challenge at that point.

2. My little sister is learning to tell time.

3. Careful reading of instructions should become a habit.

4. Her leaving was a disappointment to all of us.

5. Surely the teacher plans to return.

6. Father enjoys some housework, vacuuming and ironing.

7. Did you forget to do your homework?

8. Our intention is to play ball after school and to do our homework after dinner.

9. My uncle devotes much time to his hobby, sailing his boat.

10. Emily regretted losing that match; she had hoped to win the tournament.

11. Constant showing off may be a sign of immaturity.

12. I had only one option, to agree.

13. Our job is counting the ballots and recording the results.

14. That person's greatest failing is leaving everything until the last minute.

15. The little girl enjoys everything except doing the dishes.

16. To work hard for something and then to win it gives anyone a feeling of real satisfaction.

17. One aspect of maturity, behaving responsibly, requires self-discipline.

18. One form of immaturity is ridiculing another person for making a slight mistake.

19. To save money is hard for some people.

20. Being awarded the trophy was a "dream come true."

Understanding and Using Good Grammar

TEST 1: Recognizing Gerund and Infinitive Phrases Used as Nouns

> The next reproducible page contains two copies of one half-page Test. Cut each duplicated page in half; give each student one half-page.

The half-page Tests on pages 255 and 258 are of equal difficulty. You may want to give one as a trial test and record the score in pencil. After the class has had a chance to improve their understanding by studying the returned Test, give them the second Test. The recorded grade for each student will be the higher of the two scores.

Suggested Grading:

Count each phrase for three points:
    ½ point for each parenthesis mark
    1 point for the phrase label
    1 point for the label that identifies the use of the phrase in the sentence

Grading scale: 30 points

−1, 97	−3, 90	−5, 83	−7, 77	−9, 70	−11, 63	−13, 57
−2, 93	−4, 87	−6, 80	−8, 73	−10, 67	−12, 60	−14, 53

Students are instructed to mark or label all sentence parts outside the phrases as an aid in analyzing the use of each phrase. If you decide to grade these markings, there are 34, with this percentage scale:

−1, 97	−3, 91	−5, 85	−7, 79	−9, 74	−11, 68	−13, 62
−2, 94	−4, 88	−6, 82	−8, 76	−10, 71	−12, 65	−14, 59

TEST 1: Recognizing Gerund
and Infinitive Phrases
Used as Nouns

Instructions: Enclose the phrases in parentheses; label them **Ger. Ph.** or **Inf. Ph.** and write their use in the sentence. Mark verbs, subjects, adjectives, adverbs, and prepositional phrases; label **LV, LVC–N, D.O., I.O., prep., O.P.,** and **Appos.**

1. Emily regretted (losing that match); she had hoped (to win the tournament.)

2. That boy has the tiresome tendency (of (jumping to conclusions).)

3. My ambition is (to graduate from high school) and (to attend college.)

4. (Careful saving now) should enable us (to afford a nice summer vacation.)

5. My uncle devoted much time (to his hobby), (sailing his boat.)

6. I had only one option, (to agree with my parents.)

7. One common human fault is (making derogatory remarks about others.)

TEST 1: Recognizing Gerund and Infinitive Phrases Used as Nouns

Name _____

Date _____

Instructions: Enclose the phrases in parentheses; label them **Ger. Ph.** or **Inf. Ph.** and write their use in the sentence. Mark verbs, subjects, adjectives, adverbs, and prepositional phrases; label **LV, LVC–N, D.O., I.O., prep., O.P.,** and **Appos.**

1. Emily regretted losing that match; she had hoped to win the tournament.

2. That boy has the tiresome tendency of jumping to conclusions.

3. My ambition is to graduate from high school and to attend college.

4. Careful saving now should enable us to afford a nice summer vacation.

5. My uncle devoted much time to his hobby, sailing his boat.

6. I had only one option, to agree with my parents.

7. One common human fault is making derogatory remarks about others.

TEST 1: Recognizing Gerund and Infinitive Phrases Used as Nouns

Name _____

Date _____

Instructions: Enclose the phrases in parentheses; label them **Ger. Ph.** or **Inf. Ph.** and write their use in the sentence. Mark verbs, subjects, adjectives, adverbs, and prepositional phrases; label **LV, LVC–N, D.O., I.O., prep., O.P.,** and **Appos.**

1. Emily regretted losing that match; she had hoped to win the tournament.

2. That boy has the tiresome tendency of jumping to conclusions.

3. My ambition is to graduate from high school and to attend college.

4. Careful saving now should enable us to afford a nice summer vacation.

5. My uncle devoted much time to his hobby, sailing his boat.

6. I had only one option, to agree with my parents.

7. One common human fault is making derogatory remarks about others.

Understanding and Using Good Grammar

TEST 2: Recognizing Gerund and Infinitive Phrases Used as Nouns

> The next reproducible page contains two copies of one half-page Test. Cut each duplicated page in half; give each student one half-page.

Suggested Grading:

Count each phrase for three points:

    ½ point for each parenthesis mark

    1 point for correct phrase label; 1 point for correct use label

    Total points: 33 (Subtract 3% for each error.)

If you decide to grade markings outside phrases, there are 30, with this percentage scale:

−1, 97	−3, 90	−5, 83	−7, 77	−9, 70	−11, 63	−13, 57
−2, 93	−4, 87	−6, 80	−8, 73	−10, 67	−12, 60	−14, 53

TEST 2: Recognizing Gerund and Infinitive Phrases Used as Nouns

Instructions: Enclose the phrases in parentheses; label them **Ger. Ph.** or **Inf. Ph.** and write their use in the sentence. Mark verbs, subjects, adjectives, adverbs, and prepositional phrases; label **LV**, **LVC–N**, **D.O.**, **I.O.**, **prep.**, **O.P.**, **Appos.**, and **N.A.**

1. One aspect (of maturity,) (appreciating individual differences among one's peers,) develops [slowly] (in some teenagers.)

2. (To work hard for something) and [then] (to attain it) gives anyone a (feeling of real satisfaction.)

3. Almost everyone enjoys (being given a sincere compliment.)

4. (Having two elections a year) permits more students (to participate in student government.)

5. (Being selected outstanding girl of the class) was a surprise (to Gina.)

6. Mom, had Dad decided (to wait for the girls) or (to leave without them?)

7. Alan [never] fails (to do his homework.)

Name _____

Date _____

TEST 2: Recognizing Gerund and Infinitive Phrases Used as Nouns

Instructions: Enclose the phrases in parentheses; label them **Ger. Ph.** or **Inf. Ph.** and write their use in the sentence. Mark verbs, subjects, adjectives, adverbs, and prepositional phrases; label **LV**, **LVC–N**, **D.O.**, **I.O.**, **prep.**, **O.P.**, **Appos.**, and **N.A.**

1. One aspect of maturity, appreciating individual differences among one's peers, develops slowly in some teenagers.

2. To work hard for something and then to attain it gives anyone a feeling of real satisfaction.

3. Almost everyone enjoys being given a sincere compliment.

4. Having two elections a year permits more students to participate in student government.

5. Being selected outstanding girl of the class was a surprise to Gina.

6. Mom, had Dad decided to wait for the girls or to leave without them?

7. Alan never fails to do his homework.

Name _____

Date _____

TEST 2: Recognizing Gerund and Infinitive Phrases Used as Nouns

Instructions: Enclose the phrases in parentheses; label them **Ger. Ph.** or **Inf. Ph.** and write their use in the sentence. Mark verbs, subjects, adjectives, adverbs, and prepositional phrases; label **LV**, **LVC–N**, **D.O.**, **I.O.**, **prep.**, **O.P.**, **Appos.**, and **N.A.**

1. One aspect of maturity, appreciating individual differences among one's peers, develops slowly in some teenagers.

2. To work hard for something and then to attain it gives anyone a feeling of real satisfaction.

3. Almost everyone enjoys being given a sincere compliment.

4. Having two elections a year permits more students to participate in student government.

5. Being selected outstanding girl of the class was a surprise to Gina.

6. Mom, had Dad decided to wait for the girls or to leave without them?

7. Alan never fails to do his homework.

Understanding and Using Good Grammar

Facts About Adjectives

The information presented on the following two Facts sheets was covered in detail, with ample drill work, in *Steps to Good Grammar*, pages 32–45 and 250–261. If your students need more practice in applying these facts, duplicate appropriate worksheets in *Steps to Good Grammar* for them to use.

Adjectives with irregular comparatives are listed in *Steps to Good Grammar*, page 251.

As you read aloud the basic facts included in *A* and *B*, quiz students to be sure they remember (1) what adjectives tell about the words they modify, (2) the rules for the formation of comparatives and superlatives, and (3) the two usage errors to avoid.

In the Practice sentences, be sure students make the necessary corrections. In recording the grade, there are 16 corrections; subtract 6% for each uncorrected error. Return this page for students to use in preparing for the Test on page 267.

Facts About Adjectives

A. *DEFINITION:* An **adjective** modifies a noun or pronoun. It may tell *which one, what kind, how many,* or *whose* about that word.

Example: (Those) (eight) (tart) apples are (for (Grandmother's) pie.)
                (which ones)(how many)(what kind)   (whose)

B. Use of Adjectives to Compare Nouns

1. To one-syllable adjectives (*cheap*) and two-syllable adjectives ending in *-le* (*simple*) or *-y* (*easy*), add **-er** (*two* letters) to compare *two* nouns, add **-est** (*three* letters) to compare *three* or more nouns.

   (a) Of the *two* projects, this will be the cheap**er**, simpl**er**, and easi**er**.
   (b) Of the *three*, this will be the cheap**est**, simpl**est**, and easi**est**.

2. With all other adjectives of two or more syllables, use **more** before the adjective to compare *two* nouns (notice: *-re/-er* for two). Use **most** (notice: *-st/-est*) to compare *three* or more nouns.

   (a) Of the *two*, Fiona is **more** reliable and **more** athletic.
   (b) Of the *three*, Fiona is **most** reliable and **most** athletic.

3. Avoid using double comparisons: Do not use *more* before an adjective ending in *-er*; do not use *most* before an adjective ending in *-est*.

   (a) My horse is ~~more~~ gentler than his.
   (b) That puppy is the ~~most~~ wiggliest I've ever seen.

4. In comparing one person with others in the same group, use **other** after **any**.

   (a) *Not clear:* Angelo is taller than any boy in his class.
   (b) *Clear:* Angelo is taller than any **other** boy in his class.

PRACTICE: Above each error in adjective usage, write the correct form.

1. The ~~more~~ *most* expensive of these six cars may not be the ~~better~~ *best* one.

2. Of the two bikes, Toni's is the ~~newest~~ *newer* and ~~most smooth~~ *smoother* to ride.

3. Ike is shorter than any *other* boy in his class.

4. I've never seen ~~more icy~~ *icier* roads!

5. Isn't his mother the ~~patientest~~ *most patient* person?

6. This book has been more popular than any *other* this year.

7. Natasha is much ~~more~~ shorter than Brett.

8. Comparing the two, Norm is ~~most~~ *more* athletic and Nate is ~~most~~ *more* studious.

9. No one could feel ~~more lazy~~ *lazier* than I today!

10. This one is the ~~simpler~~ *simplest* and ~~more~~ *most* workable of the three plans.

11. Bridget is a better student than any *other* girl I know.

12. Comparing my two brothers' rooms, Jay's is the ~~most neatest~~ *neater*.

Facts About Adjectives

Name _____

Date _____

A. *DEFINITION:* An **adjective** modifies a noun or pronoun. It may tell *which one, what kind, how many,* or *whose* about that word.

Example:
(Those) (eight) (tart) apples are (for (Grandmother's) pie.)
(which ones)(how many)(what kind)   (whose)

B. Use of Adjectives to Compare Nouns

1. To one-syllable adjectives (*cheap*) and two-syllable adjectives ending in *-le* (*simple*) or
   -y (*easy*), add **-er** (*two* letters) to compare *two* nouns, add **-est** (*three* letters) to compare
   three or more nouns.
   (a) Of the *two* projects, this will be the cheap**er**, simpl**er**, and easi**er**.
   (b) Of the *three*, this will be the cheap**est**, simpl**est**, and easi**est**.

2. With all other adjectives of two or more syllables, use **more** before the adjective to compare
   two nouns (notice: *-re/-er* for two). Use **most** (notice: *-st/-est*) to compare *three* or more
   nouns.
   (a) Of the *two*, Fiona is **more** reliable and **more** athletic.
   (b) Of the *three*, Fiona is **most** reliable and **most** athletic.

3. Avoid using double comparisons: Do not use *more* before an adjective ending in *-er*, do not
   use *most* before an adjective ending in *-est*.
   (a) My horse is ~~more~~ gentler than his.
   (b) That puppy is the ~~most~~ wiggliest I've ever seen.

4. In comparing one person with others in the same group, use **other** after **any**.
   (a) *Not clear:* Angelo is taller than any boy in his class.
   (b) *Clear:* Angelo is taller than any **other** boy in his class.

PRACTICE: Above each error in adjective usage, write the correct form.

1. The more expensive of these six cars may not be the better one.

2. Of the two bikes, Toni's is the newest and most smooth to ride.

3. Ike is shorter than any boy in his class.

4. I've never seen more icy roads!

5. Isn't his mother the patientest person?

6. This book has been more popular than any this year.

7. Natasha is much more shorter than Brett.

8. Comparing the two, Norm is most athletic and Nate is most studious.

9. No one could feel more lazy than I today!

10. This one is the simpler and more workable of the three plans.

11. Bridget is a better student than any girl I know.

12. Comparing my two brothers' rooms, Jay's is the most neatest.

Understanding and Using Good Grammar

Facts About Adjectives
(continued)

In fact *D* point out:

1. The plural of *this* is *these*; the plural of *that* is *those*.

2. Use *this/these* to refer to items close at hand.

3. Use *that/those* to refer to items at a distance.

Have students write this added information on the back of their sheets.

This is a Final Practice before the Test on page 267. Be sure students have the information on page 261, as well as this page, for review.

Facts About Adjectives
(continued)

C. Avoid Adjective/Adverb Confusion.

  1. Use the adjectives **well** and **bad** in referring to health or feeling.

LV LVC-A   LV LVC-A
Mary feels well [today]; she felt bad [yesterday].

  2. Use the adverbs **well** or **badly** in telling how something is or was done.

prep. O.P.
I did [badly (on (the) test]; Paolo did [quite][well].

D. Adjectives **this, that, these, those** (Never use *them* as an adjective.)

  1. Use the singular *this/that* to modify the singular nouns *kind, sort,* and *type.*

D.O. prep. O.P.   D.O.
I like (this) kind (of shoes); (my) sister likes (that) kind.

  2. Use the plural *these/those* to modify the plural nouns *kinds, sorts,* and *types.*

LV LVC-A   LV LVC-A
(These) kinds (of books) are popular; (those) kinds are popular [also].

E. Adjectives **each, either, neither, every,** or **some** (meaning an unknown *one*) all mean *one*; pronouns referring to them should mean *one.*

D.O.   prep.   O.P.   D.O.
(Neither) girl had (her) pencil. (Each) one (of (the) boys) knows (his) combination.
D.O.
Does (either) student [ever] forget (his or her) book?

FINAL PRACTICE: Above each error in adjective usage, write the correct form.

1. Can any student bring ~~their~~ *his/her* friend to the dance?

2. My big sister surely does ~~good~~ *well* in school.

3. ~~Those~~ *That* sort of fish lives in fresh water.

4. Has either one of the girls finished ~~their~~ *her* homework?

5. Joe felt ~~badly~~ *bad* about losing the match.

6. ~~These~~ *This* kind of scissors is rather expensive.

7. Dad felt ~~badly~~ *bad* this morning, but he feels ~~good~~ *well* now.

8. Neither girl is apt to forget ~~their~~ *her* homework or ~~their~~ *her* lunch.

9. Neither one of the workmen had brought ~~their~~ *his* tools.

10. Of the two, the blue one is the ~~best~~ *better* value.

11. ~~These~~ *This* kind of sneakers wears ~~good~~ *well*.

12. Every little dog was wagging ~~their~~ *its* tail.

13. It was much ~~more rainy~~ *rainier* today.

14. Linnea always seems ~~more~~ calmer than any *other* person in her family.

15. Of all my friends, Marita is ~~fairer~~ *fairest* and ~~more~~ *most* supportive.

16. Some girl always leaves ~~their~~ *her* purse.

Name _____

Date _____

Facts About Adjectives
(continued)

C. Avoid Adjective/Adverb Confusion.

1. Use the adjectives **well** and **bad** in referring to health or feeling.

   Mary feels well today; she felt bad yesterday.

2. Use the adverbs **well** or **badly** in telling how something is or was done.

   I did badly on the test; Paolo did quite well.

D. Adjectives **this, that, these, those** (Never use *them* as an adjective.)

1. Use the singular *this/that* to modify the singular nouns *kind*, *sort*, and *type*.

   I like this kind of shoes; my sister likes that kind.

2. Use the plural *these/those* to modify the plural nouns *kinds*, *sorts*, and *types*.

   These kinds of books are popular; those kinds are popular also.

E. Adjectives **each, either, neither, every,** or **some** (meaning an unknown *one*) all mean *one*; pronouns referring to them should mean *one*.

   Neither girl had her pencil.   Each one of the boys knows his combination.

   Does either student ever forget his or her book?

FINAL PRACTICE: Above each error in adjective usage, write the correct form.

1. Can any student bring their friend to the dance?

2. My big sister surely does good in school.

3. Those sort of fish lives in fresh water.

4. Has either one of the girls finished their homework?

5. Joe felt badly about losing the match.

6. These kind of scissors is rather expensive.

7. Dad felt badly this morning, but he feels good now.

8. Neither girl is apt to forget their homework or their lunch.

9. Neither one of the workmen had brought their tools.

10. Of the two, the blue one is the best value.

11. These kind of sneakers wears good.

12. Every little dog was wagging their tail.

13. It was much more rainy today.

14. Linnea always seems more calmer than any person in her family.

15. Of all my friends, Marita is fairer and more supportive.

16. Some girl always leaves their purse.

Understanding and Using Good Grammar

TEST:
Facts About Adjectives

> The next reproducible page contains two copies of one half-page Test. Cut each duplicated page in half; give each student one half-page.

Before students start the Test, make it clear to them that they are to correct errors in the use of adjectives (in one sentence, in the use of adverbs that tell "how" something was done). They should not change nouns, pronouns, or verbs! For example:

Sentence 4: ~~These~~ *This* kind of scissors is ~~expensiver~~ *more expensive* than ~~those~~ *that* kind.

(Three adjective errors correctly corrected!)

These ~~kind~~ *kinds* of scissors ~~is expensiver~~ *are more expensive* than those ~~kind~~ *kinds*.

(Corrected in this manner, the student has a perfect understanding of the concept. Write: "Excellent sentence; –7% for failure to follow instructions!")

Suggested Grading:

There are 20 items. Subtract 5% for each error.

TEST:
Facts About Adjectives

Instructions: Above each error, write the correct form.

1. Has either girl brought ~~their~~ *her* report?

2. Of all the plans, this one is the ~~more simpler~~ *simplest* and ~~more easy~~ *easiest* to follow.

3. Grandfather felt ~~badly~~ *bad* yesterday, but he feels ~~good~~ *well* today.

4. *This* ~~These~~ kind of scissors is ~~expensiver~~ *more expensive* than ~~those~~ *that* kind.

5. Every one of the boys occasionally forgets ~~their~~ *his* books or ~~their~~ *his* lunch.

6. We had never driven on a ~~more bumpy~~ *bumpier* road.

7. That guard is shorter than any *other* player on the basketball team.

8. Of the two girls, Julie is the ~~capabler~~ *more capable* student and the ~~most~~ *more* reliable.

9. I like ~~these~~ *this* type of books better than any *other* kind.

10. Has each candidate drawn up ~~their~~ *his/her* platform?

11. I think I did ~~bad~~ *badly* on the test; Kenny said he did ~~good~~ *well* on it.

12. Is this the ~~cheapest~~ *cheaper* of the two?

TEST: Facts About Adjectives

Name _____

Date _____

Instructions: Above each error, write the correct form.

1. Has either girl brought their report?

2. Of all the plans, this one is the more simpler and more easy to follow.

3. Grandfather felt badly yesterday, but he feels good today.

4. These kind of scissors is expensiver than those kind.

5. Every one of the boys occasionally forgets their books or their lunch.

6. We had never driven on a more bumpy road.

7. That guard is shorter than any player on the basketball team.

8. Of the two girls, Julie is the capabler student and the most reliable.

9. I like these type of books better than any kind.

10. Has each candidate drawn up their platform?

11. I think I did bad on the test; Kenny said he did good on it.

12. Is this the cheapest of the two?

TEST: Facts About Adjectives

Name _____

Date _____

Instructions: Above each error, write the correct form.

1. Has either girl brought their report?

2. Of all the plans, this one is the more simpler and more easy to follow.

3. Grandfather felt badly yesterday, but he feels good today.

4. These kind of scissors is expensiver than those kind.

5. Every one of the boys occasionally forgets their books or their lunch.

6. We had never driven on a more bumpy road.

7. That guard is shorter than any player on the basketball team.

8. Of the two girls, Julie is the capabler student and the most reliable.

9. I like these type of books better than any kind.

10. Has each candidate drawn up their platform?

11. I think I did bad on the test; Kenny said he did good on it.

12. Is this the cheapest of the two?

Understanding and Using Good Grammar

Prepositional Phrases Used as Adjectives

Few practice sentences are given since students have already studied prepositional phrases extensively. You may want to review the information given on pages 35–46 in this book and pages 105–111 in *Steps to Good Grammar.*

Write these two sentences on the overhead or chalkboard to demonstrate the importance of careful placement of the phrases:

1. The inspector was watching the house in his car.   (Not clear)

    (In his car), the inspector was watching the house.   (Clear)

2. Behind the school, Chloe was walking up the street.   (Not clear)

    Chloe was walking (up the street)(behind the school.)   (Clear)

Point out that the prepositional phrase, *up the street,* functions as an adverb that tells "where" about the verb, *was walking.* The next unit deals with phrases used as adverbs.

As you proceed through the rest of the study pages, encourage the students to use each new form of expression in their writing assignments.

Students should complete the Practice sentences individually. When all have finished, they should correct their own work as some in the class volunteer to give their analyses. They will need this information pages to review before the Unit Test on page 282 or 285.

Prepositional Phrases
Used as Adjectives

DEFINITION: A **phrase** is a group of related words that function together as a single part of speech. It does not have a subject and verb.

Reminder: In the preceding unit you learned that main sentence parts, such as subjects and direct objects, are not necessarily one-word nouns or pronouns. Gerund and infinitive phrases can be used instead to communicate a specifically detailed and expanded idea in any main sentence part. Knowing this, practice using these various types of sentence structure whenever you write.

1. We could [not] leave [then]. It was [not] wise.

2. (To have decided to leave at that moment) would [not] have been wise.

3. (Our leaving at that moment) seemed unwise (for several reasons.)

Phrases Used as Adjectives to Modify Nouns/Pronouns

The **prepositional phrase** begins with a preposition and ends with a noun/pronoun object.

1. Often the phrase contains a description that could not be expressed in a single adjective:
   apple *on the table*; boy *in the blue sweater*

2. Depending upon the purpose of your writing, you may use:

   (a) A single adjective: The cabin, in a (wooded) area, was hard to find.

   (b) Prepositional phrases: The cabin, (in a heavily shaded area) (of towering redwood trees) was hard to find.

3. Place the phrase as close as possible to the word it modifies:

   Poor: We bought some strawberries at the market with a delicious flavor. (The market had a delicious flavor?!)

   Better: We bought some strawberries with a delicious flavor at the market. (The delicious flavor was only at the market?!)

   Best: (At the market) we bought (some) strawberries (with a delicious flavor.) (Clear picture! Effective writing!)

PRACTICE: Mark or label all sentence parts; draw an arrow from the phrase to the word modified (see Example).

Example: Dad lost (two) keys, (the) one (to (his) car) and (the) one (to (our) front) door.)

1. (The) expressions (on (the) faces) (of (several) of (the (nearby) observers) showed (their) annoyance (with (the) delay.)

2. (Your) suggestion (about (the) program) (for (the) kindergarteners) is being considered.

3. (The (most) (treacherous) trail (in (this) (entire) area) is (the) one (to (the) top) (of (the) mountain.)

4. Coach [just] gave (the) boy (in (the (front) row) (the) award (for (most (improved) player.)

5. (In (her) new (majorette) uniform,) (with (great) confidence,) Annella strutted.

Name _____

Date _____

Prepositional Phrases Used as Adjectives

DEFINITION: A **phrase** is a group of related words that function together as a single part of speech. It does not have a subject and verb.

Reminder: In the preceding unit you learned that main sentence parts, such as subjects and direct objects, are not necessarily one-word nouns or pronouns. Gerund and infinitive phrases can be used instead to communicate a specifically detailed and expanded idea in any main sentence part. Knowing this, practice using these various types of sentence structure whenever you write.

1. We could [not] leave [then]. It was [not] wise.
2. (To have decided to leave at that moment) would [not] have been wise.
3. (Our leaving at that moment) seemed unwise (for (several) reasons.)

Phrases Used as Adjectives to Modify Nouns/Pronouns

The **prepositional phrase** begins with a preposition and ends with a noun/pronoun object.

1. Often the phrase contains a description that could not be expressed in a single adjective: apple *on the table*; boy *in the blue sweater*

2. Depending upon the purpose of your writing, you may use:

    (a) A single adjective: The cabin, in a (wooded) area, was hard to find.
    (b) Prepositional phrases: The cabin, (in a heavily shaded area) (of towering redwood trees) was hard to find.

3. Place the phrase as close as possible to the word it modifies:

    Poor: We bought some strawberries at the market with a delicious flavor. (The market had a delicious flavor?!)

    Better: We bought some strawberries with a delicious flavor at the market. (The delicious flavor was only at the market?!)

    Best: (At (the) market) we bought (some) strawberries (with (a) (delicious) flavor.) (Clear picture! Effective writing!)

PRACTICE: Mark or label all sentence parts; draw an arrow from the phrase to the word modified (see Example).

Example: Dad lost (two) keys, (the) one (to (his) car) and (the) one (to (our) (front) door.)

1. The expressions on the faces of several of the nearby observers showed their annoyance with the delay.

2. Your suggestion about the program for the kindergarteners is being considered.

3. The most treacherous trail in this entire area is the one to the top of the mountain.

4. Coach just gave the boy in the front row the award for most improved player.

5. In her new majorette uniform, with great confidence, Annella strutted.

Participial Phrases Used as Adjectives

The use of participial phrases as adjectives is a new concept. Go over every phase of the instruction very carefully with the students. Arouse the students' interest with the information that participial phrase adjectives, which add an extra action, are picture-making devices. Instruct them to observe the "enlivening" effect each such phrase has in the sentences on this page.

Inform students that the participle in an adjective phrase is in *active voice* if the word it modifies *does the action* as in Example *2a*:

"Captains," modified by "having chosen the boys . . . ," did the action of the participle; the participle is in *active voice*.

The participle in an adjective phrase is in *passive voice* if the word it modifies *receives the action* of the participle as in Example *2b*:

"Newcomer," modified by "(not) having been chosen . . . ," received the action; the participle is in *passive voice*.

For item 3 write these two sentences to emphasize the importance of placing an adjective phrase as close as possible to the word it modifies in order to make the meaning instantly clear to the reader:

Part. Ph. Adj.

Not clear: (Wading happily in a shallow little stream), the

searchers found the two small children.

D.O.

Clear: (The) searchers found (the)(two)(small) children

Part. Ph.   Adj.

(wading happily . . .)

Not clear: We took the shorter of the two trails having

limited time.

Part. Ph. Adj.

Clear: (Having limited time), we took (the)(shorter)

prep.   O.P.

(of (the)(two) trails.)

Encourage students to use participial phrase adjectives to improve their writing style—to enable their readers to visualize better the persons and scenes they describe in their writings.

Participial Phrases Used as Adjectives

The **participial phrase**, beginning with a verb participle and containing complements/modifiers, may be used to describe a noun or pronoun. (To be labeled: **Part. Ph. Adj.**)

1. Participles of the verb *choose*: *choosing* (present), *chosen* (past), *having chosen* (perfect), *being chosen* (present, passive voice), *having been chosen* (perfect, passive voice)

2. *Examples:*

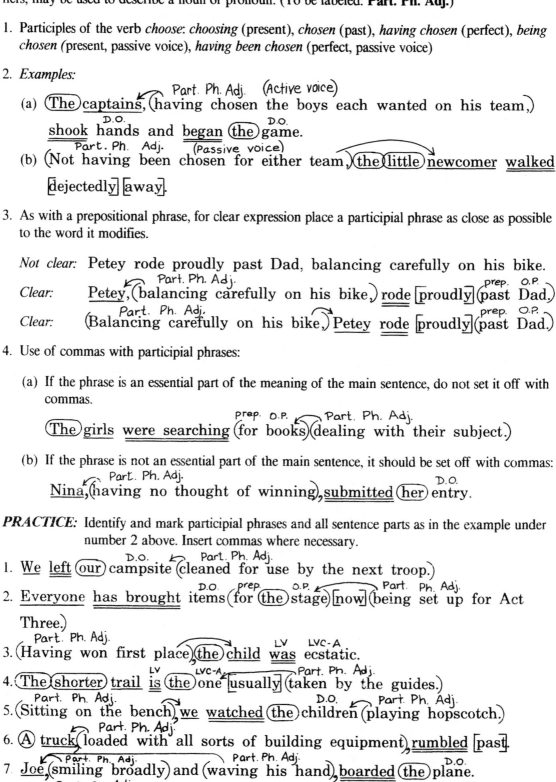

    Part. Ph. Adj. (Active voice)
  (a) The captains, (having chosen the boys each wanted on his team,) shook hands and began the game.
    Part. Ph. Adj. (Passive voice)
  (b) (Not having been chosen for either team,) the little newcomer walked dejectedly away.

3. As with a prepositional phrase, for clear expression place a participial phrase as close as possible to the word it modifies.

Not clear: Petey rode proudly past Dad, balancing carefully on his bike.
Clear: Petey, (balancing carefully on his bike,) rode proudly (past Dad.)
Clear: (Balancing carefully on his bike,) Petey rode proudly (past Dad.)

4. Use of commas with participial phrases:

  (a) If the phrase is an essential part of the meaning of the main sentence, do not set it off with commas.

    The girls were searching (for books) (dealing with their subject.)

  (b) If the phrase is not an essential part of the main sentence, it should be set off with commas:

    Nina, (having no thought of winning,) submitted her entry.

PRACTICE: Identify and mark participial phrases and all sentence parts as in the example under number 2 above. Insert commas where necessary.

1. We left our campsite (cleaned for use by the next troop.)

2. Everyone has brought items (for the stage) now (being set up for Act Three.)

3. (Having won first place) the child was ecstatic.

4. The shorter trail is the one usually (taken by the guides.)

5. (Sitting on the bench) we watched the children (playing hopscotch.)

6. A truck (loaded with all sorts of building equipment) rumbled past.

7. Joe, (smiling broadly) and (waving his hand,) boarded the plane.

8. (Having been badly shaken in the accident) the man, (huddled in a blanket,) was sitting (on the curb.)

Participial Phrases Used as Adjectives

Name _____

Date _____

The **participial phrase**, beginning with a verb participle and containing complements/modifiers, may be used to describe a noun or pronoun. (To be labeled: **Part. Ph. Adj.**)

1. Participles of the verb *choose*: *choosing* (present), *chosen* (past), *having chosen* (perfect), *being chosen* (present, passive voice), *having been chosen* (perfect, passive voice)

2. *Examples:*

   (a) The captains, (having chosen the boys each wanted on his team,) shook hands and began the game.

   (b) (Not having been chosen for either team,) the little newcomer walked dejectedly away.

3. As with a prepositional phrase, for clear expression place a participial phrase as close as possible to the word it modifies.

   Not clear: Petey rode proudly past Dad, balancing carefully on his bike.

   Clear: Petey, (balancing carefully on his bike,) rode proudly (past Dad.)

   Clear: (Balancing carefully on his bike,) Petey rode proudly (past Dad.)

4. Use of commas with participial phrases:

   (a) If the phrase is an essential part of the meaning of the main sentence, do not set it off with commas.

   The girls were searching (for books) (dealing with their subject.)

   (b) If the phrase is not an essential part of the main sentence, it should be set off with commas:

   Nina, (having no thought of winning,) submitted her entry.

PRACTICE: Identify and mark participial phrases and all sentence parts as in the example under number 2 above. Insert commas where necessary.

1. We left our campsite cleaned for use by the next troop.

2. Everyone has brought items for the stage now being set up for Act Three.

3. Having won first place the child was ecstatic.

4. The shorter trail is the one usually taken by the guides.

5. Sitting on the bench we watched the children playing hopscotch.

6. A truck loaded with all sorts of building equipment rumbled past.

7. Joe smiling broadly and waving his hand boarded the plane.

8. Having been badly shaken in the accident the man huddled in a blanket was sitting on the curb.

Understanding and Using Good Grammar

Infinitive Phrases Used as Adjectives

While many students are able to differentiate among and understand the various uses of verb forms, sentence verbs and verbals, some may become confused. It is for them that the **Understand** items are included.

Copy the following sentences on the overhead or chalkboard. Point out to students that the study of the use of phrases opens new vistas for them on ways to express their ideas:

1. (Elmer's) tendency (to jump to conclusions) is [really] annoying.

2. Elmer has (a) tendency (to jump to conclusions.)

3. (Elmer's) [most] (annoying) tendency is (to jump to conclusions.)

4. (To jump to conclusions) is (Elmer's) (bad) tendency.

5. Elmer tends (to jump to conclusions.)

Volunteers could come to the chalkboard or overhead to underline and label the sentence parts.

Infinitive Phrases Used as Adjectives

Infinitives and infinitive phrases may be used as adjectives.

1. An **infinitive** is the plain form of a verb preceded by **to**: *to try, to run.*
   Do not confuse it with a prepositional phrase that begins with the preposition *to* and ends with a noun or pronoun object: *to the bank.*

2. An **infinitive phrase** includes the infinitive and its complements and/or modifiers: *to win easily, to complete the project.*

   Examples: It is (his) expectation (to win the election easily.)

   (The) girls asked (for (more) time) (to complete their project.)

UNDERSTAND:

1. Do not mistake an infinitive for the sentence verb.

2. Remember that the verb in a sentence is the word that tells what is being done or is in the list of helping verbs.

3. In the example sentences, the infinitives, *to win* and *to complete*, have no subject.

4. The other verb words do have subjects: It is; girls asked.

5. An infinitive phrase used as an adjective answers the question, "What kind?" about the noun or pronoun it modifies:

   It is (his) expectation (what kind of expectation?) (to win . . . .)

PRACTICE:
Mark or label all sentence parts as in the examples. Put parentheses around the phrase, write **Inf./Inf. Ph. Adj.** above the infinitive, and draw an arrow to the word modified.

1. (Your) suggestion (to leave early in the morning) is [quite] sensible.

2. They have (several) (serious) problems (to consider) and (to resolve.)

3. (The) package (to be wrapped next) is (a) [rather] (awkward) shape.

4. (The) question (to be decided) is (which) day (to leave.)

5. Will you have (enough) time (to make the dessert for twenty guests?)

6. [Yesterday], (at (the) (bake) sale,) mine was (the) (last) cake (to be sold.)

7. I [really] need (new) boots (to wear for hiking.)

8. We should set [aside] (some) time (to study for the test.)

9. (Mom's) decision (to buy a new car) [really] surprised us.

10. Clancy has (a) (real) ability (to influence others.)

11. (The) (little) boy had (a) (good) reason (to hurry home.)

Name _____

Date _____

Infinitive Phrases Used as Adjectives

Infinitives and infinitive phrases may be used as adjectives.

1. An **infinitive** is the plain form of a verb preceded by **to**: *to try, to run*.
   Do not confuse it with a prepositional phrase that begins with the preposition *to* and ends with a noun or pronoun object: *to the bank*.

2. An **infinitive phrase** includes the infinitive and its complements and/or modifiers: *to win easily, to complete the project*.

   Examples: It is (his) expectation (to win the election easily.)

   (The) girls asked (for (more) time)(to complete their project)

UNDERSTAND:

1. Do not mistake an infinitive for the sentence verb.

2. Remember that the verb in a sentence is the word that tells what is being done or is in the list of helping verbs.

3. In the example sentences, the infinitives, *to win* and *to complete*, have no subject.

4. The other verb words do have subjects: It is;   girls asked.

5. An infinitive phrase used as an adjective answers the question, "What kind?" about the noun or pronoun it modifies:

   It is (his) expectation (what kind of expectation?)(to win . . . .)

PRACTICE:
Mark or label all sentence parts as in the examples. Put parentheses around the phrase, write **Inf./Inf. Ph. Adj.** above the infinitive, and draw an arrow to the word modified.

1. Your suggestion to leave early in the morning is quite sensible.

2. They have several serious problems to consider and to resolve.

3. The package to be wrapped next is a rather awkward shape.

4. The question to be decided is which day to leave.

5. Will you have enough time to make the dessert for twenty guests?

6. Yesterday, at the bake sale, mine was the last cake to be sold.

7. I really need new boots to wear for hiking.

8. We should set aside some time to study for the test.

9. Mom's decision to buy a new car really surprised us.

10. Clancy has a real ability to influence others.

11. The little boy had a good reason to hurry home.

Understanding and Using Good Grammar

FINAL PRACTICE:
Recognizing Prepositional, Participial, and Infinitive Phrases Used as Adjectives

To remind students of the makeup of the phrases, write on the chalkboard or overhead:

Prepositional phrase = (prep. + noun or pronoun O.P.)
Participial phrase = (verb with a participial ending -*ing*, -*ed*, etc.)
Infinitive phrase = (*to* + plain form of verb)

In order for the phrases to stand out, you may tell students not to label the other sentence parts. When students have completed the Final Practice, be sure they understand the following points in these sentences:

Sentence 4: *To the soldiers* is an adverbial prep. phrase; the arrow should go to *came*.

6: Prep. ph., *of the music*, is essential to the meaning of the inf. ph. and should be included in it.

14: Part. ph., *showing no license*, should be labeled separately since it modifies *motorboat* and in no way describes *man*.

Students should have this page to review before the Test.

FINAL PRACTICE:
Recognizing Prepositional, Participial, and Infinitive Phrases Used as Adjectives

Instructions: Put parentheses around each phrase, label appropriately **prep./O.P.**, **Part. Ph.**, and **Inf. Ph.**, and draw an arrow to the word modified. Mark or label all other sentence parts. One sentence has an **Inf. Ph. LVC-A.**

1. (Bill's) attitude (toward teachers and homework) is unfortunate.

2. Mr. James is (the) teacher (sitting to your left.)

3. (Perched on the cage door,) (the) parakeet seemed (to be looking around questioningly.)

4. (The) order (to advance over the rough terrain) came (to the soldiers.)

5. I watched (the) actress (in the torn calico dress.)

6. (The) pianist needs someone (to turn the pages of the music.)

7. (Thor Heyerdahl's) raft, (made of balsa logs), reached Polynesia.

8. Does Debbie have (enough) time (to make a telephone call?)

9. (Which) road would be (the) (best) one (to take?)

10. (The) girl (in the blue sweater) has (the) (best) chance (to be elected.)

11. (The) package (being sent today) is a [very] (valuable) one.

12. I do [not] know (the) answer (to your question.)

13. (The) boy could touch (the) (long) icicles (hanging from the roof.)

14. A man (in a motorboat) (showing no license) zipped [past].

15. We have (no) right (to question his decision.)

16. (The) student (at the head) (of the line) seems nervous.

17. Has Dad read (that) (long) letter (describing Uncle Ed's tour of Alaska?)

18. (The) (whole) family admired (the) tree (decorated simply with crystal icicles.)

19. (The) floodwaters (covering the grass in the meadow) were receding.

20. (No) one had (any) reason (to doubt the stranger's explanation.)

FINAL PRACTICE:
Recognizing Prepositional, Participial, and Infinitive Phrases Used as Adjectives

Name _____

Date _____

Instructions: Put parentheses around each phrase, label appropriately **prep./O.P.**, **Part. Ph.**, and **Inf. Ph.**, and draw an arrow to the word modified. Mark or label all other sentence parts. One sentence has an **Inf. Ph. LVC–A.**

1. Bill's attitude toward teachers and homework is unfortunate.

2. Mr. James is the teacher sitting to your left.

3. Perched on the cage door, the parakeet seemed to be looking around questioningly.

4. The order to advance over the rough terrain came to the soldiers.

5. I watched the actress in the torn calico dress.

6. The pianist needs someone to turn the pages of the music.

7. Thor Heyerdahl's raft, made of balsa logs, reached Polynesia.

8. Does Debbie have enough time to make a telephone call?

9. Which road would be the best one to take?

10. The girl in the blue sweater has the best chance to be elected.

11. The package being sent today is a very valuable one.

12. I do not know the answer to your question.

13. The boy could touch the long icicles hanging from the roof.

14. A man in a motorboat showing no license zipped past.

15. We have no right to question his decision.

16. The student at the head of the line seems nervous.

17. Has Dad read that long letter describing Uncle Ed's tour of Alaska?

18. The whole family admired the tree decorated simply with crystal icicles.

19. The floodwaters covering the grass in the meadow were receding.

20. No one had any reason to doubt the stranger's explanation.

  Understanding and Using Good Grammar

TEST 1:
Recognizing Adjective Phrases

> The next reproducible page contains two copies of one half-page Test. Cut each
> duplicated page in half; give each student one half-page.

This is the first of two half-page Tests. You may want to have the students take this one
as a trial test, correct any errors they may have made when you give them the correct marks
and labels, and review it in preparation for Test 2.

Suggested Grading:

Sentence 3: The adverbial prepositional phrase, *for more time*, modifies *asked*; do not count it
other than to be sure that the arrow from the infinitive phrase points to *time*.

Sentence 7: Both infinitive phrases modify *reason*.

Sentence 9: In the author's mind, both participial phrases modify *I*; however, the participial
phrase *surrounded by high cliffs* could be shown to modify *canyon*.

Phrase identification (3 points for each phrase):

½ point for opening parenthesis mark. The parentheses must accurately enclose the phrase.
1 point for arrow
1 point for label
½ point for closing parenthesis mark

Grading scale: 45 points

–1, 98	–7, 84	–13, 71
–2, 96	–8, 82	–14, 69
–3, 93	–9, 80	–15, 67
–4, 91	–10, 78	–16, 64
–5, 89	–11, 76	–17, 62
–6, 87	–12, 73	–18, 60
		–19, 58

Identification of other sentence parts:

Total points: 40

–1, 97	–7, 82	–13, 67
–2, 95	–8, 80	–14, 65
–3, 92	–9, 77	–15, 62
–4, 90	–10, 75	–16, 60
–5, 87	–11, 72	–17, 57
–6, 85	–12, 70	

TEST 1:
Recognizing Adjective Phrases

Instructions: One sentence has two simple infinitives which function as adjectives. Label them **Inf.**, enclose in parentheses, and draw an arrow to the modified words. Put parentheses around adjective phrases, and label them appropriately **prep./O.P.**, **Part. Ph.**, or **Inf. Ph.** Draw an arrow to the modified word. Mark or label all other sentence parts.

1. (The) voice (heard on the intercom) sounded stern.

2. (Your) suggestion (about the program)(for the kindergarteners) is being considered.

3. (The) girls asked (for more time)(to complete their project.)

4. (Sitting on the bench), we watched (the) children (playing hopscotch.)

5. (The) question (to be decided) is (which) day (to leave.)

6. (The) child, (jumping rope happily), was chanting (a)(nursery) rhyme.

7. We have (no) reason (to question his honesty) nor (to reject his decision.)

8. (The) student (at the head)(of the line) seems ill.

9. (Standing in the box canyon)(surrounded by high cliffs,) I gazed [upward].

Name _____

Date _____

TEST 1: Recognizing Adjective Phrases

Instructions: One sentence has two simple infinitives which function as adjectives. Label them **Inf.**, enclose in parentheses, and draw an arrow to the modified words. Put parentheses around adjective phrases, and label them appropriately **prep./O.P.**, **Part. Ph.**, or **Inf. Ph.** Draw an arrow to the modified word. Mark or label all other sentence parts.

1. The voice heard on the intercom sounded stern.
2. Your suggestion about the program for the kindergarteners is being considered.
3. The girls asked for more time to complete their project.
4. Sitting on the bench, we watched the children playing hopscotch.
5. The question to be decided is which day to leave.
6. The child, jumping rope happily, was chanting a nursery rhyme.
7. We have no reason to question his honesty nor to reject his decision.
8. The student at the head of the line seems ill.
9. Standing in the box canyon, surrounded by high cliffs, I gazed upward.

Name _____

Date _____

TEST 1: Recognizing Adjective Phrases

Instructions: One sentence has two simple infinitives which function as adjectives. Label them **Inf.**, enclose in parentheses, and draw an arrow to the modified words. Put parentheses around adjective phrases, and label them appropriately **prep./O.P.**, **Part. Ph.**, or **Inf. Ph.** Draw an arrow to the modified word. Mark or label all other sentence parts.

1. The voice heard on the intercom sounded stern.
2. Your suggestion about the program for the kindergarteners is being considered.
3. The girls asked for more time to complete their project.
4. Sitting on the bench, we watched the children playing hopscotch.
5. The question to be decided is which day to leave.
6. The child, jumping rope happily, was chanting a nursery rhyme.
7. We have no reason to question his honesty nor to reject his decision.
8. The student at the head of the line seems ill.
9. Standing in the box canyon, surrounded by high cliffs, I gazed upward.

Understanding and Using Good Grammar

TEST 2:
Recognizing Adjective Phrases

The next reproducible page contains two copies of one half-page Test. Cut each duplicated page in half; give each student one half-page.

Advise students to be alert! They should be sure to:

1. Label the compound participial adjective in one sentence.
2. Write *You* as the subject of a command in one sentence.
3. Write *to* before the verb word where it has been left out in one infinitive phrase.

Suggested Grading:

Phrase identification:

For each phrase, 3 points as shown on page 280. Total points: 45

Identification of other sentence parts:

Total points: 36

–1, 97	–4, 89	–7, 81	–10, 72	–14, 64
–2, 94	–5, 86	–8, 78	–11, 70	–15, 61
–3, 92	–6, 83	–9, 75	–12, 67	–16, 58

TEST 2:
Recognizing Adjective Phrases

Instructions: Put parentheses around adjective phrases, and label them appropriately **prep./O.P.**, **Part. Ph.**, or **Inf. Ph.** Draw an arrow to the modified word. Mark or label all other sentence parts.

1. The expressions (on the faces) (of several) (of the nearby observers) betrayed their annoyance.

2. Marcella has something (exciting and surprising) (to tell you.)

3. (Hearing the dog's vicious growl,) the little boy clutched my hand.

4. The elderly man, (looking rather helpless,) needed someone (to hold the rickety ladder.)

5. The girl (in the blue sweater) has the best chance (to be elected.)

6. (You) Take time (to read the instructions carefully) and (mark your answers clearly.)

7. A man (in a motorboat) (showing no license) zipped [past].

8. (Looking disappointed,) Amanda walked [away].

TEST 2: Recognizing Adjective Phrases

Name _____

Date _____

Instructions: Put parentheses around adjective phrases, and label them appropriately **prep./O.P.**, **Part. Ph.**, or **Inf. Ph.** Draw an arrow to the modified word. Mark or label all other sentence parts.

1. The expressions on the faces of several of the nearby observers betrayed their annoyance.

2. Marcella has something exciting and surprising to tell you.

3. Hearing the dog's vicious growl, the little boy clutched my hand.

4. The elderly man, looking rather helpless, needed someone to hold the rickety ladder.

5. The girl in the blue sweater has the best chance to be elected.

6. Take time to read the instructions carefully and mark your answers clearly.

7. A man in a motorboat showing no license zipped past.

8. Looking disappointed, Amanda walked away.

TEST 2: Recognizing Adjective Phrases

Name _____

Date _____

Instructions: Put parentheses around adjective phrases, and label them appropriately **prep./O.P.**, **Part. Ph.**, or **Inf. Ph.** Draw an arrow to the modified word. Mark or label all other sentence parts.

1. The expressions on the faces of several of the nearby observers betrayed their annoyance.

2. Marcella has something exciting and surprising to tell you.

3. Hearing the dog's vicious growl, the little boy clutched my hand.

4. The elderly man, looking rather helpless, needed someone to hold the rickety ladder.

5. The girl in the blue sweater has the best chance to be elected.

6. Take time to read the instructions carefully and mark your answers clearly.

7. A man in a motorboat showing no license zipped past.

8. Looking disappointed, Amanda walked away.

Clauses Used as Adjectives

Remind students:

1. As with other noun/pronoun modifiers, an adjective clause tells *which one, what kind, how many,* or *whose* about the word it modifies.

2. And, as with all other information sheets, students should keep this one after you check the work, record scores, and return the papers.

3. On the chalkboard or overhead, write this sentence which has an adjective clause modifying an indirect object. Select a volunteer to analyze the sentence parts.

Joey's grandfather bequeathed us, who are very distant relatives, a large sum of money.

4. Work with students in marking or labeling sentence parts in sentences 1–5 in "An adjective clause may modify."

Clauses Used as Adjectives

DEFINITIONS:

1. A **clause** is a group of words having a verb and subject.

2. An **independent clause** has a verb and subject and expresses a complete thought.

   Example: Gold is a soft, yellow, malleable element.

3. A **dependent clause** has a verb and subject but does not express a complete thought. It functions as a modifier.

   Example: which is corrosion-resistant.

4. A **complex sentence** is made up of an independent clause, the main sentence, and at least one dependent clause.

   Example: Gold is a soft, yellow, malleable element which is corrosion-resistant.

5. An **adjective clause** is a dependent clause used to modify a noun or pronoun in an independent clause, the main sentence, and usually follows the noun it modifies. In this study, pointed brackets will be used to identify an adjective clause.

   Example: Gold is (a)(soft)(yellow)(malleable) element ⟨which is corrosion-resistant.⟩

Words that introduce adjective clauses connect the clause to the word it modifies in the main sentence:

1. Relative pronouns: **who, whom, whose, which, that**

2. Subordinate conjunctions (occasionally): **when, where, since, while**

An adjective clause may modify: (Mark or label all sentence parts.)

1. *Subject:* (The) man ⟨who [just] drove [past] is (my) uncle.

2. *Linking verb complement:* This is (the) house ⟨(that) Dad wants (to buy.)⟩

3. *Direct object:* (Most) students respect Mario, ⟨(whom) I told you (about.)⟩

4. *Appositive:* Jody Harvey, (the) girl ⟨who sits (beside me)(in science)⟩ is [very] intelligent.

5. *Object of preposition:* I've forgotten (the) name (of (the) town ⟨where] Dad was born.⟩

Punctuating adjective clauses

1. An adjective clause that supplies information essential to the meaning of the sentence should not be set off with commas.

2. An adjective clause that gives only incidental information about the word it modifies should be set off with commas.

   Example: (The) argument, ⟨while it was stimulating,⟩ did [not] resolve (the) problem.

Name _____

Date _____

Clauses Used as Adjectives

DEFINITIONS:

1. A **clause** is a group of words having a verb and subject.

2. An **independent clause** has a verb and subject and expresses a complete thought.

    Example: Gold is a soft, yellow, malleable element.

3. A **dependent clause** has a verb and subject but does not express a complete thought. It functions as a modifier.

    Example: which is corrosion-resistant.

4. A **complex sentence** is made up of an independent clause, the main sentence, and at least one dependent clause.

    Example: Gold is a soft, yellow, malleable element which is corrosion-resistant.

5. An **adjective clause** is a dependent clause used to modify a noun or pronoun in an independent clause, the main sentence, and usually follows the noun it modifies. In this study, pointed brackets will be used to identify an adjective clause.

    Example: Gold is (a)(soft)(yellow)(malleable) element which is corrosion-resistant.

Words that introduce adjective clauses connect the clause to the word it modifies in the main sentence:

1. Relative pronouns: **who, whom, whose, which, that**

2. Subordinate conjunctions (occasionally): **when, where, since, while**

An adjective clause may modify: (Mark or label all sentence parts.)

1. *Subject:* The man who just drove past is my uncle.

2. *Linking verb complement:* This is the house that Dad wants to buy.

3. *Direct object:* Most students respect Mario, whom I told you about.

4. *Appositive:* Jody Harvey, the girl who sits beside me in science, is very intelligent.

5. *Object of preposition:* I've forgotten the name of the town where Dad was born.

Punctuating adjective clauses

1. An adjective clause that supplies information essential to the meaning of the sentence should not be set off with commas.

2. An adjective clause that gives only incidental information about the word it modifies should be set off with commas.

    Example: (The) argument, (while it was stimulating) did [not] resolve (the) problem.

Recognizing Adjective Clauses

Pointed brackets are used to identify adjective clauses. In addition, it would be helpful to students to write the label **Adj. Cl.** above the clause.

Point out to students:

1. An adjective clause may modify a noun or pronoun in any major part of a sentence. For example, in the example sentence it modifies an object of the preposition; in sentence 1, a direct object; and in sentence 2, a subject.

2. The word that introduces the adjective clause may function in different ways within the clause. For example:

   Example sentence: *who*, subject
         Sentence 1: *which*, subject
         Sentence 3: *whose*, possessive adjective
         Sentence 5: *which*, direct object
         Sentence 7: *where*, adverb

3. In sentences where the adjective clause has been set off with commas, sentences 1, 2, 5, 8, 9, 11, and 14, the clauses are not essential to the meaning of the sentence. Stress use of commas!

Return this practice paper to the students before the Test on page 297.

Recognizing Adjective Clauses

Instructions: Mark or label all sentence parts in the main sentence and in the adjective clause; insert commas where needed; put pointed brackets around the clause; draw an arrow from the clause to the word it modifies.

Example: That book belongs (to the girl) who shares my locker.

1. We have eaten all the dessert, which was really delicious.

2. Sarah, who is a champion tennis player, is my next-door neighbor.

3. Jay Bennett is an author whose books have become quite popular.

4. The magician performed tricks that absolutely amazed the children.

5. This book, which many students have read recently, is very good.

6. Perhaps people who always arrive late at school should get up earlier.

7. Santa Cruz is one place where nearly everyone has fun.

8. Floy, whom we just passed on the stairs, is a very accomplished pianist.

9. A stranger, who looks very much like Uncle Pat, is at the front door.

10. My horse is one possession which I could never give away or sell.

11. One girl who lives near the house that your parents are buying is Candice Baker, whom I know very well.

12. A person who has an extreme excess of self-confidence may be boring to others.

13. Do you have any idea when Gabe plans to arrive?

14. Gary, who was born in Canada, has become, along with his parents, a citizen of the U.S.

15. The days since the accident occurred have been like a nightmare.

16. My class and extracurricular schedules leave me little time when I can have just plain fun.

17. The gift that I am giving Mom is really neat.

Recognizing Adjective Clauses

Name _____

Date _____

Instructions: Mark or label all sentence parts in the main sentence and in the adjective clause; insert commas where needed; put pointed brackets around the clause; draw an arrow from the clause to the word it modifies.

Example: (That) book belongs (to (the) girl)(who shares (my) locker.)

1. We have eaten all the dessert which was really delicious.

2. Sarah who is a champion tennis player is my next-door neighbor.

3. Jay Bennett is an author whose books have become quite popular.

4. The magician performed tricks that absolutely amazed the children.

5. This book which many students have read recently is very good.

6. Perhaps people who always arrive late at school should get up earlier.

7. Santa Cruz is one place where nearly everyone has fun.

8. Floy whom we just passed on the stairs is a very accomplished pianist.

9. A stranger who looks very much like Uncle Pat is at the front door.

10. My horse is one possession which I could never give away or sell.

11. One girl who lives near the house that your parents are buying is Candice Baker whom I know very well.

12. A person who has an extreme excess of self-confidence may be boring to others.

13. Do you have any idea when Gabe plans to arrive?

14. Gary who was born in Canada has become, along with his parents, a citizen of the U.S.

15. The days since the accident occurred have been like a nightmare.

16. My class and extracurricular schedules leave me little time when I can have just plain fun.

17. The gift that I am giving Mom is really neat.

Understanding and Using Good Grammar

Recognizing Adjective Clauses

Explain to students:

Sentence 12: *hard to believe* is an infinitive adverb phrase which they will study in the next unit.

Sentence 17: It is not essential that the clause *who is only four years old* be set off with commas.

An interesting exercise which helps students to recognize the descriptive value of dependent adjective clauses is to call on individuals to analyze the adjective clause and tell what the reader can infer or imagine about the whole situation. For example, in sentence 7:

1. The speaker/writer is showing someone, or is writing to someone, about the huge trout.

2. *We* indicates that several people were in the fishing party.

3. *Huge* implies that the lake is probably big, deep, and secluded; *huge* fish aren't caught in small, shallow, frequently fished lakes.

4. Possibly they had fished in several places, but Lincoln Lake produced the fine catch.

5. The speaker/writer is not selfish about sharing the location.

Students have also enjoyed analyzing sentences 1, 9, 11, 12, and 14.

Return this practice paper to the students before the Test on page 291.

Recognizing Adjective Clauses

Instructions: Mark or label all sentence parts in the independent clause. In the adjective clause: underline verb and subject; identify the function of the introductory word, and draw an arrow from it to modified word; enclose it in pointed brackets. Insert necessary commas.

1. Jane, who is quite athletic, is a better-than-average student.

2. The Louvre, which is now a museum, was once the home of the French kings.

3. All students whose reports are due today should turn them in now.

4. May, the girl who had raised her hand, gave a very concise answer.

5. Are you the brother of the girl who won the ski race?

6. Uncle Theo lighted the candles which were standing on the table.

7. The lake where we caught those huge native trout is Lincoln Lake.

8. Are he and I the ones whom you were calling?

9. Richard, who has the highest academic record among the athletes, is walking toward us.

10. The student who borrowed this book should return it to the library.

11. The test that I spent hours to prepare for has been postponed.

12. The thief told a story that the police found hard to believe.

13. Miguel returned the skateboard which he had borrowed from us.

14. That book behind the others on the shelf is the one which Hugh lost.

15. The driver of the car that just cut in front of us is certainly reckless.

16. I made a report on the book which my aunt had given me for Christmas.

17. The kite which is highest is being flown by my little brother who is only four years old.

18. The girl who just left brought some good news.

Name _____

Date _____

Recognizing Adjective Clauses

Instructions: Mark or label all sentence parts in the independent clause. In the adjective clause: underline verb and subject; identify the function of the introductory word, and draw an arrow from it to modified word; enclose it in pointed brackets. Insert necessary commas.

1. Jane who is quite athletic is a better-than-average student.

2. The Louvre which is now a museum was once the home of the French kings.

3. All students whose reports are due today should turn them in now.

4. May the girl who had raised her hand gave a very concise answer.

5. Are you the brother of the girl who won the ski race?

6. Uncle Theo lighted the candles which were standing on the table.

7. The lake where we caught those huge native trout is Lincoln Lake.

8. Are he and I the ones whom you were calling?

9. Richard who has the highest academic record among the athletes is walking toward us.

10. The student who borrowed this book should return it to the library.

11. The test that I spent hours to prepare for has been postponed.

12. The thief told a story that the police found hard to believe.

13. Miguel returned the skateboard which he had borrowed from us.

14. That book behind the others on the shelf is the one which Hugh lost.

15. The driver of the car that just cut in front of us is certainly reckless.

16. I made a report on the book which my aunt had given me for Christmas.

17. The kite which is highest is being flown by my little brother who is only four years old.

18. The girl who just left brought some good news.

Understanding and Using Good Grammar

TEST: Recognizing and Punctuating Adjective Clauses

> The next reproducible page contains two copies of one half-page Test. Cut each duplicated page in half; give each student one half-page.

Suggested Grading:

Dependent adjective clause:

½ point for each pointed bracket. The pointed brackets enclosing the clause must be accurately placed.

1 point for each introductory word label

1 point for the subject if not introductory

1 point for verb

Sentence	Points	Sentence	Points
1	14	5	5
2	5	6	5
3	5	7	5
4	8	8	5
		Total points:	52 (minus 2% each error)

Independent clause labels and commas:

Total points: 50 (minus 2% each error)

TEST: Recognizing and Punctuating Adjective Clauses

Instructions: Mark or label all sentence parts in the independent clause. In the adjective clause: underline the verb and subject; identify the function of the introductory word, and draw an arrow from it to modified word; enclose it in pointed brackets. Insert necessary commas.

1. (One) girl ⟨who lives near the house⟩⟨that your parents are buying⟩ is Candice Baker, ⟨whom I know very well.⟩

2. (All) students ⟨whose reports are due today⟩ should turn them [in] [now].

3. (Nearly) everyone admires Mike, (the) boy ⟨whom I told you about.⟩

4. (The) kite ⟨which is highest⟩ is being flown (by (my) (little) brother) ⟨who is only four years old.⟩

5. Do you have (any) idea ⟨[when] Gabe plans to arrive?⟩

6. (The) days ⟨[since] the accident occurred⟩ have been (like (a) nightmare.)

7. (The) argument, ⟨[while] it was stimulating,⟩ got us [nowhere].

8. I've forgotten (the) name (of (the) town) ⟨[where] Dad was born.⟩

TEST: Recognizing and Punctuating Adjective Clauses

Name _____

Date _____

Instructions: Mark or label all sentence parts in the independent clause. In the adjective clause: underline the verb and subject; identify the function of the introductory word, and draw an arrow from it to modified word; enclose it in pointed brackets. Insert necessary commas.

1. One girl who lives near the house that your parents are buying is Candice Baker whom I know very well.

2. All students whose reports are due today should turn them in now.

3. Nearly everyone admires Mike the boy whom I told you about.

4. The kite which is highest is being flown by my little brother who is only four years old.

5. Do you have any idea when Gabe plans to arrive?

6. The days since the accident occurred have been like a nightmare.

7. The argument while it was stimulating got us nowhere.

8. I've forgotten the name of the town where Dad was born.

TEST: Recognizing and Punctuating Adjective Clauses

Name _____

Date _____

Instructions: Mark or label all sentence parts in the independent clause. In the adjective clause: underline the verb and subject; identify the function of the introductory word, and draw an arrow from it to modified word; enclose it in pointed brackets. Insert necessary commas.

1. One girl who lives near the house that your parents are buying is Candice Baker whom I know very well.

2. All students whose reports are due today should turn them in now.

3. Nearly everyone admires Mike the boy whom I told you about.

4. The kite which is highest is being flown by my little brother who is only four years old.

5. Do you have any idea when Gabe plans to arrive?

6. The days since the accident occurred have been like a nightmare.

7. The argument while it was stimulating got us nowhere.

8. I've forgotten the name of the town where Dad was born.

Understanding and Using Good Grammar

Facts About Adverbs

Students should add this page to their collection of information pages.

Remind students:

1. They should use their dictionary if they are in doubt about the correct form of an adverb.

    Example: quick, *adj.*, quicker, quickest; *adv.*, quickly (From their own knowledge they supply *more/most* to form the comparatives.)

2. Often they can determine the correct form by saying a sentence aloud.

    Example: Adj. low, lower, lowest: (Her) score was low.

    fast, faster, fastest: (The) clock was fast.

    Adv. The same words are used:

    She scored [low].   (The) clock was running [fast].

    (No one would say, She scored "lowly." The clock ran "fastly.")

    Return this page to students before they take the Test on page 310.

    If students need more practice in applying the basic facts about adverbs, duplicate for them appropriate pages from *Steps to Good Grammar*, pages 46–57 and 262–273.

Facts About Adverbs

DEFINITION: An **adverb** modifies a verb, an adjective, or another adverb. It may tell *how, when, where,* or *how much* about the word it modifies.

Example: We <u>could walk</u> ⌈rather⌉ ⌈quickly⌉ and <u>arrive</u> ⌈there⌉ ⌈soon⌉.
⠀⠀⠀⠀⠀⠀⠀⠀⠀⠀⠀(how much)⠀(how)⠀⠀⠀⠀⠀⠀⠀⠀⠀⠀⠀(where)⠀(when)

A. Forms of Adverbs

1. Many adverbs are formed by adding **-ly** or **-y** to an adjective: slow—slowly; merry—merrily; idle—idly; courageous—courageously.

   (a) Note that not all words that end in *-ly* are adverbs:
   ⠀⠀⠀⠀{ (lonely) child
   ⠀⠀⠀⠀{ (ugly) situation

   (b) In **making comparisons** using adverbs ending in **-ly,** use **more** or **less** before the adverb to compare two, **most** or **least** to compare three or more.

   > *Example:* Belle works quickly; Belinda works *more/less* quickly than Belle; Bertha works *most/least* quickly of the three.

2. A few adverbs add **-er** to compare two, and **-est** to compare three or more.

   <u>scored</u> low, lower, lowest; <u>worked</u> hard, harder, hardest; <u>came</u> early, earlier, earliest; <u>arrived</u> soon, sooner, soonest/late, later, latest

3. Do not use *more* before adverbs that end in *-er;* do not use *most* before adverbs that end in *-est.*

   I ran ~~more~~ faster than Rhonda; Sonya ran ~~most~~ fastest of us three.

4. Some adverbs are compared irregularly: far, farther (further), farthest (furthest); badly, worse, worst; little, less, least; much, more, most; well, better, best.

   Note: (a) Use *farther* to refer to actual distance:

   ⠀⠀⠀⠀⠀⠀⠀The campsite was *farther* away than I'd remembered.

   ⠀⠀⠀⠀(b) Use *further* to indicate possible additional degree, time, quantity:

   ⠀⠀⠀⠀⠀⠀⠀We should give the matter *further* consideration.

   ⠀⠀⠀⠀⠀⠀⠀Could anything be *further* from the truth?

5. Many adverbs that do not end in *-ly* are not used in making comparisons:

   afterward, again, almost, always, down, ever, everywhere, here, never, not, now, rather, then, there, too, up

PRACTICE: Above each incorrect adverb form, write the correct form.

1. From school, is it ~~further~~ *farther* to your house or to hers?

2. Gina will undoubtedly win the election ~~easy~~ *easily*.

3. In unison, we all shouted ~~loud~~ *loudly*, hoping to be heard.

4. We must avoid getting ~~farther~~ *further* in debt.

5. The storm certainly came up ~~sudden~~ *suddenly*.

6. Which of those three boys drives ~~more careful~~ *most carefully*?

7. She and I should have practiced ~~more~~ oftener.

Facts About Adverbs

Name _____

Date _____

DEFINITION: An **adverb** modifies a verb, an adjective, or another adverb. It may tell *how, when, where,* or *how much* about the word it modifies.

Example: We could walk [rather] [quickly] and arrive [there] [soon].
        (how much) (how)   (where) (when)

A. Forms of Adverbs

1. Many adverbs are formed by adding **-ly** or **-y** to an adjective: slow—slowly; merry—merrily; idle—idly; courageous—courageously.

   (a) Note that not all words that end in *-ly* are adverbs: { (lonely) child (ugly) situation

   (b) In **making comparisons** using adverbs ending in **-ly**, use **more** or **less** before the adverb to compare two, **most** or **least** to compare three or more.

      Example: Belle works quickly; Belinda works *more / less* quickly than Belle; Bertha works *most / least* quickly of the three.

2. A few adverbs add **-er** to compare two, and **-est** to compare three or more.

   scored low, lower, lowest; worked hard, harder, hardest; came early, earlier, earliest; arrived soon, sooner, soonest/late, later, latest

3. Do not use *more* before adverbs that end in *-er;* do not use *most* before adverbs that end in *-est.*

   I ran ~~more~~ faster than Rhonda; Sonya ran ~~most~~ fastest of us three.

4. Some adverbs are compared irregularly: far, farther (further), farthest (furthest); badly, worse, worst; little, less, least; much, more, most; well, better, best.

   Note: (a) Use *farther* to refer to actual distance:

      The campsite was *farther* away than I'd remembered.

      (b) Use *further* to indicate possible additional degree, time, quantity:

      We should give the matter *further* consideration.

      Could anything be *further* from the truth?

5. Many adverbs that do not end in *-ly* are not used in making comparisons:

   afterward, again, almost, always, down, ever, everywhere, here, never, not, now, rather, then, there, too, up

PRACTICE: Above each incorrect adverb form, write the correct form.

1. From school, is it further to your house or to hers?

2. Gina will undoubtedly win the election easy.

3. In unison, we all shouted loud, hoping to be heard.

4. We must avoid getting farther in debt.

5. The storm certainly came up sudden.

6. Which of those three boys drives more careful?

7. She and I should have practiced more oftener.

Understanding and Using Good Grammar

Facts About Adverbs
(continued)

Emphasize: bad ⎫ *adjectives* used after a linking
well ⎬ verb to refer to feeling/appearance

badly⎫ *adverbs* used after a doing verb
well ⎬ to tell *how* someone does something.

When reviewing the corrected Practice sentences, point out another correct form for sentence 5:

Benito hardly ever pitches badly . . .

Return this page to students to prepare for the test on page 310. The instruction on this page, as well as on page 301, was covered in detail, with ample practice work, in *Steps to Good Grammar*.

Facts About Adverbs
(continued)

B. Adjective/Adverb Confusion

ADJECTIVES

1. Adjectives modify nouns and pronouns.

2. **Good** is always an adjective.

   His behavior <u>was</u> good. *(LV, LVC-A)*

   I admire his (good) behavior. *(D.O.)*

3. **Well** may be used as an adjective after a linking verb to describe feeling or appearance.

   Adeline { feels *(LV)* / is *(LVC-A)* / <u>looks</u> } well.

4. **Bad** is used as an adjective after a linking verb to describe feeling or appearance.

   Adeline { feels *(LV)* / <u>looks</u> } bad today. *(LVC-A)*

5. **Sure, easy, real**: No one uses these adjectives incorrectly.

   I <u>felt</u> quite sure about it. *(LV, LVC-A)*

   We needed a (sure) cure. *(D.O.)*

   The problem <u>was</u> easy. *(LV, LVC-A)*

   It was an (easy) problem. *(LVC-N)*

   We have a (real) problem. *(D.O.)*

   The problem <u>is</u> real. *(LV, LVC-A)*

ADVERBS

1. Adverbs modify verbs, adjectives, and adverbs.

2. **Good** is never an adverb.

   He <u>behaved</u> (~~good~~, [well]).

   The team <u>had played</u> (~~good~~, [well]).

3. **Well** may be used as an adverb after a doing verb to tell *how* someone does something.

   Adeline { listens / does / dresses } [well].

4. **Badly** is used as an adverb after a doing verb to tell *how* someone does something.

   Adeline <u>did</u> [badly] on the test.

   Adeline <u>played</u> rather [badly].

5. **Surely, easily, really**: Sometimes people carelessly misuse these adjective-derived adverbs.

   It was (~~sure~~, surely) an error.

   I (~~sure~~, surely) wanted it.

   Everyone did it (~~easy~~, easily).

   It was done (~~easy~~, easily).

   I solved it (~~real~~, really) easily.

   I am (~~real~~, really) sure about it.

C. Avoid the double negative: do not combine the adverbs *not/n't*, *hardly*, or *scarcely* with other negative words: *none, no, no one, nobody, nothing, never, nowhere.*

Incorrect: We don't never go nowhere.
Correct: We do**n't** ever go anywhere.   We **n**ever go anywhere.   We go *nowhere*.

PRACTICE: Above errors in usage, write the correct form.

1. Hardly ~~nobody~~ *anybody* in the class

   could do the problem.

2. Some stores ~~don't have~~ *don't have* ~~scarcely~~ *scarcely* enough clerks.

3. Did~~n't~~ they have ~~no~~ money? *Didn't they have any money?*

4. Some committee members ~~haven't done nothing~~. *(haven't done anything)*

5. Benito ~~don't hardly~~ *doesn't* ever pitch ~~bad~~ *badly*

   during an important game.

6. We ~~sure~~ *surely* enjoyed the program.

7. Dana sang her solo ~~real good~~ *really well.*

8. We'll win this game ~~easy~~ *easily.*

Name _____

Date _____

Facts About Adverbs
(continued)

B. Adjective/Adverb Confusion

ADJECTIVES	ADVERBS

ADJECTIVES

1. Adjectives modify nouns and pronouns.

2. **Good** is always an adjective.
   His behavior <u>was</u> good.
   LV LVC-A
   I admire his (good) behavior.
   D.O.

3. **Well** may be used as an adjective after a linking verb to describe feeling or appearance.
   LV
   Adeline { feels   LVC-A
            { is   well.
            { <u>looks</u>

4. **Bad** is used as an adjective after a linking verb to describe feeling or appearance.
   LV
   Adeline { feels   LVC-A
            { <u>looks</u>   bad today.

5. **Sure, easy, real**: No one uses these adjectives incorrectly.
   LV   LVC-A
   I <u>felt</u> quite sure about it.
   D.O.
   We needed a (sure) cure.
   LV LVC-A
   The problem <u>was</u> easy.
   LV   LVC-N
   It <u>was</u> an (easy) problem.
   D.O.
   We have a (real) problem.
   LV LVC-A
   The problem <u>is</u> real.

ADVERBS

1. Adverbs modify verbs, adjectives, and adverbs.

2. **Good** is never an adverb.
   He <u>behaved</u> (~~good~~, [well]).
   The team <u>had played</u> (~~good~~, [well]).

3. **Well** may be used as an adverb after a doing verb to tell *how* someone does something.
   { listens
   Adeline { does   [well].
   { <u>dresses</u>

4. **Badly** is used as an adverb after a doing verb to tell *how* someone does something.
   Adeline <u>did</u> [badly] on the test.
   Adeline <u>played</u> rather [badly].

5. **Surely, easily, really**: Sometimes people carelessly misuse these adjective-derived adverbs.
   It was (~~sure~~, surely) an error.
   I (~~sure~~, surely) wanted it.
   Everyone did it (~~easy~~, easily).
   It was done (~~easy~~, easily).
   I solved it (~~real~~, really) easily.
   I am (~~real~~, really) sure about it.

C. Avoid the double negative: do not combine the adverbs *not/n't*, *hardly*, or *scarcely* with other negative words: *none, no, no one, nobody, nothing, never, nowhere.*

Incorrect: We don't never go nowhere.
Correct: We do*n't* ever go anywhere.   We *n*ever go anywhere.   We go *no*where.

PRACTICE: Above errors in usage, write the correct form.

1. Hardly nobody in the class could do the problem.

2. Some stores don't have scarcely enough clerks.

3. Didn't they have no money?

4. Some committee members haven't done nothing.

5. Benito don't hardly ever pitch bad during an important game.

6. We sure enjoyed the program.

7. Dana sang her solo real good.

8. We'll win this game easy.

Understanding and Using Good Grammar

FINAL DRILL:
Facts About Adverbs

> The next reproducible page contains two copies of one half-page Drill. Cut each duplicated page in half; give each student one half-page.

This page may be used as a trial test with each student correcting his or her own errors.

When reviewing corrections with students, point out the following alternative correct forms:

Sentence 2: (a) Do you do nothing foolish?

                  (b) Don't you ever do anything foolish?

Sentence 12:   . . . really surprised that Lars found nobody. . . .

FINAL DRILL:
Facts About Adverbs

Instructions: Above errors in usage, write the correct form.

1. We both studied ~~good~~ *well* and should pass the test ~~easy~~ *easily*.

2. Don't you never do ~~nothing~~ *anything* foolish?

3. We should turn around ~~careful~~ *carefully* and move ~~real slow~~ *really slowly* down the cliff.

4. All three girls sing ~~good~~ *well* but the ~~shorter~~ *shortest* one sings ~~better~~ *best*.

5. We traveled 20 miles ~~further~~ *farther* than we needed to.

6. I ~~sure~~ *surely* am tired; we worked ~~constant~~ *constantly* today.

7. The wind blew ~~soft~~ *softly* and the rain fell ~~steady~~ *steadily*.

8. I felt ~~badly~~ *bad* yesterday, but I feel ~~real good~~ *really well* today.

9. We simply must not get ~~farther~~ *further* into debt.

10. Of the two men, Mr. Stone arrived ~~earliest~~ *earlier* and stayed ~~longest~~ *longer*.

11. The home team was playing quite ~~good~~ *well* while the visiting team was playing rather ~~bad~~ *badly*.

12. Grandpa was ~~real~~ *really* surprised that Lars didn't find ~~nobody~~ *anybody* at the cabin.

13. Peg could run ~~more~~ faster if she wanted to.

FINAL DRILL:
Facts About Adverbs

Name _____

Date _____

Instructions: Above errors in usage, write the correct form.

1. We both studied good and should pass the test easy.

2. Don't you never do nothing foolish?

3. We should turn around careful and move real slow down the cliff.

4. All three girls sing good but the shorter one sings better.

5. We traveled 20 miles further than we needed to.

6. I sure am tired; we worked constant today.

7. The wind blew soft and the rain fell steady.

8. I felt badly yesterday, but I feel real good today.

9. We simply must not get farther into debt.

10. Of the two men, Mr. Stone arrived earliest and stayed longest.

11. The home team was playing quite good while the visiting team was playing rather bad.

12. Grandpa was real surprised that Lars didn't find nobody at the cabin.

13. Peg could run more faster if she wanted to.

Name _____

Date _____

FINAL DRILL:
Facts About Adverbs

Instructions: Above errors in usage, write the correct form.

1. We both studied good and should pass the test easy.

2. Don't you never do nothing foolish?

3. We should turn around careful and move real slow down the cliff.

4. All three girls sing good but the shorter one sings better.

5. We traveled 20 miles further than we needed to.

6. I sure am tired; we worked constant today.

7. The wind blew soft and the rain fell steady.

8. I felt badly yesterday, but I feel real good today.

9. We simply must not get farther into debt.

10. Of the two men, Mr. Stone arrived earliest and stayed longest.

11. The home team was playing quite good while the visiting team was playing rather bad.

12. Grandpa was real surprised that Lars didn't find nobody at the cabin.

13. Peg could run more faster if she wanted to.

TEST:
Facts About Adverbs

> The next reproducible page contains two copies of one half-page Test. Cut each duplicated page in half; give each student one half-page.

When reviewing corrections with students, point out the following alternative correct forms:

Sentence 2: Do you never travel anywhere . . .
              Don't you ever travel . . .

Sentence 9: There is no ice cream left.   ⎫ Acceptable, though neither expresses
              There isn't any ice cream left.   ⎬ the idea of "scarcely."
                                                   ⎭

Suggested Grading:

There are 24 corrections.

–1, 96	–4, 83	–7, 71	–10, 58
–2, 92	–5, 79	–8, 67	–11, 54
–3, 88	–6, 75	–9, 63	–12, 50

TEST:
Facts About Adverbs

Instructions: Above errors in usage, write the correct form.

1. The team played rather ~~bad~~ *badly* yesterday; it's playing ~~real~~ ~~good~~ *really well* today.

2. Don't you ~~never~~ *ever* travel ~~nowhere~~ *anywhere* during the summer?

3. We ~~sure~~ *surely* shouldn't drive ~~further~~ *farther* until we have been informed ~~farther~~ *further* about the roads.

4. Masashi stood ~~quiet~~ *quietly* and planned his next pitch ~~careful~~ *carefully*.

5. Of the two girls, Clarissa worked ~~hardest~~ *harder* and finished ~~quickest~~ *more quickly*.

6. Nothing was ~~farther~~ *further* from my mind than the idea that I should run ~~further~~ *farther*.

7. Meghan felt ~~real~~ ~~badly~~ *really bad* about losing; she had hoped to play ~~good~~ *well* and win ~~easy~~ *easily*.

8. The truck's motor is idling ~~more~~ smoother.

9. There ~~isn't~~ *is* scarcely ~~no~~ *any* ice cream left.

10. Of the three teachers, that one works ~~harder~~ *hardest* and helps us ~~more~~ *most*.

11. Who drives most ~~careful~~ *carefully*?

Name _____

Date _____

TEST:
Facts About Adverbs

Instructions: Above errors in usage, write the correct form.

1. The team played rather bad yesterday; it's playing real good today.
2. Don't you never travel nowhere during the summer?
3. We sure shouldn't drive further until we have been informed farther about the roads.
4. Masashi stood quiet and planned his next pitch careful.
5. Of the two girls, Clarissa worked hardest and finished quickest.
6. Nothing was farther from my mind than the idea that I should run further.
7. Meghan felt real badly about losing; she had hoped to play good and win easy.
8. The truck's motor is idling more smoother.
9. There isn't scarcely no ice cream left.
10. Of the three teachers, that one works harder and helps us more.
11. Who drives most careful?

Name _____

Date _____

TEST:
Facts About Adverbs

Instructions: Above errors in usage, write the correct form.

1. The team played rather bad yesterday; it's playing real good today.
2. Don't you never travel nowhere during the summer?
3. We sure shouldn't drive further until we have been informed farther about the roads.
4. Masashi stood quiet and planned his next pitch careful.
5. Of the two girls, Clarissa worked hardest and finished quickest.
6. Nothing was farther from my mind than the idea that I should run further.
7. Meghan felt real badly about losing; she had hoped to play good and win easy.
8. The truck's motor is idling more smoother.
9. There isn't scarcely no ice cream left.
10. Of the three teachers, that one works harder and helps us more.
11. Who drives most careful?

© 1992, 1997 J. Weston Walch, Publisher   *Understanding and Using Good Grammar*

Prepositional Phrases Used as Adverbs

Regarding the first example sentences:

1. Adverbial nouns have not been studied as such in this book. Students should easily recognize that *Every morning* is a noun phrase that tells *how much* or *how often* about the verb *have ridden*.

2. Having studied infinitives used as nouns and as adjectives, it should not be difficult for students to understand that in this sentence the infinitive phrase *to prepare themselves* is used as an adverb that tells *why* about the verb.

   In Sentence 2 of the Practice the use of the comma after *day* indicates that the writer intends that both prepositional phrases should modify the LVC–A, *highest*.

   In Sentence 3 (From (last) summer's) is an elliptical prepositional phrase where the possessive noun serves as the object of the preposition, replacing "weather," the omitted true object of the preposition.

Prepositional Phrases Used as Adverbs

A. A **prepositional phrase**, beginning with a preposition and ending with a noun or pronoun object, may be used to modify a verb, an adjective, or another adverb.

1. An **adverb phrase** tells *how, when, where, how much,* or *why* about the word it modifies:

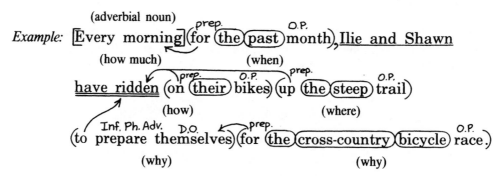

2. Remember that the placement of modifiers may determine the exact meaning of the sentence:

Example: (a) Sis [nearly] lost (ten) dollars. (Fortunately, she didn't!)

Sis lost [nearly] (ten) dollars. (Fortunately it wasn't more!)

(b) (Four) students are waiting (in (the) office.) (Others are waiting in the hall!)

(Four) students (in (the) office) are waiting. (The others left!)

3. In making a comparison using the word *different,* follow it with a prepositional phrase beginning with *from*:

Example: (My) grade (on (the) test) was [certainly] different (from yours or his.)

(Avoid this substandard usage: "...different *than* yours or his" *Than,* as a subordinate conjunction used to introduce dependent clauses, will be studied in the next section.)

PRACTICE: Mark or label all sentence parts, including parentheses around the phrases and arrows from the phrase to the word modified.

1. (During (the) storm) we stayed (in (the) cabin) (for (several) hours.)

2. (My) energy is [certainly] highest (on (a) cool, sunny) day) (in (the) early) morning.)

3. (This) summer's) weather has been [very] different (from (last) summer's.)

4. (At (that) moment) (a) stranger appeared (from behind (a) huge) rock) and seated himself (on (a) stump) (beside (the) stream.)

5. (Around (the) street) light,) (feathery) snowflakes floated [aimlessly] (in (the) still) air) (like (small) white) moths.)

6. (The) little) girl looks [quite] different (from (her) sister.)

Prepositional Phrases
Used as Adverbs

Name _____

Date _____

A. A **prepositional phrase**, beginning with a preposition and ending with a noun or pronoun object, may be used to modify a verb, an adjective, or another adverb.

1. An **adverb phrase** tells *how, when, where, how much,* or *why* about the word it modifies:

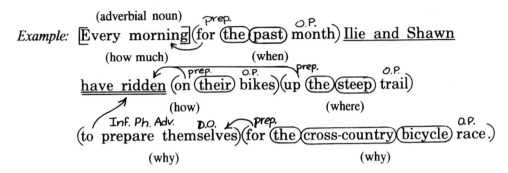

Example:

2. Remember that the placement of modifiers may determine the exact meaning of the sentence:

Example: (a) Sis ⌈nearly⌋ lost⟨ten⟩ dollars. (Fortunately, she didn't!)

Sis lost ⌈nearly⟨ten⟩ dollars. (Fortunately it wasn't more!)

(b) ⟨Four⟩ students are waiting(in (the) office.) (Others are waiting in the hall!)

⟨Four⟩ students(in (the) office) are waiting. (The others left!)

3. In making a comparison using the word *different*, follow it with a prepositional phrase beginning with *from*:

Example: ⟨My⟩ grade(on (the) test) was ⌈certainly⌋ different(from yours or his.)

(Avoid this substandard usage: "...different *than* yours or his" *Than*, as a subordinate conjunction used to introduce dependent clauses, will be studied in the next section.)

PRACTICE: Mark or label all sentence parts, including parentheses around the phrases and arrows from the phrase to the word modified.

1. During the storm we stayed in the cabin for several hours.

2. My energy is certainly highest on a cool, sunny day, in the early morning.

3. This summer's weather has been very different from last summer's.

4. At that moment a stranger appeared from behind a huge rock and seated himself on a stump beside the stream.

5. Around the street light, feathery snowflakes floated aimlessly in the still air like small white moths.

6. The little girl looks quite different from her sister.

Understanding and Using Good Grammar

Infinitive Phrases Used as Adverbs

In Example 2 point out to students that a comma is used after an introductory adverbial infinitive phrase:

To avoid being seen, we moved . . .

Under **Avoid Careless Usage**, note that the split infinitive and dangling infinitive phrase were presented on page 246. Restudy, plus practice, is desirable.

For the second Practice instruct students to write at least the words of the correct form (see below) on the reverse side of the paper.

Sentence 1: . . . try to be ready.

2: . . . one/we/you should move into . . .
or
. . . It would be wise for us to move . . .

3: . . . he really needed to pass . . .

4: . . . to try to arrive on time for once.

5: . . . to object strongly.

6: . . . one/a gardener/he or she should irrigate regularly.
or
. . . it is necessary to irrigate regularly.

Infinitive Phrases Used as Adverbs

B. Infinitives and infinitive phrases may be used as adverbs.

REMEMBER:

1. An **infinitive** is the plain form of a verb preceded by **to**: *to qualify, to avoid.*

2. An **infinitive phrase** includes the infinitive and its complements/modifiers: *to qualify for the race, to avoid being seen.*

3. An **adverbial infinitive or infinitive phrase** answers the question *why?* about the word it modifies. Use the label **Inf. Adv./Inf. Ph. Adv.**, enclose the phrase in brackets, and draw an arrow to the modified word.

   Examples: 1. Ellie competed (in some earlier races) to qualify for this one.
   2. [To avoid being seen], we moved deeper (into the cave.)

PRACTICE: Mark parts of speech, including adverbial infinitives and infinitive phrases as in the examples above.

1. I was glad [to accept.]

2. Stan ran [out] (on the court) [to practice.]

3. (The angry, disheveled) customer waited [to see the manager.]

4. [To attract our attention], Dad had whistled [shrilly,] [repeatedly.]

5. Coach moved [forward] (with authority) [to stop the argument.]

6. Mr. Adams spoke [loudly] [enough] [to be heard by everyone.]

AVOID CARELESS USAGE

1. **Split infinitive**—using a word(s) between "to" and the verb.

   Poor: If you want to *really* help, be quiet!
   Standard: If you **really** want to help, be quiet!

2. **Dangling infinitive phrase**—does not tell who does the action.

   Poor: To see well, *moving* to different seats was necessary.
   Standard: To see well, we **moved** to different seats.

3. **Substituting "and" for "to":** *try and* rather than *try to.*

   Poor: You should *try and* get some rest.
   Standard: You should **try to** get some rest.

PRACTICE: Rewrite these sentences, using standard form. (Answers may vary.)

1. Next time, you should try ~~and~~ *to* be ready.

2. To take the off ramp, ~~moving~~ *move* into the right-hand lane is ~~wise~~.

3. Undoubtedly, he needed to (really) pass that test.

4. Joan and I had jogged to school to try ~~and~~ *to* (for once) arrive on time.

5. Claude had a reason to (strongly) object.

6. To grow good vegetables, ~~regular irrigation~~ *it* is necessary *to irrigate regularly.*

Name _____

Date _____

Infinitive Phrases Used as Adverbs

B. Infinitives and infinitive phrases may be used as adverbs.

REMEMBER:

1. An **infinitive** is the plain form of a verb preceded by **to**: *to qualify, to avoid.*

2. An **infinitive phrase** includes the infinitive and its complements/modifiers: *to qualify for the race, to avoid being seen.*

3. An **adverbial infinitive or infinitive phrase** answers the question *why?* about the word it modifies. Use the label **Inf. Adv./Inf. Ph. Adv.**, enclose the phrase in brackets, and draw an arrow to the modified word.

Examples: 1. Ellie competed (in some earlier races) to qualify for this one.
2. To avoid being seen we moved deeper (into the cave.)

PRACTICE: Mark parts of speech, including adverbial infinitives and infinitive phrases as in the examples above.

1. I was glad to accept.

2. Stan ran out on the court to practice.

3. The angry, disheveled customer waited to see the manager.

4. To attract our attention, Dad had whistled shrilly, repeatedly.

5. Coach moved forward with authority to stop the argument.

6. Mr. Adams spoke loudly enough to be heard by everyone.

AVOID CARELESS USAGE

1. **Split infinitive**—using a word(s) between "to" and the verb.

   Poor: If you want to *really* help, be quiet!
   Standard: If you **really** want to help, be quiet!

2. **Dangling infinitive phrase**—does not tell who does the action.

   Poor: To see well, *moving* to different seats was necessary.
   Standard: To see well, we **moved** to different seats.

3. **Substituting "and" for "to":** *try and* rather than *try to.*

   Poor: You should *try and* get some rest.
   Standard: You should **try to** get some rest.

PRACTICE: Rewrite these sentences, using standard form.

1. Next time, you should try and be ready.

2. To take the off ramp, moving into the right-hand lane is wise.

3. Undoubtedly, he needed to really pass that test.

4. Joan and I had jogged to school to try and for once arrive on time.

5. Claude had a reason to strongly object.

6. To grow good vegetables, regular irrigation is necessary.

Understanding and Using Good Grammar

FINAL PRACTICE:
Recognizing and Using Adverb Phrases

Practice A

Encourage students to label the parts of a prepositional phrase. This is a well-established habit that the students should continue.

When students have completed Practice A, have volunteers identify the sentence parts. Remind the others to correct any errors they may have made in their own sentences.

Practice B

The following are alternative corrections:

Sentence 3: The adverb *really* may precede Dino or come after *wants.*

Sentence 7: The adverb *definitely* may precede *I* or follow *need.*

FINAL PRACTICE:
Recognizing and Using
Adverb Phrases

A. Instructions: Mark or label all sentence parts including bracketing and labeling **Inf. Adv.** and **Inf. Ph. Adv.** and drawing an arrow to the modified word.

1. Grandmother was [really] surprised [to see us on the six o'clock TV news.]

2. (No) one has come [in] [to claim the reward.]

3. Some (of (the) Scouts) had left [early] [to prepare the campsite.]

4. [To earn spending money,] Tricia and Byron bargained (with (the) neighbors) [to mow their lawns.]

5. [To be rested enough] [to leave at 5:30 A.M.,] we all went (to bed) [early.]

6. Lyle stepped (over the low picket fence,) moved [warily] (past the sleeping dog,) and [cautiously] ascended (the) (porch) steps.

7. (Without much practice) but (with great optimism,) Karl entered the race.

B. Instructions: Correct (edit) careless usage. If necessary, rewrite the sentence on the reverse side of the paper. Be alert to sentences in which *different* is not correctly modified.

1. Shouldn't we try ~~and~~ *to* be finished before dinner?

2. This assignment is certainly different ~~than~~ *from* yesterday's.

3. Dino ^*really* wants to ~~really~~ be elected.

4. To finish on schedule, ~~working systematically was decided upon.~~ *we decided to work systematically*

5. Mom's decision was different ~~than~~ *from* what I'd expected.

6. Dad is going to try ~~and~~ *to* arrange definite vacation dates.

7. I ^*definitely* need to ~~definitely~~ study for that test.

8. To impress our grandmother, ~~our room was quickly cleaned.~~ *we quickly cleaned our room*

9. Uncle Paul was embarrassed that his left sock was different ~~than~~ *from* his right one.

FINAL PRACTICE:
Recognizing and Using
Adverb Phrases

Name _____

Date _____

A. Instructions: Mark or label all sentence parts including bracketing and labeling **Inf. Adv.** and **Inf. Ph. Adv.** and drawing an arrow to the modified word.

1. Grandmother was really surprised to see us on the six o'clock TV news.

2. No one has come in to claim the reward.

3. Some of the Scouts had left early to prepare the campsite.

4. To earn spending money, Tricia and Byron bargained with the neighbors to mow their lawns.

5. To be rested enough to leave at 5:30 A.M., we all went to bed early.

6. Lyle stepped over the low picket fence, moved warily past the sleeping dog, and cautiously ascended the porch steps.

7. Without much practice but with great optimism, Karl entered the race.

B. Instructions: Correct (edit) careless usage. If necessary, rewrite the sentence on the reverse side of the paper. Be alert to sentences in which *different* is not correctly modified.

1. Shouldn't we try and be finished before dinner?

2. This assignment is certainly different than yesterday's.

3. Dino wants to really be elected.

4. To finish on schedule, working systematically was decided upon.

5. Mom's decision was different than what I'd expected.

6. Dad is going to try and arrange definite vacation dates.

7. I need to definitely study for that test.

8. To impress our grandmother, our room was quickly cleaned.

9. Uncle Paul was embarrassed that his left sock was different than his right one.

Understanding and Using Good Grammar

TEST:
Recognizing and Using
Adverb Phrases

Suggested Grading:

Part A

Before students begin the Test, inform them that it is not necessary to mark all sentence parts. In *A* they will be graded on their identification of the adverb phrases, 3 points for each phrase:

½ point each for beginning and ending parenthesis or bracket

1 point for correct label (**prep./O.P.** or **Inf. Ph. Adv.**)

1 point for correctly placed arrow

Sentence	Points	Sentence	Points
1	3	5	3
2	9	6	6
3	3	7	6
4	12	8	9

Total points: 51 (Each point: 2%)

Highlighting the markings on the phrases on the Answer Key may facilitate grading.

Part B

All corrections count for 1 point except in sentences 4 and 9 where the correction requires a subject and verb and counts for 2 points. Total points: 11 (9% each)

TEST:
Recognizing and Using Adverb Phrases

A. Instructions: Put parentheses around the adverb prepositional phrases and label them **prep./O.P.** Put brackets around the adverb infinitive phrases and label them **Inf. Ph. Adv.** Draw an arrow from each adverb phrase to the word it modifies.

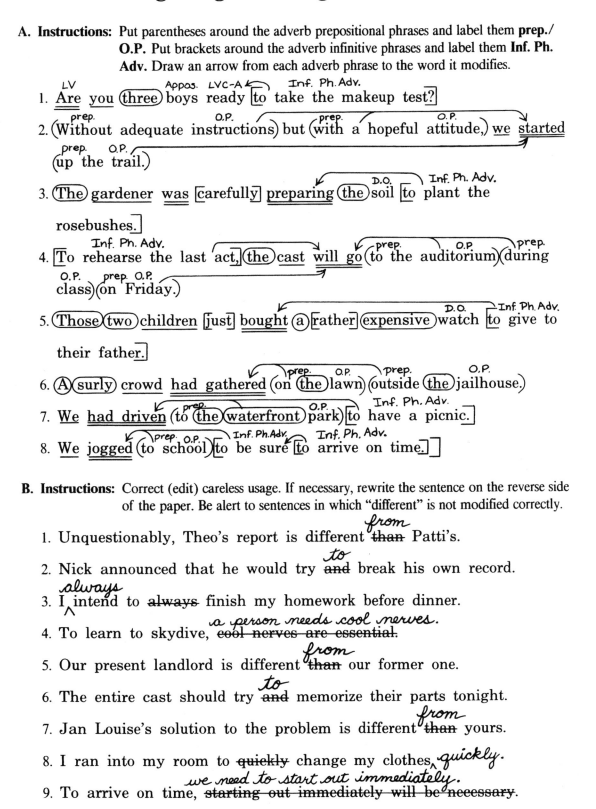

1. Are you (three) boys ready [to take the makeup test?]

2. (Without adequate instructions) but (with a hopeful attitude,) we started (up the trail.)

3. (The) gardener was [carefully] preparing (the) soil [to plant the rosebushes.]

4. [To rehearse the last act,] (the) cast will go (to the auditorium) (during class) (on Friday.)

5. (Those) (two) children [just] bought (a) [rather] (expensive) watch [to give to their father.]

6. (A) (surly) crowd had gathered (on (the) lawn) (outside (the) jailhouse.)

7. We had driven (to (the) waterfront) park) [to have a picnic.]

8. We jogged (to school) [to be sure [to arrive on time.]]

B. Instructions: Correct (edit) careless usage. If necessary, rewrite the sentence on the reverse side of the paper. Be alert to sentences in which "different" is not modified correctly.

1. Unquestionably, Theo's report is different ~~than~~ *from* Patti's.

2. Nick announced that he would try ~~and~~ *to* break his own record.

3. I intend to ~~always~~ *always* finish my homework before dinner.

4. To learn to skydive, ~~cool nerves are essential.~~ *a person needs cool nerves.*

5. Our present landlord is different ~~than~~ *from* our former one.

6. The entire cast should try ~~and~~ *to* memorize their parts tonight.

7. Jan Louise's solution to the problem is different ~~than~~ *from* yours.

8. I ran into my room to ~~quickly~~ change my clothes, *quickly.*

9. To arrive on time, ~~starting out immediately will be necessary.~~ *we need to start out immediately.*

Name _____

Date _____

TEST: Recognizing and Using Adverb Phrases

A. Instructions: Put parentheses around the adverb prepositional phrases and label them **prep./ O.P.** Put brackets around the adverb infinitive phrases and label them **Inf. Ph. Adv.** Draw an arrow from each adverb phrase to the word it modifies.

1. Are you three boys ready to take the makeup test?

2. Without adequate instructions but with a hopeful attitude, we started up the trail.

3. The gardener was carefully preparing the soil to plant the rosebushes.

4. To rehearse the last act, the cast will go to the auditorium during class on Friday.

5. Those two children just bought a rather expensive watch to give to their father.

6. A surly crowd had gathered on the lawn outside the jailhouse.

7. We had driven to the waterfront park to have a picnic.

8. We jogged to school to be sure to arrive on time.

B. Instructions: Correct (edit) careless usage. If necessary, rewrite the sentence on the reverse side of the paper. Be alert to sentences in which "different" is not modified correctly.

1. Unquestionably, Theo's report is different than Patti's.

2. Nick announced that he would try and break his own record.

3. I intend to always finish my homework before dinner.

4. To learn to skydive, cool nerves are essential.

5. Our present landlord is different than our former one.

6. The entire cast should try and memorize their parts tonight.

7. Jan Louise's solution to the problem is different than yours.

8. I ran into my room to quickly change my clothes.

9. To arrive on time, starting out immediately will be necessary.

Understanding and Using Good Grammar

Tense and Voice of Infinitives— Supplementary Lesson

This supplementary lesson is designed to interest perceptive students who enjoy analyzing sentence forms as a possible means of improving the effectiveness of their expression.

Emphasize the fact that the only difference between the active voice and the passive voice in the *present tense* is the use of *be* in the *passive*. In the *past tense*, the difference is that *been* is used in the *passive*.

Since the point of this lesson is to enlighten the students about the makeup of infinitive phrases, it is not necessary for them to identify the parts of the entire sentence.

Tense and Voice of Infinitives—
Supplementary Lesson

REMINDER: **Infinitives and infinitive phrases** may function as **nouns, as adjectives, or as adverbs**.

Infinitives may be in present or past tense and in active or passive voice:

	Active Voice	**Passive Voice**
Present	to see	to be seen
Past	to have seen	to have been seen

A. An infinitive is in **active voice** if the subject does the action of the infinitive verb form.

1. *Present:* Bernie stood on tiptoe [to see over the hedge.] *Inf. Ph.*
    (Bernie was the one "to see over.")

2. *Past:* Pieter was pleased [to have seen Felix get the award.] *Inf. Ph.*
    (Pieter was the one "to have seen Felix.")

B. An infinitive is in **passive voice** if the subject receives the action implied in the infinitive verb form. Passive voice always uses a form of the verb *to be.*

1. *Present:* [To be seen by the audience,] the short children stood on *Inf. Ph.*
    a riser on stage. (The children received the "seeing.")

2. *Past:* For the girls, it was a "claim to fame" [to have been seen *Inf. Ph.*
    with the rock star.] (The girls received the "seeing.")

PRACTICE: Put brackets around the phrase; at the end of the sentence write the tense and voice of the infinitive.

1. The tennis match [to have been played today] will be played tomorrow. *Past tense–Passive*
2. The carpenters were urged [to work more quickly.] *Present tense–Active*
3. The students were warned [to be prepared for the test.] *Present tense–Passive*
4. All the evidence appears [to have been removed completely.] *Past tense–Passive*
5. Meg borrowed my eraser [to correct her mistakes.] *Present tense–Active*
6. Without headlights, it was impossible for her [to have seen the warning.] *Past tense–Active*
7. Cleo was really surprised [to have been elected.] *Past tense–Passive*
7. Jon had expected [to be met at the airport by Dylan.] *Present tense–Passive*
9. Jackie was supposed [to have left her report on my desk.] *Past tense–Active*
10. I shall be really pleased [to visit my cousin again.] *Present tense–Active*

Tense and Voice of Infinitives— Supplementary Lesson

Name _____

Date _____

REMINDER: **Infinitives and infinitive phrases** may function as **nouns, as adjectives, or as adverbs**.

Infinitives may be in present or past tense and in active or passive voice:

	Active Voice	**Passive Voice**
Present	to see	to be seen
Past	to have seen	to have been seen

A. An infinitive is in **active voice** if the subject does the action of the infinitive verb form.

    1. *Present:* Bernie stood on tiptoe [to see over the hedge.]   Inf. Ph.
       (Bernie was the one "to see over.")

    2. *Past:* Pieter was pleased [to have seen Felix get the award.]   Inf. Ph.
       (Pieter was the one "to have seen Felix.")

B. An infinitive is in **passive voice** if the subject receives the action implied in the infinitive verb form. Passive voice always uses a form of the verb *to be*.

    1. *Present:* [To be seen by the audience,] the short children stood on a riser on stage. (The children received the "seeing.")   Inf. Ph.

    2. *Past:* For the girls, it was a "claim to fame" [to have been seen with the rock star.] (The girls received the "seeing.")   Inf. Ph.

PRACTICE: Put brackets around the phrase; at the end of the sentence write the tense and voice of the infinitive.

1. The tennis match to have been played today will be played tomorrow.

2. The carpenters were urged to work more quickly.

3. The students were warned to be prepared for the test.

4. All the evidence appears to have been removed completely.

5. Meg borrowed my eraser to correct her mistakes.

6. Without headlights, it was impossible for her to have seen the warning.

7. Cleo was really surprised to have been elected.

7. Jon had expected to be met at the airport by Dylan.

9. Jackie was supposed to have left her report on my desk.

10. I shall be really surprised to visit my cousin again.

                            Understanding and Using Good Grammar

Clauses Used as Adverbs

Remember items 1–4 repeat information given on page 288, introducing clauses used as adjectives. Point out that a *de*pendent clause depends or relies on an *in*dependent (not dependent) clause for communicating the complete meaning.

Items 5, 6, and 7 contain new information about adverb clauses. Point out that some of the words listed here as subordinate conjunctions may also function as prepositions or adverbs:

$$\overline{[\text{Where}]} \ \underline{\underline{\text{are}}} \ \underline{\underline{\text{you}}} \ \underline{\underline{\text{going}}} \overset{prep. \quad O.P.}{(\text{after} \ \text{lunch}?)}$$

In Practice sentence 3 the clause *that I felt dizzy* modifies the two-word adverb *so fast*.

In sentence 7 be sure students write in the understood subject, *you*, for the verb, *check*.

In checking students' papers, each half of a pair of brackets or parentheses should be correctly placed and be given ½-point credit.

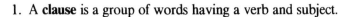

Clauses Used as Adverbs

REMEMBER:

1. A **clause** is a group of words having a verb and subject.

2. An **independent clause** has a verb and subject and expresses a complete thought:

   Our family often eats (on the patio.)

3. A **dependent clause** has a verb and subject but does not express a complete thought:

   when the weather is warm.

4. A **complex sentence** is made up of an independent clause (the main sentence) and at least one dependent clause:

   Our family often eats (on the patio) [when the weather is warm.]

5. An **adverb clause** is a dependent clause used to modify a verb, as in number 4 above, an adjective, or an adverb:

   Modifies adjective: Dad was [so] tired [that he went right (to bed.)]

   Modifies adverb: I had run [so] [fast] [that I was (out of breath.)]

6. **Subordinate conjunctions** introduce adverb clauses. Some are:

after	because	since	unless	wherever
although	before	so, so that	until	whether
as, as if	even though	than	when	while
as though	how	that	whenever	why
as soon as	if	though	where	

7. An **introductory adverb clause** is followed by a comma; an adverb clause placed after the independent clause needs no comma:

   [After you left] the phone rang.   The phone rang [after you left.]

PRACTICE: In the main sentence, mark or label all sentence parts. Place square brackets around the adverb clause. Within the clause draw a box around the subordinate conjunction; underline the verb twice, the subject once; draw an arrow to the modified word; insert necessary commas; label **Adv. Cl.**

1. The (little) boy was sorry [that he had scratched his little sister.]

2. [Even though rain was expected,] the troop went (on the overnight hike.)

3. The merry-go-round was going [so] [fast] [that I felt dizzy.]

4. [Until visibility improves,] none (of the planes) will take off.

5. I'll call you [after I eat dinner.]

6. Dad becomes [very] quiet [when he's really angry.]

7. [Before you hand in your papers,] check (your) answers.

Name _____   **Clauses Used as Adverbs**

Date _____

REMEMBER:

1. A **clause** is a group of words having a verb and subject.

2. An **independent clause** has a verb and subject and expresses a complete thought:

   Our family often eats (on the patio.)

3. A **dependent clause** has a verb and subject but does not express a complete thought:

   when the weather is warm.

4. A **complex sentence** is made up of an independent clause (the main sentence) and at least one dependent clause:

   Our family often eats (on the patio) when the weather is warm.

5. An **adverb clause** is a dependent clause used to modify a verb, as in number 4 above, an adjective, or an adverb:

   Modifies adjective: Dad was so tired that he went right (to bed.)

   Modifies adverb: I had run so fast that I was (out of breath.)

6. **Subordinate conjunctions** introduce adverb clauses. Some are:

after	because	since	unless	wherever
although	before	so, so that	until	whether
as, as if	even though	than	when	while
as though	how	that	whenever	why
as soon as	if	though	where	

7. An introductory adverb clause is followed by a comma; an adverb clause placed after the independent clause needs no comma:

   After you left the phone rang.   The phone rang after you left.

PRACTICE: In the main sentence, mark or label all sentence parts. Place square brackets around the adverb clause. Within the clause draw a box around the subordinate conjunction; underline the verb twice, the subject once; draw an arrow to the modified word; insert necessary commas; label **Adv. Cl.**

1. The little boy was sorry that he had scratched his little sister.

2. Even though rain was expected the troop went on the overnight hike.

3. The merry-go-round was going so fast that I felt dizzy.

4. Until visibility improves none of the planes will take off.

5. I'll call you after I eat dinner.

6. Dad becomes very quiet when he's really angry.

7. Before you hand in your papers check your answers.

Understanding and Using Good Grammar

Reminders: Use of Adverb Clauses

A. In a clearly stated elliptical clause that expresses comparison the subject is included and the verb is omitted. On the chalkboard or overhead, write these pairs of sentences to demonstrate the confusion that occurs if *both* the subject and the verb are omitted and the direct object or object of the preposition is used.

Clear	*Confusing or Ungrammatical*

1. Do you play tennis with
   El. Adv. Cl.
   her as often ⌈as I?⌉(play

   with her)?

2. Dad writes Caitlin more
   El. Adv. Cl.
   regularly ⌈than I.⌉(write

   her).

1. Do you play tennis with her as
   prep.   O.P.
   often ⌈as (you play with) me?⌉

2. Dad writes Caitlin more regularly
   D.O.
   ⌈than (he writes) me.⌉

Remind students of polite order in using nominative (subject) pronouns:

    First: you   *Next:* he, she, it, they, (nouns)   *Last:* I, we

B. The subordinator *that* is the correct word to introduce a dependent clause that explains a reason:

The reason I hurried home was (that, ~~because~~) Mom needed my help; *that* was the only reason! (Not: *because* was the only reason!)

C. 1. Agree with students that "freedom of speech" permits them to use as many colloquialisms as they wish in communicating with one another! However, it really is best for them to avoid using them in formal speech or writing.

   2. Using *like* as a preposition with a noun or pronoun object is always correct:

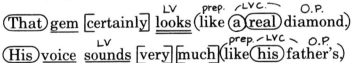

Reminders: Use of Adverb Clauses

A. Elliptical clauses are incomplete. They have a subject but do not have a verb. Elliptical clauses that express a comparison are introduced by the subordinating conjunction **as** or **than**.

Don can run [faster [than I.] (can/can run)   Don can run [as fast [as I.] (can/can run)

REMEMBER: I, a subject pronoun, is the subject of the verb *can/can run.* Never use *me,* or any object pronoun, in that position.

PRACTICE: In the blanks, write your choice of pronouns, remembering to use polite order. Bracket the elliptical clause and insert the omitted words of the clause. Label: **El. Adv. Cl.**

1. Mary Beth enjoys backpacking as much [as *you* and *we*].
   (enjoy it)   (us, we, you)

2. Carol did better on the test [than *you* or *I.* *(did)*   (I, you, me)

3. Has that swimmer more trophies [than *they* or *we*] ? *(have)*
   (them, we, us, they)

4. No other couples are as good dancers [as *she* and *he.*] *(are)*
   (her, she, he, him)

5. Betty's as eager to go [as *you* , *he* , or *I.*] *(are)*
   (him, you, I, he, me)

B. In using the word *reason* to explain something, do not use the subordinators *why* or *because. Reason, why,* and *because* all mean approximately the same.

The reason (~~why~~, that) I can't go is (~~because~~, that) I must work.   *OR* I can't go because I must work. Why I can't go is that I must work.

PRACTICE: Cross out unnecessary words; change incorrectly used words.

1. The reason she practiced so much was ~~because~~ *that* she hoped to win.

2. ~~Why~~ I arrived late ~~was~~ because I missed the bus.

3. Because I had to get up early, ~~was why~~ I went to bed early.

4. What was the reason ~~why~~ you didn't buy the dress?

C. Avoid Colloquial Uses of *Like*

1. Omit *like* as an expletive to provide a pause: The accident was ~~like~~ horrible. Make corrections in the following:

   The class was ~~like~~ boring.   The tennis match was ~~like~~

   The suggestion is ~~like~~ really weird.   exhausting.

   His reaction was ~~like~~ wild.   ~~Like~~ this practice should end!

2. Do not use *like* as a subordinator to introduce a full clause; use *as/as if/as though* instead. Make corrections in the following:

   The speaker really told it   She looked ~~like~~ *as if* she might cry.
   ~~like~~ *as* it is.   Don't embellish the facts; tell it
   It looks ~~like~~ *as though* we will finish   ~~like~~ *as* it was.
   early.   He took to politics ~~like~~ *as* a fish
   He spoke ~~like~~ *as if* he had authority.   takes to water.

Reminders: Use of Adverb Clauses

Name _____

Date _____

A. **Elliptical clauses** are incomplete. They have a subject but do not have a verb. Elliptical clauses that express a comparison are introduced by the subordinating conjunction **as** or **than**.

El. Adv. Cl.

Don <u>can run</u> ⌈faster⌉than⌉ I.⌉ (can/can run)   Don <u>can run</u> ⌈as⌉fast⌉as⌉ I.⌉ (can/can run)

REMEMBER: *I,* a subject pronoun, is the subject of the verb *can/can run.* Never use *me,* or any object pronoun, in that position.

PRACTICE: In the blanks, write your choice of pronouns, remembering to use polite order. Bracket the elliptical clause and insert the omitted words of the clause. Label: **El. Adv. Cl.**

1. Mary Beth enjoys backpacking as much as _____ and _____ . (us, we, you)

2. Carol did better on the test than _____ or _____ . (I, you, me)

3. Has that swimmer more trophies than _____ or _____ ? (them, we, us, they)

4. No other couples are as good dancers as _____ and _____ . (her, she, he, him)

5. Betty's as eager to go as _____ , _____ , or _____ . (him, you, I, he, me)

B. In using the word *reason* to explain something, do not use the subordinators *why* or *because.* *Reason, why,* and *because* all mean approximately the same.

The reason (~~why~~, that) I can't go is (~~because,~~ that) I must work.   *OR* I can't go because I must work. Why I can't go is that I must work.

PRACTICE: Cross out unnecessary words; change incorrectly used words.

1. The reason she practiced so much was because she hoped to win.

2. Why I arrived late was because I missed the bus.

3. Because I had to get up early was why I went to bed early.

4. What was the reason why you didn't buy the dress?

C. **Avoid Colloquial Uses of *Like***

1. Omit *like* as an expletive to provide a pause: The accident was ~~like~~ horrible. Make corrections in the following:

   The class was like boring.

   The suggestion is like really weird.

   His reaction was like wild.

   The tennis match was like exhausting.

   Like this practice should end!

2. Do not use *like* as a subordinator to introduce a full clause; use *as/as if/as though* instead. Make corrections in the following:

   The speaker really told it like it is.

   It looks like we will finish early.

   He spoke like he had authority.

   She looked like she might cry.

   Don't embellish the facts; tell it like it was.

   He took to politics like a fish takes to water.

Understanding and Using Good Grammar

Recognizing and Punctuating
Adverb Clauses

Remind students of earlier learnings:

Sentences 5 and 9: The participial adjectives, *yelping* and *whistling*, modify subjects.

Sentence 13: Two adjective participial phrases modify the direct object *man*.

Sentence 17: *Subjunctive mood* has been referred to occasionally in this book. Point out that *were starving* is in the subjunctive mood used after *as if* to communicate a possibility, something not known to be true. If a fact were being communicated, the expression would be in the *indicative mood*: The dog *was starving*.

Return this page to students to prepare for the Test on page 340.

Recognizing and Punctuating Adverb Clauses

Instructions: In the main sentence, mark or label all sentence parts. Place square brackets around the adverb clause and a box around the subordinate conjunction. In the adverb clause, underline the verb twice, subject once; draw an arrow to the modified word; insert needed commas; label **Adv. Cl.** or **El. Adv. Cl.**

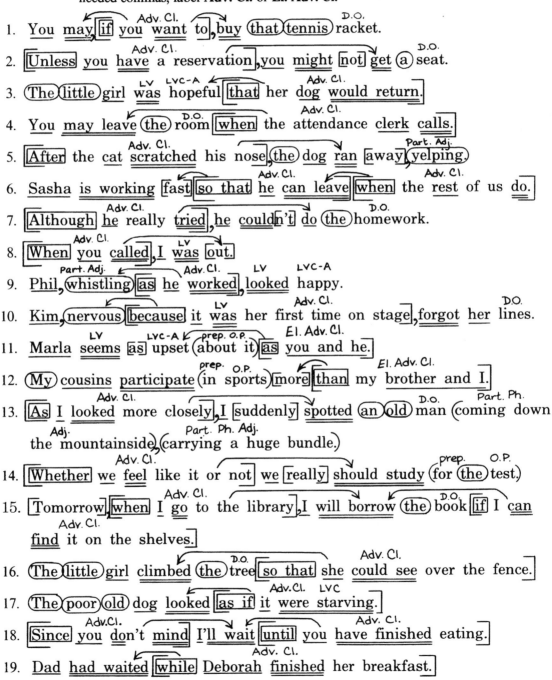

1. You may, [if you want to], buy that tennis racket.

2. [Unless you have a reservation], you might not get a seat.

3. The little girl was hopeful [that her dog would return].

4. You may leave the room [when the attendance clerk calls].

5. [After the cat scratched his nose], the dog ran away, yelping.

6. Sasha is working fast [so that he can leave] [when the rest of us do].

7. [Although he really tried], he couldn't do the homework.

8. [When you called], I was out.

9. Phil, whistling [as he worked], looked happy.

10. Kim, nervous [because it was her first time on stage], forgot her lines.

11. Marla seems as upset about it [as you and he].

12. My cousins participate in sports more [than my brother and I].

13. [As I looked more closely], I suddenly spotted an old man coming down the mountainside, carrying a huge bundle.

14. [Whether we feel like it or not] we really should study for the test.

15. Tomorrow, [when I go to the library], I will borrow the book [if I can find it on the shelves].

16. The little girl climbed the tree [so that she could see over the fence].

17. The poor old dog looked [as if it were starving].

18. [Since you don't mind] I'll wait [until you have finished eating].

19. Dad had waited [while Deborah finished her breakfast].

Name _____

Date _____

Recognizing and Punctuating Adverb Clauses

Instructions: In the main sentence, mark or label all sentence parts. Place square brackets around the adverb clause and a box around the subordinate conjunction. In the adverb clause, underline the verb twice, subject once; draw an arrow to the modified word; insert needed commas; label **Adv. Cl.** or **El. Adv. Cl.**

1. You may if you want to buy that tennis racket.

2. Unless you have a reservation you might not get a seat.

3. The little girl was hopeful that her dog would return.

4. You may leave the room when the attendance clerk calls.

5. After the cat scratched his nose the dog ran away yelping.

6. Sasha is working fast so that he can leave when the rest of us do.

7. Although he really tried he couldn't do the homework.

8. When you called I was out.

9. Phil whistling as he worked looked happy.

10. Kim nervous because it was her first time on stage forgot her lines.

11. Marla seems as upset about it as you and he.

12. My cousins participate in sports more than my brother and I.

13. As I looked more closely I suddenly spotted an old man coming down the mountainside carrying a huge bundle.

14. Whether we feel like it or not we really should study for the test.

15. Tomorrow when I go to the library I will borrow the book if I can find it on the shelves.

16. The little girl climbed the tree so that she could see over the fence.

17. The poor old dog looked as if it were starving.

18. Since you don't mind I'll wait until you have finished eating.

19. Dad had waited while Deborah finished her breakfast.

Reminders:
Use of Adverb Clauses

In sentences 3, 8, and 11, any nominative pronouns in polite order may be used. In sentence 8, you may want to point out that, in formal use, in a *negative* comparison, "not *so* good as he" is preferred to "not *as* good as he."

In sentences 4, 6, 12, 15, and 16, students may suggest several different sentence forms that are grammatically correct. Give credit for any acceptable sentence; the point is that only *one* of the three words, *reason/because/why*, should be used in each sentence.

Return this page to students to prepare for the Test on the next page.

Reminders:
Use of Adverb Clauses

Instructions: Write in, leave out, or change words to produce a grammatical sentence. Write your choice of pronouns where there are blanks. Bracket any elliptical clauses and label them **El. Adv. Cl.** (elliptical adverb clause).

Examples: 1. The way Earl played the game was ~~like~~ fantastic.

2. The reason ~~why~~ she forfeited the match was ~~because~~ *that* she developed a muscular cramp.

3. It looks ~~like~~ *as if* the storm is nearly over.

4. Ingrid finishes her work as quickly [as *you* and *I* (finish ours)] *El. Adv. Cl.*

1. The motor sounds ~~like~~ *as though* a spark plug is misfiring.

2. I am ~~like~~ tired to death!

3. Belinda always thinks things through more carefully [than *he* *El. Adv. Cl.* or *I* (do.)]

4. The reason the streets flooded was ~~because~~ *that* the storm sewers were clogged.

5. ~~Like~~ don't mention that subject to me!

6. Because it rained ~~is why~~ we didn't go.

7. Charles looks ~~like~~ *as if* he has no intention of signing up for soccer.

8. Jenna has a better record on the high jump [than *he* *El. Adv. Cl.* and *I* (have)], but not as good [as *you* (do.)] *El. Adv. Cl.*

9. You really should try to tell it ~~like~~ *as* it is.

10. Those kittens are ~~like~~ so cute!

11. Guillermo has as good a chance to win [as *they* or *we* (have.)] *El. Adv. Cl.*

12. Because he's always won~~, is why~~ he expects to win again.

13. Oh, this view! It's ~~like~~ gorgeous!

14. He stared at us ~~like~~ *as if* we were from another planet.

15. ~~Why~~ everyone likes her ~~is~~ because she doesn't act vain or selfish.

16. The reason ~~why~~ I bought my ticket early is ~~because~~ *that* I want to be sure to see the play.

17. His behavior was ~~like~~ wild.

Reminders: Use of Adverb Clauses

Name _____

Date _____

Instructions: Write in, leave out, or change words to produce a grammatical sentence. Write your choice of pronouns where there are blanks. Bracket any elliptical clauses and label them **El. Adv. Cl.** (elliptical adverb clause).

Examples: 1. The way Earl played the game was ~~like~~ fantastic.

2. The reason ~~why~~ she forfeited the match was *that* ~~because~~ she developed a muscular cramp.

3. It looks ~~like~~ *as if* the storm is nearly over.

4. Ingrid finishes her work as quickly [as *you* and *I*] (*finish ours*)
   El. Adv. Cl.

1. The motor sounds like a spark plug is misfiring.

2. I am like tired to death!

3. Belinda always thinks things through more carefully than _____ or _____ .

4. The reason the streets flooded was because the storm sewers were clogged.

5. Like don't mention that subject to me!

6. Because it rained is why we didn't go.

7. Charles looks like he has no intention of signing up for soccer.

8. Jenna has a better record on the high jump than _____ and _____ , but not as good as _____ .

9. You really should try to tell it like it is.

10. Those kittens are like so cute!

11. Guillermo has as good a chance to win as _____ *or* _____ .

12. Because he's always won is why he expects to win again.

13. Oh, this view! It's like gorgeous!

14. He stared at us like we were from another planet.

15. Why everyone likes her is because she doesn't act vain or selfish.

16. The reason why I bought my ticket early is because I want to be sure to see the play.

17. His behavior was like wild.

Understanding and Using Good Grammar

TEST: *Adverb Clauses*

A. Before students take the test, tell them to be alert to one sentence which contains two clauses. Instruct them to write, in parentheses, the words left out of an elliptical clause (two sentences), and the understood subject in another sentence.

The instruction to underline the verb and subject in both clauses is to emphasize in the students' minds the two essential components of a clause.

Suggested Grading:

In grading *A*, count only the markings of the dependent adverb clause (6 points each) and the 6 commas. Total points: 66

−1, 98	−5, 92	−9, 86	−13, 80	−17, 74	−21, 68	−25, 62
−2, 97	−6, 91	−10, 85	−14, 79	−18, 73	−22, 67	−26, 61
−3, 95	−7, 89	−11, 83	−15, 77	−19, 71	−23, 65	−27, 59
−4, 94	−8, 88	−12, 82	−16, 76	−20, 70	−24, 64	−28, 58

B. *Suggested Grading:*

Sentences 2, 6, 9, and 12: Grammatical sentences different from the ones in the Answer Key may be accepted; each must contain *one*, only, of *reason*, *why*, or *because*: **7 points**

Sentences 3, 7, and 13: Pronouns must be nominative, in polite order; label and brackets correctly placed: **15 points**

Sentences 1, 4, 5, 8, 10, and 11: *one* change each sentence: **6 points**

Total: **28 points**

−1, 96	−3, 89	−5, 82	−7, 75	−9, 68	−11, 61
−2, 93	−4, 86	−6, 79	−8, 71	−10, 64	−12, 57

When you return the tests, ask volunteers to analyze the makeup and function of *Part A*

Sentence 4: "delivering her newspapers." (gerund phrase, direct object within adverb clause)

Sentence 7: "to see the play." (infinitive phrase, direct object within adverb clause)

TEST: Adverb Clauses

A. Instructions: In both clauses underline the verb twice, the subject once. Bracket the adverb clause, draw a box around the subordinator, draw an arrow to the modified word; label the clauses **Adv. Cl.** or **El. Adv. Cl.**; insert needed commas.

1. Arthur can play soccer better [than you or she.] *(can)*   — El. Adv. Cl.

2. [As Patrick hesitantly opened the door,] the mob surged forward.   — Adv. Cl.

3. My sister is not quite so ambitious [as I.] *(am)*   — El. Adv. Cl. / LV

4. Edie ate an ice cream cone [after she finished delivering her newspapers.]   — Adv. Cl.

5. [Because he argues so much,] Clarke has lost a few friends.   — Adv. Cl.

6. Ramona, happy and excited [because she had been elected,] hurried toward us.   — Adv. Cl.

7. (You) Order your tickets now [since you really want to see the play.]   — Adv. Cl.

8. [Although he acted very self-confident,] Luther felt unsure of himself.   — Adv. Cl.

9. [If you wish,] I can wait [until you finish your chores.]   — Adv. Cl. / Adv. Cl.

B. Instructions: Make necessary changes to produce a grammatical sentence. Write correct pronouns in blanks. Bracket elliptical clauses and label them **El. Adv. Cl.**

1. Carl is ~~like~~ really handsome.

2. The reason ~~why~~ no one believes him is ~~because~~ *that* he often misrepresents the facts.

3. Aimee performs as agilely on the parallel bars [as *you* and *he*], and more agilely [than *I*].   — El. Adv. Cl.

4. My uncle acted ~~like~~ *as if* he'd never met us.

5. ~~Like~~ why would you say that?

6. ~~Why~~ I went to the movies ~~was~~ because my brother paid my way.

7. Alma didn't arrive any earlier [than *they* or *we*].   — El. Adv. Cl.

8. He is acting bored, ~~like~~ *as* he always does.

9. The reason we came back is ~~because~~ *that* we've lost the money.

10. I tried to tell it ~~like~~ *as* it was.

11. Stella acted ~~like~~ *as though* she really wanted to go.

12. Because I'm behind in math, ~~is the reason why~~ I'm not going.

13. Zack played as well [as *he* or *I*].   — El. Adv. Cl.

Name _____

Date _____

TEST: Adverb Clauses

A. Instructions: In both clauses underline the verb twice, the subject once. Bracket the adverb clause, draw a box around the subordinator, draw an arrow to the modified word; label the clauses **Adv. Cl.** or **El. Adv. Cl.**; insert needed commas.

1. Arthur can play soccer better than you or she.

2. As Patrick hesitantly opened the door the mob surged forward.

3. My sister is not quite so ambitious as I.

4. Edie ate an ice cream cone after she finished delivering her newspapers.

5. Because he argues so much Clarke has lost a few friends.

6. Ramona happy and excited because she had been elected hurried toward us.

7.   Order your tickets now since you really want to see the play.

8. Although he acted very self-confident Luther felt unsure of himself.

9. If you wish I can wait until you finish your chores.

B. Instructions: Make necessary changes to produce a grammatical sentence. Write correct pronouns in blanks. Bracket elliptical clauses and label them **El. Adv. Cl.**

1. Carl is like really handsome.

2. The reason why no one believes him is because he often misrepresents the facts.

3. Aimee performs as agilely on the parallel bars as _____ and _____ , and more agilely than _____ .

4. My uncle acted like he'd never met us.

5. Like why would you say that?

6. Why I went to the movies was because my brother paid my way.

7. Alma didn't arrive any earlier than _____ or _____ .

8. He is acting bored, like he always does.

9. The reason we came back is because we've lost the money.

10. I tried to tell it like it was.

11. Stella acted like she really wanted to go.

12. Because I'm behind in math is the reason why I'm not going.

13. Zack played as well as _____ or _____ .

Recognizing the Function of Noun Clauses

Complete these steps with students to help them recognize the use of a noun clause as a main sentence part:

Sentence 1: (a) First, locate and draw two lines under the verbs: <u>had escaped</u>   <u>was</u> (LV)

(b) Second, locate and draw a box around the introductory word: [That]

(c) Third, locate and draw one line under the subjects: <u>Gerald</u>   ??

Obviously, the subject of <u>was</u> (LV) is ([That] <u>Gerald</u> <u>escaped</u> injury) — Noun Cl. Subj. / D.O.

Sentence 2: ([when] I <u>was</u> (LV) [really] embarrassed) (LVC-A) is in apposition to (one) time (D.O.). — Noun Cl. Appos.

Remind students that an appositive may be substituted for the noun it describes and the meaning of the sentence remains the same.

<u>I</u> <u>remember</u> ([when] <u>I</u> <u>was</u> [really] embarrassed.) — Noun Cl. D.O. / LVC-A

Sentence 6: Requires writing the understood subject: (<u>You</u>)

Sentence 9: Contains two dependent noun clauses which function as major parts of the sentence.

Notice that pages 346 and 349 require students to recognize and underline only the verbs and subjects since these are the essential components of a clause.

Work carefully with the students through all the practice sentences to be sure they have marked or labeled the clauses and other sentence parts correctly. Collect the worksheets, grade them, record scores, and return them to students.

Recognizing the Function
of Noun Clauses

UNDERSTAND: 1. A **dependent noun clause** may be used in a sentence as a noun or pronoun; it may function as a subject, a linking verb complement, a direct object, an object of a preposition, an indirect object, or an appositive. (To be labeled: **Noun Cl.** plus the appropriate function symbol, **Subj.**, **D.O.**, etc.)

2. A **noun clause may be introduced** by one of the following: **who, whom, whoever, whomever, that, what, whatever, whether, how, however, when, where, wherever, why,** etc.

Subject: (Whoever finds (Dad's) wallet) will be given (a substantial) reward.

LVC: The (warden's) idea is (that (the) escapee had (inside) help.)

D.O.: I (really) wonder (if she will come.)

O.P.: (Many (alert) people profit (from (what they hear and see.)

IO.: (The) coach will give (whoever has (the best) qualifications) (the) job.

Appos.: (The) news (that (the dangerous) criminal had escaped) frightened me.

PRACTICE: Draw a box around the introductory word and heavy parentheses around the clause. Above the clause, label its function. Mark and label all sentence parts as usual.

1. (That Gerald had escaped injury) was (really) surprising.

2. I remember (one) time (when I was (really) embarrassed.)

3. (Many) witnesses described (what they had seen.)

4. (Reassuring) news was (what we were hoping for.)

5. (A beautiful) trophy will be given (to (whoever wins (this) match.))

6. (You) Give (whoever answers (the) doorbell) (the) message.

7. (That (our) team would win) became evident (early) (in (the) game.)

8. (A (long, (pleasant) (summer) vacation was (what we all needed.)

9. (What (that (spoiled) (little) child asks for) is (what he (usually) gets.)

10. I had been informed (that (some) students were staying (after school.))

Recognizing the Function of Noun Clauses

Name _____

Date _____

UNDERSTAND: 1. A **dependent noun clause** may be used in a sentence as a noun or pronoun; it may function as a subject, a linking verb complement, a direct object, an object of a preposition, an indirect object, or an appositive. (To be labeled: **Noun Cl.** plus the appropriate function symbol, **Subj.**, **D.O.**, etc.)

2. A **noun clause may be introduced** by one of the following: **who, whom, whoever, whomever, that, what, whatever, whether, how, however, when, where, wherever, why,** etc.

Subject: (Whoever finds Dad's wallet) will be given a substantial reward.

LVC: The warden's idea is (that the escapee had inside help.)

D.O.: I really wonder (if she will come.)

O.P.: Many alert people profit from (what they hear and see.)

IO.: The coach will give (whoever has the best qualifications) the job.

Appos.: The news (that the dangerous criminal had escaped) frightened me.

PRACTICE: Draw a box around the introductory word and heavy parentheses around the clause. Above the clause, label its function. Mark and label all sentence parts as usual.

1. That Gerald had escaped injury was really surprising.

2. I remember one time when I was really embarrassed.

3. Many witnesses described what they had seen.

4. Reassuring news was what we were hoping for.

5. A beautiful trophy will be given to whoever wins this match.

6.   Give whoever answers the doorbell the message.

7. That our team would win became evident early in the game.

8. A long, pleasant summer vacation was what we all needed.

9. What that spoiled little child asks for is what he usually gets.

10. I had been informed that some students were staying after school.

Understanding and Using Good Grammar

Recognizing the Function
of Noun Clauses

As you proceed through the Practice, emphasize the fact that an introductory word begins the clause which functions as a major sentence part.

Sentence 1: *Verbs:* <u>does</u>, <u>is</u>; *Introductory word:* What

Dependent clause: (What she <u>does</u> with her money)

<u>is</u> a mystery to me.

Sentence 4: *Verbs:* <u>'d like</u>, <u>is</u>, <u>phoned</u>; *Introductory words:* What   who

Dependent clause: (What I<u>'d like</u> to know) <u>is</u>

(who <u>phoned</u> me last night.)

Notice that noun clauses function as subjects in sentences 1, 2, and 3; as linking verb complements in sentences 5, 6, and 7, etc. Grouped repetition should be helpful.

Also notice that *who* (sentence 4) and *whoever* (sentences 12, 13, 15) function as *subjects* within the clause. *Whom* functions as an object of the preposition in sentence 11 and, in sentence 18, as a direct object within the clause.

To simplify grading this worksheet, check, grade, and record scores for sentences 1, 5, 8, 11, 14, and 17 which are representative of all the other sentences.

Recognizing the Function of Noun Clauses

PRACTICE: Draw a box around an introductory word and heavy parentheses around the noun clause. Above the clause label its function. Underline verbs twice and subjects once.

1. (What she does with her money) is a mystery to me.

2. (Whether or not we go on the picnic) depends upon the weather.

3. (Why Calvin was chosen) is easy to understand.

4. (What I'd like to know) is (who phoned me last night.)

5. Our vacation will be (whatever days Mom and Dad can take off from work.)

6. His orders are (that we should leave now.)

7. The mystery was (why anyone would want to break into the old warehouse.)

8. (You) Donate (whatever you can to the town library.)

9. Mom showed us exactly (how she budgets our money.)

10. (Whatever you say,) I'll believe.

11. The manager is a man (in (whom Dad has complete confidence.))

12. I shall offer help (to (whoever needs it most.))

13. (You) Return this report (to (whoever wrote it.))

14. (You) Give (whatever child hasn't any) these donated toys.

15. The teacher gave (whoever requested one) a pass to the library.

16. I shall give (whichever paper carrier needs it most) my old ten-speed.

17. McDougal's cave was the place (where the treasure was found.)

18. I do not know the person (whom she has married.)

19. The information (that Norman is a contestant) surprises me.

20. (When it's dark and the wind is howling) is a great time for telling ghost stories.

21. Mr. Gray told us (how he won the Purple Heart.)

22. (That some of the students hadn't prepared for the test) was fairly obvious.

Name _____

Date _____

Recognizing the Function of Noun Clauses

PRACTICE: Draw a box around an introductory word and heavy parentheses around the noun clause. Above the clause label its function. Underline verbs twice and subjects once.

1. What she does with her money is a mystery to me.

2. Whether or not we go on the picnic depends upon the weather.

3. Why Calvin was chosen is easy to understand.

4. What I'd like to know is who phoned me last night.

5. Our vacation will be whatever days Mom and Dad can take off from work.

6. His orders are that we should leave now.

7. The mystery was why anyone would want to break into the old warehouse.

8. Donate whatever you can to the town library.

9. Mom showed us exactly how she budgets our money.

10. Whatever you say, I'll believe.

11. The manager is a man in whom Dad has complete confidence.

12. I shall offer help to whoever needs it most.

13. Return this report to whoever wrote it.

14. Give whatever child hasn't any these donated toys.

15. The teacher gave whoever requested one a pass to the library.

16. I shall give whichever paper carrier needs it most my old ten-speed.

17. McDougal's cave was the place where the treasure was found.

18. I do not know the person whom she has married.

19. The information that Norman is a contestant surprises me.

20. When it's dark and the wind is howling is a great time for telling ghost stories.

21. Mr. Gray told us how he won the Purple Heart.

22. That some of the students hadn't prepared for the test was fairly obvious.

Understanding and Using Good Grammar

FINAL PRACTICE:
Recognizing the Function
of Noun Clauses

Sentences on the Test, page 352, will be taken from the practice sheets dealing with noun clauses. Be sure students' pages 343, 346, and 349 have been returned to them to prepare for the Test. The instructions on the Test will be the same as on pages 346 and 349.

FINAL PRACTICE:
Recognizing the Function
of Noun Clauses

Instructions: Draw a box around an introductory word and heavy parentheses around the noun clause. Above the clause label its function. Underline verbs twice and subjects once.

1. (Why I was chosen) was a mystery to me.

2. Dorothy's suggestion is (that we should go tomorrow, not today.)

3. Teachers usually give extra help (to (whoever asks for it.))

4. Do you know (how the magician did that trick?)

5. (You) Give (whoever comes in next) this complimentary ticket.

6. I remember the time (when I fell through the ice.)

7. Dwight always buys (whomever he is going with at the time) some

   really nice presents.

8. Everyone had assumed (that Abigail would win the girls' tennis

   tournament.)

9. (Whoever is responsible for the damage) will be severely punished.

10. I really believe (that he meant no harm.)

11. (When the committee should meet again) is (what we must decide.)

12. Brenda told her dad (that she was not planning to return to college.)

13. You may send invitations (to (whomever you wish.))

14. (You) Give (whoever is the rightful owner) the pen.

15. The surprise party for our parents is (what we're talking about.)

16. (How you spend your allowance) is your affair.

17. I'll buy my ticket (from (whoever asks me first.))

18. Have you ever seen the shack (where they supposedly had hidden the

    money?)

19. Carlos told about one time (when he was very frightened.)

FINAL PRACTICE:
Recognizing the Function
of Noun Clauses

Name _____

Date _____

Instructions: Draw a box around an introductory word and heavy parentheses around the noun clause. Above the clause label its function. Underline verbs twice and subjects once.

1. Why I was chosen was a mystery to me.

2. Dorothy's suggestion is that we should go tomorrow, not today.

3. Teachers usually give extra help to whoever asks for it.

4. Do you know how the magician did that trick?

5. Give whoever comes in next this complimentary ticket.

6. I remember the time when I fell through the ice.

7. Dwight always buys whomever he is going with at the time some really nice presents.

8. Everyone had assumed that Abigail would win the girls' tennis tournament.

9. Whoever is responsible for the damage will be severely punished.

10. I really believe that he meant no harm.

11. When the committee should meet again is what we must decide.

12. Brenda told her dad that she was not planning to return to college.

13. You may send invitations to whomever you wish.

14. Give whoever is the rightful owner the pen.

15. The surprise party for our parents is what we're talking about.

16. How you spend your allowance is your affair.

17. I'll buy my ticket from whoever asks me first.

18. Have you ever seen the shack where they supposedly had hidden the money?

19. Carlos told about one time when he was very frightened.

Understanding and Using Good Grammar

TEST: Recognizing the Function of Noun Clauses

> The next reproducible page contains two copies of one half-page Test. Cut each duplicated page in half; give each student one half-page.

Sentence 3: The understood subject, *you*, must be written.

Sentence 5: Parentheses should be drawn around the prepositional phrase and the **prep.** label written.

Sentence 9: *Whom*ever is an objective word, the object of the preposition *with*.

Grading Scale:

Each of a pair of parentheses must be correctly placed and is worth ½ point. All markings required in the instructions must be graded.

Total points: 70

–1, 99	–6, 92	–11, 85	–16, 78	–21, 71	–26, 64
–2, 97	–7, 90	–12, 83	–17, 76	–22, 69	–27, 62
–3, 96	–8, 89	–13, 82	–18, 75	–23, 68	–28, 61
–4, 94	–9, 87	–14, 80	–19, 73	–24, 66	–29, 59
–5, 93	–10, 86	–15, 79	–20, 72	–25, 65	–30, 58

TEST: Recognizing the Function of Noun Clauses

Instructions: Draw a box around an introductory word and heavy parentheses around a noun clause. Above the clause, label its function. Underline verbs twice and subjects once.

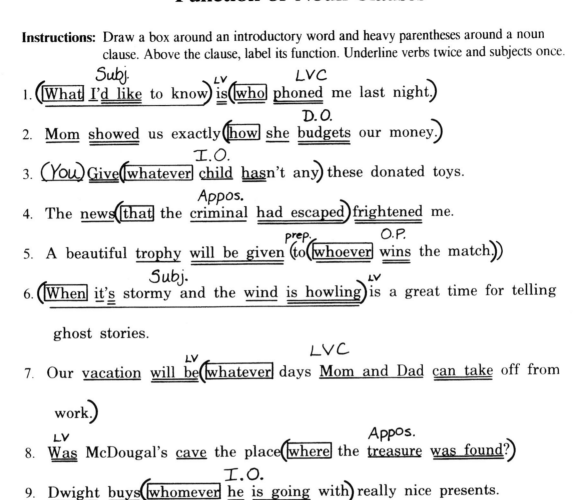

1. (What I'd like to know) is (who phoned me last night.)

2. Mom showed us exactly (how she budgets our money.)

3. (You) Give (whatever child hasn't any) these donated toys.

4. The news (that the criminal had escaped) frightened me.

5. A beautiful trophy will be given (to (whoever wins the match.))

6. (When it's stormy and the wind is howling) is a great time for telling

   ghost stories.

7. Our vacation will be (whatever days Mom and Dad can take off from

   work.)

8. Was McDougal's cave the place (where the treasure was found?)

9. Dwight buys (whomever he is going with) really nice presents.

Name _____

Date _____

TEST: Recognizing the Function of Noun Clauses

Instructions: Draw a box around an introductory word and heavy parentheses around a noun clause. Above the clause, label its function. Underline verbs twice and subjects once.

1. What I'd like to know is who phoned me last night.

2. Mom showed us exactly how she budgets our money.

3.   Give whatever child hasn't any these donated toys.

4. The news that the criminal had escaped frightened me.

5. A beautiful trophy will be given to whoever wins the match.

6. When it's stormy and the wind is howling is a great time for telling ghost stories.

7. Our vacation will be whatever days Mom and Dad can take off from work.

8. Was McDougal's cave the place where the treasure was found?

9. Dwight buys whomever he is going with really nice presents.

Name _____

Date _____

TEST: Recognizing the Function of Noun Clauses

Instructions: Draw a box around an introductory word and heavy parentheses around a noun clause. Above the clause, label its function. Underline verbs twice and subjects once.

1. What I'd like to know is who phoned me last night.

2. Mom showed us exactly how she budgets our money.

3.   Give whatever child hasn't any these donated toys.

4. The news that the criminal had escaped frightened me.

5. A beautiful trophy will be given to whoever wins the match.

6. When it's stormy and the wind is howling is a great time for telling ghost stories.

7. Our vacation will be whatever days Mom and Dad can take off from work.

8. Was McDougal's cave the place where the treasure was found?

9. Dwight buys whomever he is going with really nice presents.

Understanding and Using Good Grammar

Recognizing Adjective, Adverb, and Noun Clauses

Work carefully with students on sentences 1–7 to be sure that each one understands the analysis and has made correct markings. Sentences 8–14 could be done as individual work in the classroom or as homework with each student correcting his or her own paper as you give them the correct markings. You may wish to highlight on the Answer Key the correct markings pertaining to clauses.

Return this paper to students before they take the Test on page 361. Some of the Test sentences are taken from this page.

Complete Analysis of Sentence Parts

The sentences on this worksheet contain many of the special sentence forms the students have studied in this book. The page could be used as a comprehensive review with the students marking every word.

To the instructions on the page, add: Box words that introduce dependent clauses. Mark and label all words.

Sentence

1:   An introductory adverb clause containing a D.O. noun clause: must be followed by a comma; an arrow to LVC–A in independent clause.

2:   Introductory word, *that*, is the subject of the adjective clause.

3:   Contains introductory *there*, unrelated grammatically to the sentence; LVC–N *Claire* follows the subject and should be set off with commas; *whom everyone liked* is an appos. since it could replace *Claire*.

4:   Noun clause functions as sentence D.O.; adjective clause modifies D.O. in noun clause.

5:   Remind students that the D.O. answers the question "What?" asked after the subject-verb: "Moira told *what*?" Moira told *why she wouldn't be a . . .*" is the D.O. The I.O. gets the D.O.: "Who got told?" The clause, *whoever asked her*, is the I.O.

6:   The infinitive, *to determine*, functions as the D.O. in the noun clause LVC.

7:   Small parentheses enclosing prepositional phrase also enclose heavy parentheses of the O.P. clause.

8:   *That* in *that house* is not an introductory word to a clause; it is a demonstrative pronoun used as an adjective to tell "which" house; the adjective clause which describes *house* gives incidental information and should be set off with commas.

9:   This sentence has the same construction as sentence 1.

10:   Understood subject, *you*, should be written for verb, *skip*, but is not necessary for verb, *go*.

11:   Nothing unusual.

12:   (To) *do* and (to) *say* are examples of an elliptical "to" in an infinitive form; the phrases *us (to) do* and *us (to) say* function as D.O.'s to *see* and *hear*.

13:   Sentence is in natural order, so no commas are necessary.

14:   The introductory adverb, *eventually*, is set off with a comma; *listening and concentrating* are gerund subjects of the adverb clause.

Recognizing Adjective, Adverb, and Noun Clauses

PRACTICE: Draw heavy parentheses around noun clauses; above them label their use. Draw pointed brackets around adjective clauses and square brackets around adverb clauses; from them draw arrows to the words they modify. Insert commas where appropriate. Underline verbs twice and subjects once.

1. [When] I heard (that I had passed the test) I was [really] pleased.

2. (Why the roofers left early today) is a question (that should be answered.)

3. [When] I was (in fourth grade) there was one girl, Claire (whom everyone liked.)

4. Did you think (that you had previously seen the tall stranger (who [just] left?))

5. Moira [frankly] told (whoever asked her (why she wouldn't be a candidate.)

6. (How the prisoner escaped) was (what the police had (to determine.))

7. The argument (over (where the junior prom will be held) must be settled [before the committee adjourns.]

8. [Because it has been declared a historical site] that house (which is (in [such a dilapidated condition) will be restored.

9. [When] I discovered (that I had forgotten my homework) I was disgusted.

10. [If you are [not] sure (of an answer) (to a question)] skip it and go [back] (to it [after you finish the test.]

11. [Although she spoke [very] firmly] I couldn't tell (how serious Mom was.)

12. [Even though some (of us) might [not] realize it] our reputations are based (upon (what other people see us do and hear us say.))

13. Most students will give (whoever is elected) their complete support [after the campaign excitement dies [down.]

14. Eventually, students become convinced (that listening and concentrating (in the classroom) are important.]

Recognizing Adjective, Adverb, and Noun Clauses

Name _____

Date _____

PRACTICE: Draw heavy parentheses around noun clauses; above them label their use. Draw pointed brackets around adjective clauses and square brackets around adverb clauses; from them draw arrows to the words they modify. Insert commas where appropriate. Underline verbs twice and subjects once.

1. When I heard that I had passed the test I was really pleased.

2. Why the roofers left early today is a question that should be answered.

3. When I was in fourth grade there was one girl Claire whom everyone liked.

4. Did you think that you had previously seen the tall stranger who just left?

5. Moira frankly told whoever asked her why she wouldn't be a candidate.

6. How the prisoner escaped was what the police had to determine.

7. The argument over where the junior prom will be held must be settled before the committee adjourns.

8. Because it has been declared a historical site that house which is in such a dilapidated condition will be restored.

9. When I discovered that I had forgotten my homework I was disgusted.

10. If you are not sure of an answer to a question skip it and go back to it after you finish the test.

11. Although she spoke very firmly I couldn't tell how serious Mom was.

12. Even though some of us might not realize it our reputations are based upon what other people see us do and hear us say.

13. Most students will give whoever is elected their complete support after the campaign excitement dies down.

14. Eventually students become convinced that listening and concentrating in the classroom are important.

Understanding and Using Good Grammar

TRIAL TEST:
Recognizing Adjective, Adverb, and Noun Clauses

Students may complete this page as individual work in the classroom or as homework. However it is handled, as you give the correct markings, each student should correct any errors he or she may have made in order to have a perfect paper to review for the Test on page 361. Some of these sentences appear on the Test.

The instructions require 118 analytical marks; therefore, each point has a value of .85. Students may determine their grades by multiplying .85 by the number of errors they made.

For example:

$$
\begin{array}{r}
.85 \\
\times\ 15 \text{ errors} \\
\hline
425 \\
85 \\
\hline
12.75 = 13
\end{array}
\qquad
\begin{array}{r}
100 \\
-\ 13 \\
\hline
87\% \text{ grade}
\end{array}
$$

TRIAL TEST:
Recognizing Adjective, Adverb, and Noun Clauses

Instructions: Draw heavy parentheses around noun clauses; above them label their use. Draw pointed brackets around adjective clauses and square brackets around adverb clauses; from them draw arrows to the words they modify. Insert commas where appropriate. Underline verbs twice and subjects once.

1. Linus was surprised [when Dad told him (who the man was.)]

2. (Whoever lost this purse) will be frantic [when she realizes it.]

3. I certainly remember the time (when I first went water skiing.)

4. Colton complained (that his schedule left him little time (when he could have fun.))

5. I agree (with (whoever made the suggestion) (that the test should be postponed.)

6. (When we should sign up for the tournament) is (what we need to know.)

7. [Although some of us might not realize it,] our reputations are based (upon (what other people see us do and hear us say.))

8. [After I read the book (that my aunt had given me,] I wrote a book report on it.

9. Several witnesses (who had seen the holdup) described quite accurately (what had happened.)

10. Frieda frankly admitted (that she had neglected to do her homework.)

11. Most adults remember at least one teacher (who had a positive influence on their lives.)

12. Jerry usually knows (when it's 6:00 P.M.) [because he gets hunger pangs.]

13. Moira told (whoever asked her) (why she wouldn't be a candidate.)

Name _____

Date _____

TRIAL TEST: Recognizing Adjective, Adverb, and Noun Clauses

Instructions: Draw heavy parentheses around noun clauses; above them label their use. Draw pointed brackets around adjective clauses and square brackets around adverb clauses; from them draw arrows to the words they modify. Insert commas where appropriate. Underline verbs twice and subjects once.

1. Linus was surprised when Dad told him who the man was.

2. Whoever lost this purse will be frantic when she realizes it.

3. I certainly remember the time when I first went water skiing.

4. Colton complained that his schedule left him little time when he could have fun.

5. I agree with whoever made the suggestion that the test should be postponed.

6. When we should sign up for the tournament is what we need to know.

7. Although some of us might not realize it our reputations are based upon what other people see us do and hear us say.

8. After I read the book that my aunt had given me I wrote a book report on it.

9. Several witnesses who had seen the holdup described quite accurately what had happened.

10. Frieda frankly admitted that she had neglected to do her homework.

11. Most adults remember at least one teacher who had a positive influence on their lives.

12. Jerry usually knows when it's 6:00 P.M. because he gets hunger pangs.

13. Moira told whoever asked her why she wouldn't be a candidate.

                 Understanding and Using Good Grammar

TEST: Recognizing Adjective, Adverb, and Noun Clauses

> The next reproducible page contains two copies of one half-page Test. Cut each duplicated page in half; give each student one half-page.

Emphasize to the students that the objective of the study of clauses has been to enable them to understand completely the makeup and uses of clauses. This understanding is of real value to them for two reasons:

1. They can recognize clauses and appreciate the effect their use has in the writings of outstanding authors.

2. They can include clauses purposefully in their own writings to improve and/or add variety to their expression. Knowledge is a tool.

Prior to starting the Test, remind students to indicate the prepositional phrase using small parentheses and the labels **prep.** and **O.P.** in sentence 6.

Grading Scale:

The markings required in the instructions and shown on the Answer Key total 77.

–1, 99	–6, 92	–11, 86	–16, 79	–21, 73	–26, 66
–2, 97	–7, 91	–12, 84	–17, 78	–22, 71	–27, 65
–3, 96	–8, 90	–13, 83	–18, 77	–23, 70	–28, 64
–4, 95	–9, 88	–14, 82	–19, 75	–24, 69	–29, 62
–5, 93	–10, 87	–15, 80	–20, 74	–25, 67	–30, 61
					–31, 60

TEST: Recognizing Adjective, Adverb, and Noun Clauses

Instructions: Draw heavy parentheses around noun clauses; above them label their use. Draw pointed brackets around adjective clauses and square brackets around adverb clauses; from them draw arrows to the words they modify. Insert needed commas. Underline verbs twice and subjects once.

1. (You) Give (whoever comes in next) — I.O. (whatever coupons are left over.) — D.O.

2. [When I was in fifth grade], there was one girl, Claire, (whom everyone liked.) — Appos.

3. (When we should sign up for the tournament) — Subj. is (what we need to know.) — LV LVC

4. [Because it has been declared a historical site], that house, (which is in such a dilapidated condition), will be completely restored.

5. Jerry usually knows (when it's 6:00 P.M.) [because he gets hunger pangs.] — D.O.

6. I agree (with (whoever made the suggestion) (that we should participate.)) — prep. O.P. D.O.

7. Several witnesses (who saw the holdup) described (what they had seen.) — D.O.

TEST: Recognizing Adjective, Adverb, and Noun Clauses

Name _____ _____

Date _____

Instructions: Draw heavy parentheses around noun clauses; above them label their use. Draw pointed brackets around adjective clauses and square brackets around adverb clauses; from them draw arrows to the words they modify. Insert needed commas. Underline verbs twice and subjects once.

1. Give whoever comes in next whatever coupons are left over.

2. When I was in fifth grade there was one girl Claire whom everyone liked.

3. When we should sign up for the tournament is what we need to know.

4. Because it has been declared a historical site that house which is in such a dilapidated condition will be completely restored.

5. Jerry usually knows when it's 6:00 P.M. because he gets hunger pangs.

6. I agree with whoever made the suggestion that we should participate.

7. Several witnesses who saw the holdup described what they had seen.

TEST: Recognizing Adjective, Adverb, and Noun Clauses

Name _____

Date _____

Instructions: Draw heavy parentheses around noun clauses; above them label their use. Draw pointed brackets around adjective clauses and square brackets around adverb clauses; from them draw arrows to the words they modify. Insert needed commas. Underline verbs twice and subjects once.

1. Give whoever comes in next whatever coupons are left over.

2. When I was in fifth grade there was one girl Claire whom everyone liked.

3. When we should sign up for the tournament is what we need to know.

4. Because it has been declared a historical site that house which is in such a dilapidated condition will be completely restored.

5. Jerry usually knows when it's 6:00 P.M. because he gets hunger pangs.

6. I agree with whoever made the suggestion that we should participate.

7. Several witnesses who saw the holdup described what they had seen.

Understanding and Using Good Grammar

Recognizing Absolute Phrases

Previous study of participles:

As *verbs:*   Lists of principal parts of irregular verbs (pages 176 and 196)

Forms of *have* plus past participle to express perfect tenses (page 211)

Forms of *be* plus present participle to express progressive tenses (page 223)

As *verbals:* Present participle used as a noun, a gerund (page 241)

Present and past participles and participial phrases used as adjectives (page 270)

In the Practice, sentence 2 contains an absolute phrase in which the participle may be omitted, but its meaning is understood.

Keep students aware of recent learnings:

Sentence 1:   *To drive* is an infinitive used as a direct object.

Sentence 2:   *To be interviewed* is an infinitive used as an adverb telling "why" about the verb *waited.*

Sentence 3:   *To end the discussion* may function as an adjective infinitive phrase to tell "what kind" about the subject, *motion,* or as an adverb to tell "why" about the verb, *was made.*

Sentence 4:   *To replace him as tackle* is an infinitive phrase used as an adverb to tell "why" about the verb, *sent.*

Collect these papers to record the score each student has earned. Return papers for them to refer to in completing page 368.

Recognizing Absolute Phrases

Absolute Phrase, Absolute Construction, Nominative Absolute: These terms all refer to the same grammatical form.

1. It is a special phrase that consists of a noun or pronoun followed and modified by a participle or participial phrase.

    Example: Our reservations having been made, we started on our vacation in spite of the predicted storm.

    (a) It is a **phrase** because it cannot stand alone as a sentence.

    (b) It is **absolute** because it modifies no single word in the main sentence; however, it has a close "thought" relationship to the entire main sentence.

2. *REMEMBER:* A **participle** is a verb form that may function as a verb or as an adjective or noun.

    (a) The **present** participle always ends in **-ing: speaking, singing, walking**

    (b) The **past** participle has various endings, according to the type of verb: **spoken, sung, walked**

    (c) The **perfect** participle consists of **having** or **having been** followed by the past participle: **having spoken, having been sung, having walked**

    (d) Writing tends to "come alive" when participles, verb forms which show action, are used (in addition to the sentence verb) in a modifying function. They help the reader to see the "picture" the writer is creating or describing.

3. **Using the Absolute Phrase**

    (a) Practice using this phrase to improve your writing style and to help your reader to visualize the person or situation that you're describing.

    (b) **Notice:** the phrase is always set off with a comma or commas.

    (c) An absolute construction is most often used at the beginning of a sentence to give obvious variety to the sentence structure. However, it may be used anyplace in the sentence where it fits in logically. The participle may be omitted but is understood.

PRACTICE: In the main sentence, underline the verb twice, subject once. In the absolute phrase, draw one wavy line under the participle and another under the noun or pronoun it follows. The first one has been done as an example.

1. Marcella not having her car, Clementine volunteered to drive.

2. I stood there, application held in hand, and waited to be interviewed.

3. A motion was made to end the discussion, no new ideas being proposed.

4. Mowrey being injured, Coach sent in Odell to replace him as tackle.

5. The football team, their uniforms caked with mud, welcomed the end of the game.

Recognizing Absolute Phrases

Name _____

Date _____

Absolute Phrase, Absolute Construction, Nominative Absolute: These terms all refer to the same grammatical form.

1. It is a special phrase that consists of a noun or pronoun followed and modified by a participle or participial phrase.

   Example: Our reservations having been made, we started on our vacation in spite of the predicted storm.

   (a) It is a **phrase** because it cannot stand alone as a sentence.

   (b) It is **absolute** because it modifies no single word in the main sentence; however, it has a close "thought" relationship to the entire main sentence.

2. *REMEMBER:* A **participle** is a verb form that may function as a verb or as an adjective or noun.

   (a) The **present** participle always ends in **-ing**: **speaking, singing, walking**

   (b) The **past** participle has various endings, according to the type of verb: **spoken, sung, walked**

   (c) The **perfect** participle consists of **having** or **having been** followed by the past participle: **having spoken, having been sung, having walked**

   (d) Writing tends to "come alive" when participles, verb forms which show action, are used (in addition to the sentence verb) in a modifying function. They help the reader to see the "picture" the writer is creating or describing.

3. **Using the Absolute Phrase**

   (a) Practice using this phrase to improve your writing style and to help your reader to visualize the person or situation that you're describing.

   (b) **Notice:** the phrase is always set off with a comma or commas.

   (c) An absolute construction is most often used at the beginning of a sentence to give obvious variety to the sentence structure. However, it may be used anyplace in the sentence where it fits in logically. The participle may be omitted but is understood.

PRACTICE: In the main sentence, underline the verb twice, subject once. In the absolute phrase, draw one wavy line under the participle and another under the noun or pronoun it follows. The first one has been done as an example.

1. Marcella not having her car, Clementine volunteered to drive.

2. I stood there, application (held) in hand, and waited to be interviewed.

3. A motion was made to end the discussion, no new ideas being proposed.

4. Mowrey being injured, Coach sent in Odell to replace him as tackle.

5. The football team, their uniforms caked with mud, welcomed the end of the game.

      Understanding and Using Good Grammar

PRACTICE and FINAL PRACTICE:
Recognizing Absolute Phrases

Practice

You may wish to work with the students in completing the half-page Practice, corroborating the sentence analysis of volunteers.

Sentence 6: The adjective participial phrase *finding our classrooms* tells "what kind" about the direct object, *trouble*.

Sentence 8: The clause *(that) we'd put out for them* (*that* is elliptical), functions as an adjective that tells "what kind" about the direct object, *seeds*.

Final Practice

You may wish to assign this Final Practice as homework, check it in class the next day, and have students retain it to prepare for the Test the following day.

Sentence 1: The infinitive phrase, *to lend Cabot my bike*, functions as a direct object.

Sentence 2: The adverb infinitive phrase, *(to) open their gifts* (*to* is elliptical), tells "why" about the verb, *watched*.

Sentence 9: The noun clause, *that she was late again*, functions as a direct object.

Sentence 10: The infinitive phrase, *to clean the docks*, functions as a direct object.

PRACTICE:
Recognizing Absolute Phrases

Instructions: In the main sentence, underline the verb twice and the subject once. In the absolute phrase, draw one wavy line under the participle and another under the noun; insert needed commas. One sentence has no participle.

1. One man having been wounded, the entire hunting party returned to the city.

2. My father, his eyebrows raised, stared questioningly at me.

3. The crowd soon scattered, the game being over.

4. Night coming, all the workers were packing up and leaving the site.

5. The student, his face flushed with pleasure, accepted the award.

6. We had trouble finding our classrooms, this being our first day.

7. The bridge having been washed out, highway patrolmen were rerouting traffic.

8. The young jays, parent birds no longer feeding them, obviously relished the seeds we'd put out for them.   *(held)*

9. Joel entered the library, his overdue book in his hand.

FINAL PRACTICE:
Recognizing Absolute Phrases

Instructions: In the main sentence, underline the verb twice and the subject once. In the absolute phrase, draw one wavy line under the participle and another under the noun; insert needed commas. One sentence has no participle.

1. His bicycle having a flat tire, I offered to lend Cabot my bike.

2. Grandpa, his face wreathed in smiles, watched the children open their gifts.

3. Jonathan has already left for school, his ride having arrived early.

4. The road having been covered by the avalanche, drivers were being halted.

5. The workmen returned to the repair shop, their job having been finished.

6. Mom, her blue eyes twinkling, handed Dad a new set of car keys. *(held)*

7. Tomas stood on the corner, lunchbox in hand, and waited for the bus.

8. Linnea closed her book and notebook, her homework being completed.

9. The tardy bell ringing sharply, Ryan realized that he was late again.

10. The ship steaming out the Golden Gate, workers began to clean the docks.

Name _____

Date _____

PRACTICE: Recognizing Absolute Phrases

Instructions: In the main sentence, underline the verb twice and the subject once. In the absolute phrase, draw one wavy line under the participle and another under the noun; insert needed commas. One sentence has no participle.

1. One man having been wounded the entire hunting party returned to the city.
2. My father his eyebrows raised stared questioningly at me.
3. The crowd soon scattered the game being over.
4. Night coming all the workers were packing up and leaving the site.
5. The student his face flushed with pleasure accepted the award.
6. We had trouble finding our classrooms this being our first day.
7. The bridge having been washed out highway patrolmen were rerouting traffic.
8. The young jays parent birds no longer feeding them obviously relished the seeds we'd put out for them.
9. Joel entered the library his overdue book in his hand.

Name _____

Date _____

FINAL PRACTICE: Recognizing Absolute Phrases

Instructions: In the main sentence, underline the verb twice and the subject once. In the absolute phrase, draw one wavy line under the participle and another under the noun; insert needed commas. One sentence has no participle.

1. His bicycle having a flat tire I offered to lend Cabot my bike.
2. Grandpa his face wreathed in smiles watched the children open their gifts.
3. Jonathan has already left for school his ride having arrived early.
4. The road having been covered by the avalanche drivers were being halted.
5. The workmen returned to the repair shop their job having been finished.
6. Mom her blue eyes twinkling handed Dad a new set of car keys.
7. Tomas stood on the corner lunchbox in hand and waited for the bus.
8. Linnea closed her book and notebook her homework being completed.
9. The tardy bell ringing sharply Ryan realized that he was late again.
10. The ship steaming out the Golden Gate began to clean the docks.

Understanding and Using Good Grammar

TEST:
Recognizing Absolute Phrases

> The next reproducible page contains two copies of one half-page Test. Cut each duplicated page in half; give each student one half-page.

Suggested Grading:

The markings required in the instructions and shown on the Answer Key total 48. It would be fair to give each point a value of 2%.

Point out to students that their knowledge about absolute phrases enables them to recognize and appreciate this effective, descriptive device in the writings of established authors. Their knowledge also provides them with another means of writing descriptively, of creating mental images in their readers' minds.

TEST:
Recognizing Absolute Phrases

Instructions: In the main sentence, underline the verb twice and the subject once. In the absolute phrase, draw one wavy line under the participle and another under the noun; insert needed commas. In one sentence, insert the appropriate participle.

1. The final curtain having fallen, the audience filed out of the theater.

2. Raul, his head aching fiercely, moved haltingly toward the door.

3. Jonathan has already left for school, his ride having arrived early.

4. My father, his eyebrows raised, stared questioningly at me.

5. Our reservations having been made, we shall start our trip tomorrow.

6. Linnea closed her book and notebook, her homework being completed.

7. Her glasses shattered totally, Eugenia stumbled around in the room.

8. The student, his face flushed with pleasure, accepted the award.

9. Julius entered the library, his overdue book *(held)* in his hand.

TEST: Recognizing Absolute Phrases

Name _____

Date _____

Instructions: In the main sentence, underline the verb twice and the subject once. In the absolute phrase, draw one wavy line under the participle and another under the noun; insert needed commas. In one sentence, insert the appropriate participle.

1. The final curtain having fallen the audience filed out of the theater.

2. Raul his head aching fiercely moved haltingly toward the door.

3. Jonathan has already left for school his ride having arrived early.

4. My father his eyebrows raised stared questioningly at me.

5. Our reservations having been made we shall start our trip tomorrow.

6. Linnea closed her book and notebook her homework being completed.

7. Her glasses shattered totally Eugenia stumbled around in the room.

8. The student his face flushed with pleasure accepted the award.

9. Julius entered the library his overdue book in his hand.

TEST: Recognizing Absolute Phrases

Name _____

Date _____

Instructions: In the main sentence, underline the verb twice and the subject once. In the absolute phrase, draw one wavy line under the participle and another under the noun; insert needed commas. In one sentence, insert the appropriate participle.

1. The final curtain having fallen the audience filed out of the theater.

2. Raul his head aching fiercely moved haltingly toward the door.

3. Jonathan has already left for school his ride having arrived early.

4. My father his eyebrows raised stared questioningly at me.

5. Our reservations having been made we shall start our trip tomorrow.

6. Linnea closed her book and notebook her homework being completed.

7. Her glasses shattered totally Eugenia stumbled around in the room.

8. The student his face flushed with pleasure accepted the award.

9. Julius entered the library his overdue book in his hand.

Understanding and Using Good Grammar

Suggested Writing Practice

The objective of this method of study is to enable students, through precept and example, to understand thoroughly all the elements of the English sentence. They learn how each element is constructed, how it functions, and how its interrelationship with other sentence parts determines its correct grammatical usage. The purpose is to provide students with the tools of communication they need to express their ideas clearly, grammatically, and fluently both in speaking and in writing.

To gain the intended maximum benefit from their learnings, students should be given opportunities to practice using each grammatical element as they study it. The practice may range from simple oral activities that occur spontaneously in class to carefully structured written assignments. When they practice using the element to describe in their own words their personal experiences, they tend to add that element effectively and permanently to their individual styles of expression. Constantly encourage each student to exercise creative thinking in utilizing the advanced grammatical elements and in selecting descriptive words to improve her or his expression.

Suggested Practice Exercises

A. Using adjectives and adverbs

Creative aspects: Students use and expand their descriptive vocabularies.

Teacher provides sentence fragments on the chalkboard, overhead, or a duplicated worksheet; indicates type of descriptive word to be used in blanks. Students fill blanks, mark or label sentence parts, and volunteer to read sentences aloud.

Further practice: Students develop their own fragment sentences and types and placement of descriptive words to share with class.

Examples:

1. *Juan's* *Chihuahua* _____ puppy ran *clumsily* *away* _____ .
   (whose?) (which one?)   (how?)   (where?)

2. *Yesterday* _____ Maya bought *three* *white* _____ D.O. shirts.
   (when?)   (how many?) (what kind?)

3. The child, *starry-eyed* and *happy*, sang *really* *well* .
   (what kind?)   (what kind?)   (how much?) (how?)

B. Teaching prepositional phrases

Creative aspects: Students imagine the situation, plan logical continuity, and choose a variety of prepositions, noun objects, and exact verbs.

Teacher provides choice of topics or each student develops her or his own. Students tell a story using only ten or twelve adverbial prepositional phrases; then, before each phrase, they supply a verb that suggests action or sound or both; they take turns reading "stories."

Example:

"Morning After Morning"

(grabbed)	from the table	(jumped)	on the bus
(burst)	out the door	(fell)	in the parking lot
(pounded)	down the steps	(shouted)	to my friend
(slithered)	across the lawn	(whispered)	inside the school
(dashed)	up the sidewalk	(hurried)	toward my classroom
(braked)	near the corner	(plopped)	into my seat

C. Building descriptive sentences

using listed verbs, nouns to be used as subjects or as objects of prepositions, adjectives, adverbs, and prepositions.

Creative aspects: Students combine given words creatively to form original sentences.

Teacher provides list of words. Students develop at least eight sentences of nine or ten words each, possibly, though not necessarily, in story continuity. Students use adjective(s) and one adjective phrase to modify the subject and use adverb(s) and one adverb phrase to modify the verb as in example sentence. They mark and label sentence parts. Groups of five critique one another's writings. Each group selects two members to read their sentences to the class.

Verbs	Nouns	Adjectives	Adverbs	Prepositions
gathered	bus	twenty	seldom	on
stood	students	noisy	very	of
lined	highway	steep	slowly	to
lay	field trip	hot	suddenly	under
reached	parents	the	usually	besides
hiked	driver	yellow	nearby	up
strolled	crowd	all	carefully	from
sat	weather	several	neatly	inside
spoke	boy	happy	occasionally	down
boarded	trail	stormy	surely	for
stopped	teacher	many	fast	around
ran	mountain	a	quietly	beside

Example: (Several) students (on (the) (field) trip) hiked [slowly] (up (the) trail.)

D. Using only present participles

followed by a modifier or an object to tell a story

Creative aspects: Students imagine the situation, plan logical continuity, and choose a variety of present participles.

Teacher suggests topics or each student provides his or her own. Using only ten or twelve present participles with an object or modifier(s), each student tells a story. Volunteers, supplying the noun they modified with the phrases, read their stories to the class.

Example: "Orchestra Practice"

(Clarissa)

pushing open the door	lifting the bow
dropping her books	raising the violin
giggling with embarrassment	squinting in the sun
sitting beside her friend	tuning the strings
getting her instrument	setting up the stand
opening the case	watching the conductor

E. Recognizing and correcting dangling participles

Remember: A participle or participial phrase must describe someone or something in the sentence.

Teacher provides these phrases; volunteers complete the sentences orally:

1. Glancing around the classroom, _____

   (Who glanced and did what?)

2. Closing the dishwasher firmly, _____

   (Who closed and did what?)

3. Mowing the lawn vigorously, _____

   (Who mowed and did what?)

4. Having eaten their dessert quickly, _____

   (Who ate and did what?)

5. Being aware of the danger, _____

   (Who was aware and did what?)

Teacher writes example sentences that demonstrate a dangling participle and the correction:

Dangling: Awakening so early in the morning, the room was still dark. (The room didn't "awaken.")

Corrected: Awakening so early (in the) morning, Mokiko could barely see (across the room.) (Who awakened and did what?) (Mokiko "awakened")

Homework assignment: Each student writes five original sentences that contain nondangling participial phrases. In class, each reads aloud his or her "outstanding" sentence.

F. Using an adjective clause to modify a noun

Creative aspects: Based upon observation, each student constructs an original sentence containing an appropriate adjective clause that describes something about a classmate. All students participate in this "Who Is It?" game.

1. I see (a) person (who has red hair.)
   (*who* is subject of the clause)

2. I see (a) person (whom I admire.)
   (*whom*, direct object of clause)

Teacher writes example sentences with marks and labels to remind students of the structure and use of adjective clauses introduced by *who, whom,* and *whose,* and identifies use of the pronoun in the clause.

3. I see (a) person (whose) sweater is red.)
   (*whose*, adjective modifies *sweater*)

4. I see (a) person (whom I often skate with.)
   (*whom*, object of preposition *with*)

Give students a few minutes to construct their sentences. When volunteers have finished reading a sentence, they should repeat the introductory pronoun, identify its use in the clause as in the example sentences, ask "Who is it?", and select a volunteer to identify the person who was described.

G. Developing and using adverb clauses

after	how	unless
although	since	until
as if	so	when
because	than	where
before	though	whether

Teacher lists some subordinate conjunctions, writes example sentences demonstrating the three possible positions of adverb clauses and the necessary commas, and marks and labels the sentence parts.

1. Jed left [hurriedly] though (many) students waited [patiently].
2. When (the) (passing) bell rang Jed left.
3. Jed, after he'd been given permission, left [hurriedly].

Each student decides upon an original subject-verb to use in writing and marking or labeling three sentences, each with a different adverb clause to demonstrate the three possible placements of such clauses. Remind students to use necessary commas.

Some students will probably substitute their own words to express essentially the same ideas as the example sentences. Others will write unique, entirely different sentences. Of course creative thinking is to be desired, but anyone who learns best by imitation should not be discouraged from doing so.

H. Expanding a speaker tag to enable the reader to visualize the speaker

Creative aspects: Students apply their knowledge of descriptive sentence elements, draw from and add to their vocabularies, and practice ways of improving their writing styles.

Class decides upon a command or short sentence to use as the base for building a description of the speaker. Teacher directs development by asking questions that call upon volunteers to suggest descriptive ideas. Following are examples you can use to demonstrate the assignment.

"Come here."

Who said it? Give it a speaker tag.
Use a more exact verb.
How does the speaker look? Use a present participle phrase.

Diann said, "Come here."
Diann whispered, "Come here."
Diann, looking frightened, whispered, "Come here."

"Don't go."

Who said it? Give it a speaker tag.
Use an adjective to describe the speaker.
How did the speaker say it? Use an adverb.
Describe the speaker's voice. Use an absolute construction.
Describe an action of the speaker. Use a present participial phrase to begin the sentence.

The stranger said, "Don't go!"
The little stranger said, "Don't go!"
The little stranger said, fearfully, "Don't go!"
The little stranger, his voice barely audible, said fearfully, "Don't go!"
Grabbing my arm frantically, the little stranger, his voice barely audible, said fearfully, "Don't go!"

"Wait!"

Who said it?
How was it said? Use an adverb.
When was it said? Use an adverb clause.

Who heard it? Use a compound subject, two nouns joined by *and*; change order of sentence.
Where were the listeners? Use a prepositional phrase to modify each of the nouns.

"Wait!" my brother called.
"Wait!" my brother called, sharply.
"Wait!" my brother called, sharply, as he stepped off the porch.
Mother and Dad heard my brother call sharply, "Wait!" as he stepped off the porch.
Mother, in the kitchen, and Dad, in the garage, heard my brother call sharply, "Wait!" as he stepped off the porch.